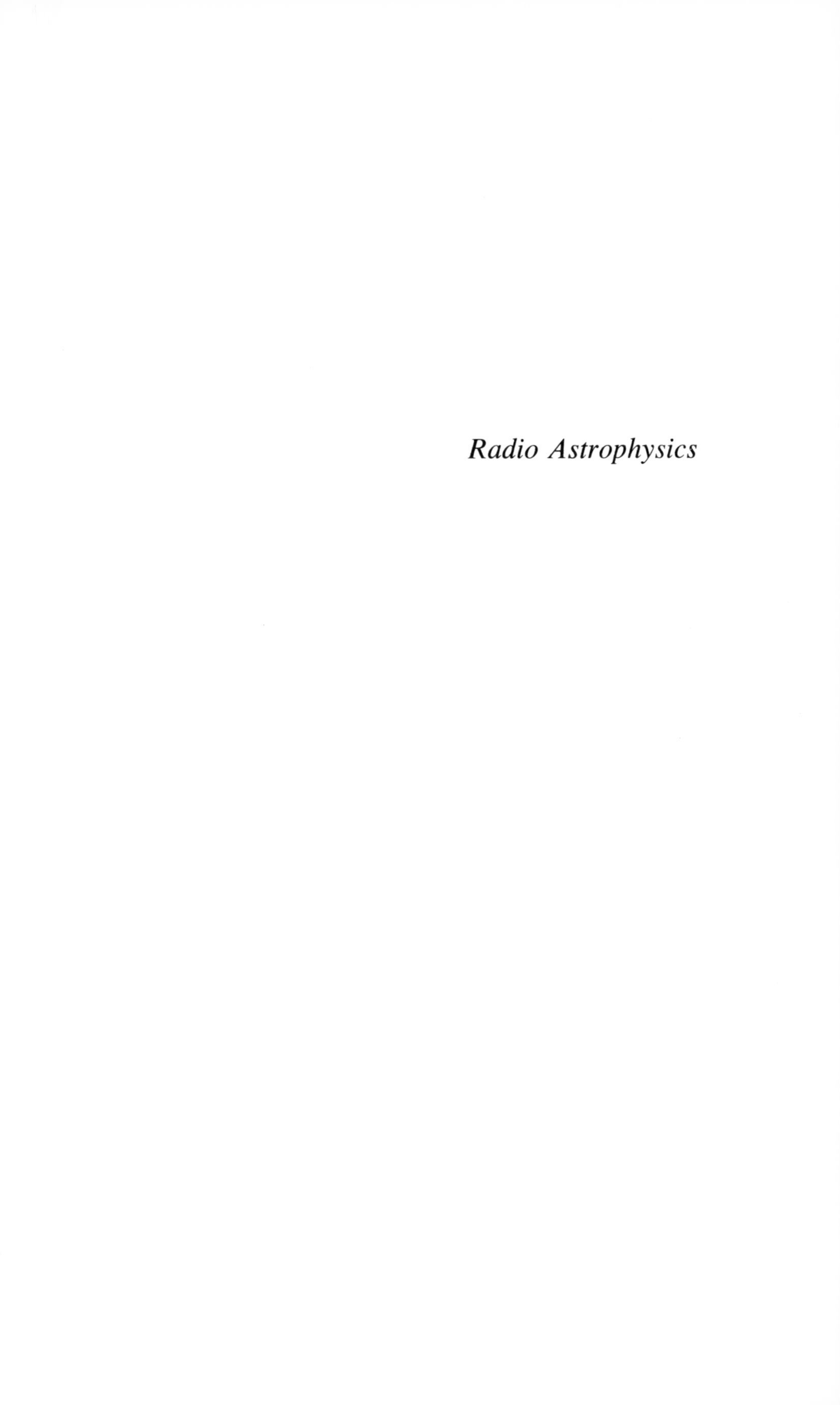

Radio Astrophysics

A Series of Books in Astronomy and Astrophysics
Editors: Geoffrey Burbidge and Margaret Burbidge

Radio Astrophysics

NONTHERMAL PROCESSES IN GALACTIC AND EXTRAGALACTIC SOURCES

A. G. Pacholczyk
Steward Observatory
The University of Arizona

W. H. FREEMAN AND COMPANY
San Francisco

Printed in the United States of America

Library of Congress Catalog Card Number: 70-95657
International Standard Book Number: 0-7167-0329-7

Wilhelminie Iwanowskiej
i Stefanowi Piotrowskiemu
którzy zbudowali podwaliny dla rozwoju
astrofizyki i radioastronomii
w moim ojczystym kraju

Dedicated to
Wilhelmina Iwanowska and Stefan Piotrowski
who built the foundations for the development
of astrophysics and radioastronomy
in my native country

Contents

3

Radiation of Relativistic Electrons in Magnetic Fields in Vacuum (Synchrotron Radiation)

4

Synchrotron Radiation in a Plasma

5

Redistribution of Energy in the Spectrum by Electron Scattering

6

Interpretation of Spectra of Discrete Radio Sources

7

Physical Conditions in Radio Sources

8

Spectral Radio Lines

Appendixes

Preface

This book is addressed primarily to observational radio astronomers and graduate students working on the interpretation of radioastronomical data. In it I have emphasized the discussion of the physical processes currently believed to be responsible for the observed radio radiation from galactic and extragalactic sources. Current interpretations and discussions of many observational results are noted only by a reference to the literature; review papers seem to be the most useful form of presentation of such problems at the present stage of development of radio astronomy.

The presentation of this material evolved from my course in radioastronomy at the University of Arizona in the years 1965–1968. I am very much indebted to many of my colleagues and students for their help and comments in preparing this book. Special thanks are due G. B. Field, who critically read the entire manuscript and offered valuable suggestions. Many of my colleagues read and commented upon various portions of the book. B. J. Bok and R. E. Williams read Chapter 8, F. D. Drake commented upon Chapter 1, W. J. Cocke commented on Chapter 2. K. I. Kellermann read Chapters 1 and 6 and Appendix 4. T. L. Swihart read Appendix 1 and R. J. Weymann read Chapter 3; the fruitful discussions with both of them as well as their suggestions during the preparation of Chapter 5 are much appreciated.

The following persons prepared figures and tables and made the necessary and sometimes tedious numerical computations: F. J. Lopez-Lopez

(Figures 3.8, 4.1, 4.2, and the nomograms in Appendix 3), W. G. Fogarty (Figures 2.3, 3.9, 6.1, 6.5, 6.6, and Tables A4, A6, A7), R. J. Weymann (Figures 3.6, 3.7 and Tables A1, A2), J. Geary and R. Wilcox (Figures 5.6, 5.7, 3.12 and 3.13) and N. D. Lubart (Table A3 and A7). I would like to express my appreciation to W. L. Bailey, Mr. Fogarty, and my wife Mary Jane for their careful editorial work on the manuscript; their work considerably improved the readability of the book. I am further grateful to Mr. Bailey, Mr. Geary and especially Mr. Fogarty and Mr. Lubart for the time-consuming and careful work of checking the equations, and to Vy Lubart for her assistance in proofreading and in preparing the index.

To all the persons named above and also to Geoffrey and Margaret Burbidge for their valuable contributions to the preparation of this book, I am most grateful.

A. G. PACHOLCZYK

The University of Arizona
Tucson, Arizona
March, 1969

Preliminary Reading List

Although no previous knowledge of astrophysics and radio astronomy is necessarily required for understanding the material presented in this book, it may prove helpful for the reader to acquaint himself with some elements of both of these sciences. As useful introductions to astrophysics and radio astronomy I recommend the following.

1. T. L. Swihart. *Astrophysics and Stellar Astronomy*. Wiley and Sons, New York, 1969.
2. J. L. Steinberg and J. Lequeux. *Radio Astronomy*. McGraw-Hill, New York, 1963.

The reader should, however, be thoroughly acquainted with the following fields of physics: (*a*) classical mechanics—to the extent of the contents of Ref. 3—and, in particular, with the relativistic mechanics of particles, as given in Chapters 1 to 3 of Ref. 4, and (*b*) classical electrodynamics, including special relativity; for example, the material presented in Chapters 4 to 9 of Ref. 4, or in Ref. 5.

3. L. D. Landau and E. M. Lifshitz. *Mechanics*. Pergamon Press, Oxford; Addison-Wesley, Reading, Mass, 1960.
4. L. D. Landau and E. M. Lifshitz. *The Classical Theory of Fields*. Pergamon Press, Oxford; Addison-Wesley, Reading, Mass., 1962.
5. J. D. Jackson. *Classical Electrodynamics*. Wiley and Sons, New York, 1962.

The reading of Chapter 8 of this book requires some acquaintance with spectroscopy—for example, with the material presented in Ref. 6— and some knowledge of the processes leading to the broadening of spectral lines, as described in Section 4 of Ref. 7.

6. G. Herzberg. *Atomic Spectra and Atomic Structure.* Dover, New York, 1944.
7. K. M. Böhm. "Basic Theory of Line Formation," In J. L. Greenstein, ed. *Stellar Atmospheres.* Univ. of Chicago Press, 1960. Chapter 3.

The reader may also find it helpful to refer occasionally to the books listed at the end of Appendix 1 (p. 218).

Notation

Since this book is addressed to astrophysicists rather than to radio engineers, the Gaussian system of units is used consistently throughout. The reader needs to convert the observed flux of radiation from radio sources, given usually in MKS units, into CGS units (Chapter 1) and no further contact with the MKS system is necessary. In order to express the flux of radiation in CGS units, one should multiply the value given in MKS units by a factor of 10^3 since

$$1\ \mathrm{W/(m^2\ sec\ Hz)} = 10^3\ \mathrm{erg/(cm^2\ sec\ Hz)};$$
$$1\ \text{flux unit} = 10^{-26}\ \mathrm{W/(m^2\ sec\ Hz)} = 10^{-23}\ \mathrm{erg/(cm^2\ sec\ Hz)}.$$

The use of one consistent set of symbols through the entire text is, unfortunately, incompatible with the retention of the notation generally accepted in the field. Therefore the notation in this book will vary slightly from one chapter to another; moreover, there will be some ambiguity due to the use of one symbol for two different quantities even within the same chapter. This ambiguity should not lead to confusion if the reading is accompanied by some degree of understanding. A list of symbols follows.

Physical constants

$c = 2.998\ E\ \ 10$	velocity of light
$h = 6.625\ E{-}27$	Planck constant
$e = 4.803\ E{-}10$	electron charge
$m = 9.108\ E{-}28$	electron mass
$k = 1.380\ E{-}16$	Boltzmann constant
$mc^2 = 8.186\ E{-}07$	rest mass energy of electron
$\Lambda_C = 2.426\ E{-}10$	Compton wavelength
$\sigma_T = 6.653\ E{-}25$	Thomson cross section

Conversion factors

1 eV = 1.602 *E*–12 erg
1 year = 3.156 *E* 07 sec
1 parsec = 3.086 *E* 18 cm

1 erg = 6.242 *E* 11 eV
1 sec = 3.169 *E*–08 years
1 cm = 3.240 *E*–19 parsecs

Marks above symbols

time derivative
quantities describing synchrotron radiation in a plasma

Subscripts and superscripts

C	inverse Compton scattering; the continuum (Chapter 8)
E	per energy interval
F	Faraday rotation
i, f	moment immediately preceding and immediately following a collision, respectively; "initial" and "final" values (Chapter 5)
I	energy loss for ionization of the medium
K	continuum
L	spectral lines; laboratory system of reference
n	Fourier harmonic n (Chapter 3)
n, m	energy states E_n and E_m, respectively
nm	transition between the energy states E_n and E_m
R	rest system
S	synchrotron radiation; measurement "on source" (Chapter 8)
T	thermal radiation
λ	per wavelength interval
ν	per frequency interval
Ω	per solid angle
(i)	the two orthogonal linear polarizations $i = 1$ and $i = 2$, direction 2 is parallel to the magnet field (Chapter 3)
$\perp, \parallel$	the two orthogonal polarizations perpendicular and parallel to a given direction, respectively
$+$	positive ions
$-$	electrons
$'$	retarded time (Chapter 3)
$*$	a unit vector

Latin Letters

$\mathbf{A}$	electromagnetic vector potential
A_e	effective aperture of the antenna
A_{nm}	Einstein coefficient of spontaneous emission
$B(T)$	Planck function [equation (A.31)]
B_{mn}	Einstein absorption coefficient
B_{nm}	Einstein coefficient of stimulated emission

BWFN	beam width between first nulls of an antenna
c_v	specific heat
D	directivity of an antenna [equation (1.15)]
e	particle charge
E	energy
$\boldsymbol{E}$	electric field
E_T	$= 1/\xi_S t$ (Chapter 6)
E_L	low energy cut-off in electron distribution
E_H	high energy cut-off in electron distribution; total energy of magnetic field in a radio source
E_e	total energy of relativistic electrons in a radio source
E_p	total energy of heavy particles in a radio source
$\mathscr{E}$	energy; emission measure [equation (6.2)]
$\mathscr{E}_E$	electrostatic energy
$\mathscr{E}_T$	thermal energy
f	distribution function of particles in phase space
F	flux
$\boldsymbol{F}$	force, in particular Lorentz force [equation (A.16)]
F_A	apparent flux of a radio source [equation (1.7)]
F_P	flux of completely polarized radiation
F_N	flux of unpolarized radiation
$\boldsymbol{\mathscr{F}}$	force density, in particular, Lorentz force density
g	statistical weight of energy level
$G(\vartheta, \varphi)$	directive gain of an antenna [equation (1.18)]
H	magnetic field intensity
HPBW	half power beam width of an antenna
$\mathscr{H}$	Hamiltonian
I	radiation intensity [equation (A.7)]
I_A	apparent brightness of a radio source [equation (1.8)]
I_N	intensity of unpolarized radiation
I_P	intensity of completely polarized radiation
I_S	average brightness of a radio source [equation (1.9)]
$\boldsymbol{j}$	net current density [equation (2.49)]
$\boldsymbol{J}$	total current density [equation (2.51)]
J	average intensity [equation (A.14)]
$\boldsymbol{J}_{\mathrm{conv}}$	convective current density [equation (2.50)]
k	wave number
$\boldsymbol{k}$	direction toward observer, $\equiv \boldsymbol{R}_0$*
L	diameter of a paraboloidal antenna; luminosity [equation (7.3)]
m	mass of a particle
M	mass of a particle
n	index of refraction; number of Fourier harmonic (Chapter 3)
$\boldsymbol{n}$	normal to a surface; direction of instantaneous electron velocity $\equiv \boldsymbol{\beta}$*
N	particle number density
N_0	constant in electron energy distribution of the form $N_E = N_0 E^{-\gamma}$

$\mathcal{N}$	number of particles
$\mathcal{N}_0$	constant in electron energy distribution of the form $\mathcal{N}_E = \mathcal{N}_0 E^{-\gamma}$
$\boldsymbol{p}$	momentum
p	power of synchrotron emission; scalar pressure
p_{rad}	radiation pressure [equation (A.20)]
$\mathfrak{p}_i$	generalized momentum
P	momentum of electron (Chapter 5)
$P(\vartheta, \varphi)$	antenna pattern
$\boldsymbol{q}$	heat flow vector [equation (2.35)]
$\mathfrak{q}_i$	generalized coordinate
$\boldsymbol{r}_C$	guiding center [equation (2.98)]
$\boldsymbol{r}_H$	radius of gyration of an electron in a magnetic field [equation (2.94)]
$\boldsymbol{r}'$	radius vector of the volume element $d\tau$ (Chapter 3)
$\boldsymbol{r}(t)$	radius vector of the point charge
R	resistance (Chapter 1)
$\boldsymbol{R}$	current coordinate or, in particular, radius vector of observer
$\boldsymbol{R}_0$	distance between observer and volume element or point charge, $= \boldsymbol{R} - \boldsymbol{r}'$
s	path length along line of sight
S	baseline of an interferometer expressed in wavelengths; source function [equation (A.23)]
t	time
t'	retarded time, $= t - [R_0(t')/c]$ (Chapter 3); time elapsed since injection of relativistic particles began (Chapter 6)
T	absolute temperature
T_A	antenna temperature [equation (1.24)]
T_B	brightness temperature [equation (1.25)]
T_e	electron temperature
T_R	noise temperature of a receiver
$\boldsymbol{u}$	peculiar velocities of particles
u_{rad}	radiation energy density [equation (A.19)]
U	Stokes parameter [equation (A.8)]
$\boldsymbol{U}$	particle velocity in phase space
$\boldsymbol{v}$	particle velocity
v_T	root mean square particle velocity
V	voltage; Stokes parameter [equation (A.9)]; amplitude of visibility function of an interferometer [equation (1.46)]
$\boldsymbol{V}$	average velocity of particles [equation (2.28)]
V_{gr}	group velocity
V_{ph}	phase velocity
V_r	radial velocity
V_A	Alfvén velocity
V_S	sound velocity
$\mathcal{V}$	complex visibility function of an interferometer [equation (1.46)]
w	velocity of magnetic inhomogeneity (magnetic mirror)
W	photon energy (Chapter 5); power; also power per unit bandwidth

W_A power delivered from an antenna
W_I average power delivered from an interferometer
W_R noise power per unit bandwidth of a receiver
x $= \nu/\nu_C$
x_H $= \nu/\nu_H$
x_L $= \nu/\nu_L$
x_M $= \nu/\nu_M$
x_T $= \nu/\nu_T$
$X_{F/R}$ ratio of Fermi threshold to rest energies [equation (2.13)]
$X_{H/R}$ ratio of magnetic to rest energies [equation (2.83)]
$X_{T/E}$ ratio of thermal to Coulomb energies [equation (2.10)]
$X_{T/F}$ ratio of thermal to Fermi threshold energies [equation (2.12)]
$X_{T/H}$ ratio of thermal to magnetic energies [equation (2.84)]
$X_{T/R}$ ratio of thermal to rest energies [equation (2.11)]
Y momentum of electron in units of mc (Chapter 5)
z redshift [equation (7.1)]
Z atomic number

Greek Letters

α $= \nu/\nu_S$; angle between direction of initial or final photon and direction of electron velocity (Chapter 5); spectral index
α_B statistical betatron acceleration parameter [equation (2.105)]
α_F statistical Fermi acceleration parameter [equation (2.110)]
$\boldsymbol{\beta}$ $= \boldsymbol{v}/c$
$\tilde{\beta}$ $= d\chi_F/ds$
β_T $= v_T/c$
γ $= E/mc^2 = (1-\beta^2)^{-1/2}$
δ $= \kappa/\tilde{\beta}$ [equation (3.68)]; angle between plane of polarization of photon and scattering plane (Chapter 5)
$\mathcal{E}$ emission coefficient
ϵ thermal energy density; photon energy in units of mc^2 (Chapter 5)
ϵ_m stray factor of an antenna [equation (1.17)]
ϵ_M beam efficiency of an antenna [equation (1.16)]
ζ $= \gamma\nu_0/\nu_C = \nu_S/\nu_0\gamma$; coefficient in equation for electron energy losses [equation (6.11)]
η $= \beta_S$ [equation (3.68)]; angle between direction $\boldsymbol{\beta}$ of electron's velocity and direction $\boldsymbol{k}$ toward observer; coefficient in equation for electron energy losses [equation (6.11)]
η_F Fermi acceleration parameter [equation (2.112)]
θ angle between directions of electron velocity and that of magnetic field; scattering angle: i.e., angle between initial and final directions of photon (Chapter 5)
ϑ angle between direction of magnetic field and direction toward observer

κ	absorption coefficient corrected for stimulated emission [equation (A.41)]
$\tilde{\kappa}$	absorption coefficient [equation (A.22)]
λ	wavelength; also $\cos\theta$, where θ is scattering angle (Chapter 5)
λ_i	critical impact parameter of particles in plasma [equation (2.1)]
λ_O	mean free path of particles in plasma [equation (2.3)]
λ_P	average distance between particles in plasma [equation (2.4)]
λ_D	Debye length [equation (2.9)]
λ_E	characteristic length of electron wave [equation (2.76)]
λ_F	mean free path against collisions with magnetic mirrors
λ_m	$= \lambda(\nu_m)$
Λ	photon wavelength (Chapter 5)
μ	$\equiv \cos\alpha$, where α is angle between plane of polarization of photon and scattering plane (Chapter 5)
ν	frequency
ν_{RF}	signal frequency
ν_{IF}	intermediate frequency of a receiver
ν_{LO}	frequency of local oscillator of a receiver
ν_C	collision frequency (Chapter 2); critical frequency [equation (3.28)]
ν_S	$= 2\nu_0^2/3\nu_G \sin\vartheta$ [equation (4.10)]
ν_0	plasma frequency [equation (2.72)]
ν_1	frequency at which optical depth is equal to unity
ν_G	Larmor frequency [equation (2.57)]
ν_H	electron gyrofrequency [equation (2.93)]; also $\nu_C(E_H)$
ν_m	$= 0.29\ \nu_C$
ν_M	$= \nu_C(E = kT)$
ν_T	$= \nu_C(E_T)$
ν_L	$= \nu_C(E_L)$; frequency of spectral line (Chapter 8)
ξ	coefficient in equation for electron energy losses [equation (6.11)]
π_{ij}	kinetic pressure tensor [equation (2.32)]
Π	degree of polarization [equation (1.39)]
Π_{ij}	total pressure tensor [equation (2.31)]
ρ	mass density [equation (2.27)]
σ	surface area; phase of visibility function of an interferometer [equation (1.46)]
Σ	total scattering cross section
$\frac{d\Sigma}{d\Omega}$	differential scattering cross section
τ	integration constant of a receiver; optical depth [equation (A.27). The term "optical depth" does not, of course, presume that the quantity refers to the optical part of the spectrum only.]
τ_m	$= \tau(\nu_m)$
τ_C	lifetime of an electron against Compton losses
τ_S	lifetime of an electron against synchrotron radiation losses
φ	electromagnetic scalar potential

ϕ	magnetic flux; electron recoil angle: i.e., angle between direction of incident photon and recoil electron (Chapter 5)
χ	angle between y-axis and projection of direction of final photon on yz plane, perpendicular to velocity of electron (see Figure 5.5)
χ_F	Faraday rotation angle
χ_H	angle defined in Figure 3.10
ψ	angle between direction of original velocity of electron (i.e., momentary velocity in plane containing magnetic field and direction toward observer) and direction toward the observer; angle between direction of polarization of intitial and scattered photons (Chapter 5)
ω	circular frequency $= 2\pi\nu$, for all subscripts
Ω	solid angle
Ω_A	beam area of an antenna, [equation (1.4)]
Ω_m	solid angle of minor lobes of an antenna [equation (1.14)]
Ω_M	solid angle of main lobe of an antenna [equation (1.13)]
Ω_S	solid angle subtended by a radio source

Radio Astrophysics

1
Radio Astronomical Measurements

1.1 Introduction; The Radio Window

The earth's atmosphere absorbs electromagnetic radiation of most wavelengths. However, there are bands in which the atmosphere is essentially transparent, and two of these are wide enough to be of major importance. The most familiar is the "optical window," which extends from a wavelength of 0.3 μ to about 1 μ. The second is the "radio window," which extends from 1 mm to about 15 m. Figure 1.1 is a schematic representation of the transparency of the earth's atmosphere.

The absorption at the short-wavelength side of the optical window is mainly molecular (ozone) (Figure 1.2). As the wavelength of the radiation approaches X-rays, atomic absorption dominates; and in the very hard X-ray and γ-ray region, nuclear absorption is the most important. The absorption band between the long-wave side of the optical window and the short-wave side of the radio window is caused mainly by infrared absorption bands of water and carbon dioxide. There are a few bands of partial transparency between 1 μ and 24 μ. In the wavelength range of 1 mm to 10 mm the absorption is due mainly to oxygen and water vapor. The radio window is cut off on the long-wave side at the critical frequency of reflection by the ionosphere. Since the critical frequency for reflection depends on the ionospheric electron density, which is variable, observations can often be made below the 20 MHz (15 m) cutoff frequency down

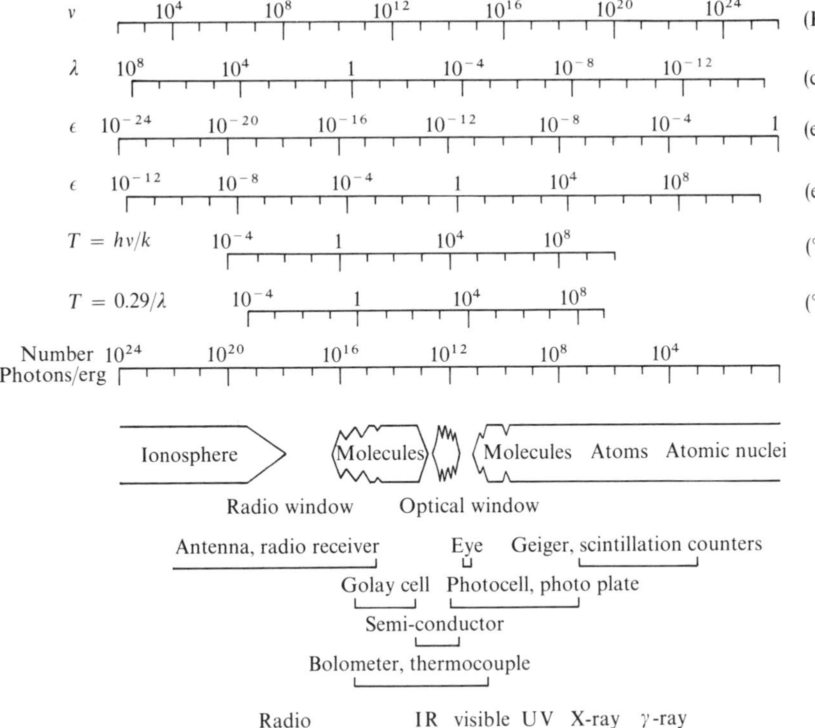

Fig. 1.1 Atmospheric transparency as a function of wavelength (schematic).

to 9 MHz and occasionally to 1 MHz. The electron density in the ionosphere varies with the time of day, geographic location of the observer, solar activity, and so on.

Both the radio and optical windows are affected by refraction due to the variations of atmospheric density and refractive index with altitude. This has the effect of making the source appear higher above the horizon than it actually is. Refraction in the short-wavelength region of the radio window is approximately twice the optical refraction, and it varies with the water content. Its typical magnitude is 0°.5 at 1° of elevation, and it decreases rapidly with increase of the elevation angle. Long waves are also affected by the ionosphere, which increases the refraction and is responsible for the long-wave cutoff in the radio window. A typical ionospheric refraction at 60 MHz is 20′ for a source 5° above the horizon. The properties of the atmosphere do not depend on source altitude alone. In the optical window local inhomogeneities cause the scintillation of stars. In the radio window the fluctuations in the electron density in the ionosphere produce the effect of scintillation for radio sources with angular sizes up to 30′. The time scale of such intensity fluctuations is of the order of one minute at wavelengths of 1.5 m and larger. Electron density fluctuations in the interplanetary medium carried along by the solar wind are the cause of a similar effect of scintillation of radio sources with a quasi-period of the order of one second. The sources must be less than about one second in size for this effect to occur. Observations of this effect are used to estimate the angular size of scintillating sources if the size is too small to be determined by interferometer techniques, or for convenience even when interferometry would succeed.

Background radiation is much more intense relative to the strength of the sources in the radio window than in the optical region. At the low-frequency end of the radio window, for example, the total background radiation is 10^4 times that of the sun. The strongest radio sources observed from the earth at low frequencies are the sun, Jupiter, and Cassiopeia A (a supernova remnant which is a galactic synchrotron source). The sun does not occupy nearly so dominant a position in the radio sky as it does in the optical sky. The flux from the quiet sun (at sunspot maximum) at 100 MHz is 4×10^{-22} W/m^2/Hz increasing to 5×10^{-22} W/m^2/Hz at 10^4 MHz, whereas the flux from Cassiopeia A is between 2×10^{-22} W/m^2/Hz at 100 MHz and 5×10^{-24} W/m^2/Hz at 10^4 MHz.

The optical window contains far more spectral lines of elements, and hence contains more information on the abundance of elements, than the radio window. The dominant mechanism producing the continuous spectrum is also different in the two regions. The optical spectra of cosmic objects are produced mainly by the thermal mechanism. The radio continua are thought to be produced by the synchrotron mechanism in the majority of radio sources and therefore yield information on cosmic magnetic fields and relativistic particles.

1.2 Response of an Antenna to Incoming Radiation

The purpose of this chapter is to familiarize the reader with the origin, character, and accuracy of the observational data which are fundamental to the astrophysical arguments aimed at the understanding of the physics and structure of radio sources. For a more detailed account of the field of observational radio astronomy, see the bibliographical notes at the end of this chapter.

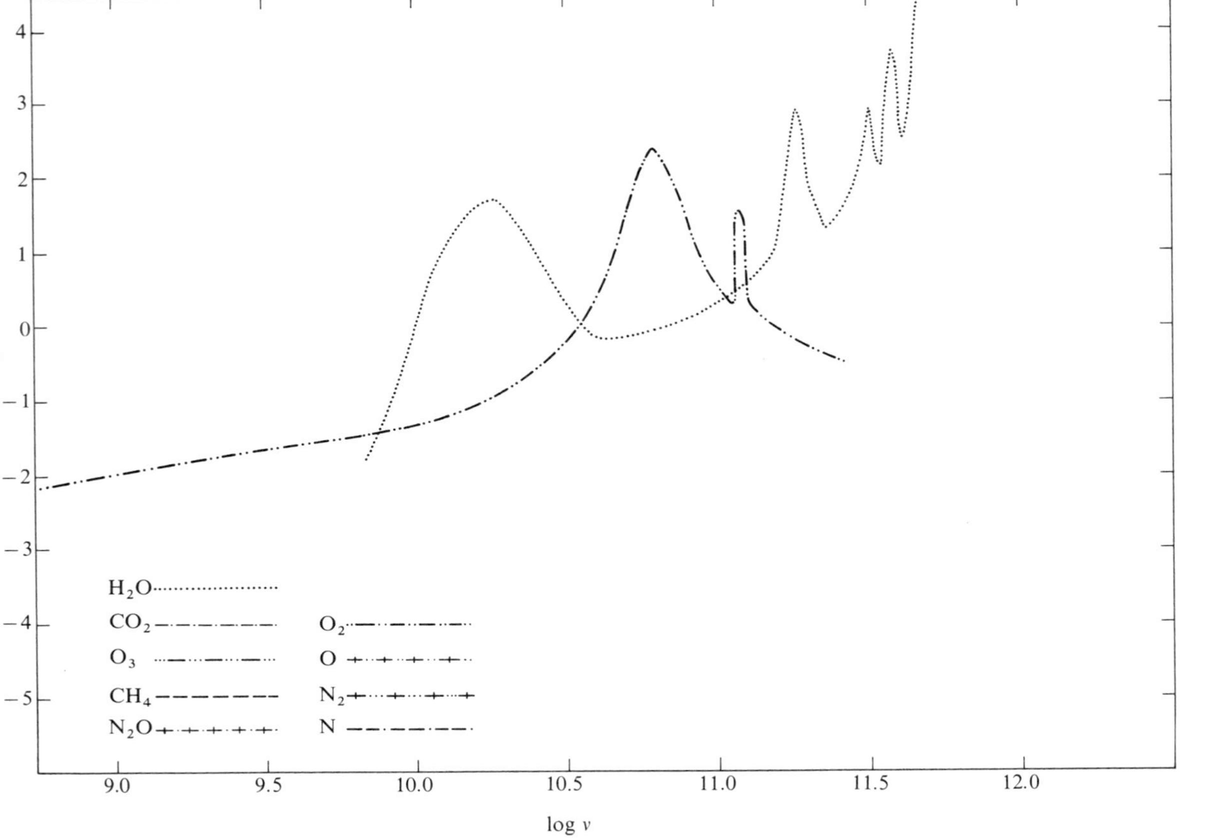

Fig. 1-2A Atmospheric absorption κ (referred to gas under normal conditions; i.e., 0°C and 760 mm Hg) as a function of frequency in the ultraviolet, visual, infrared and millimeter regions (continued on facing page).

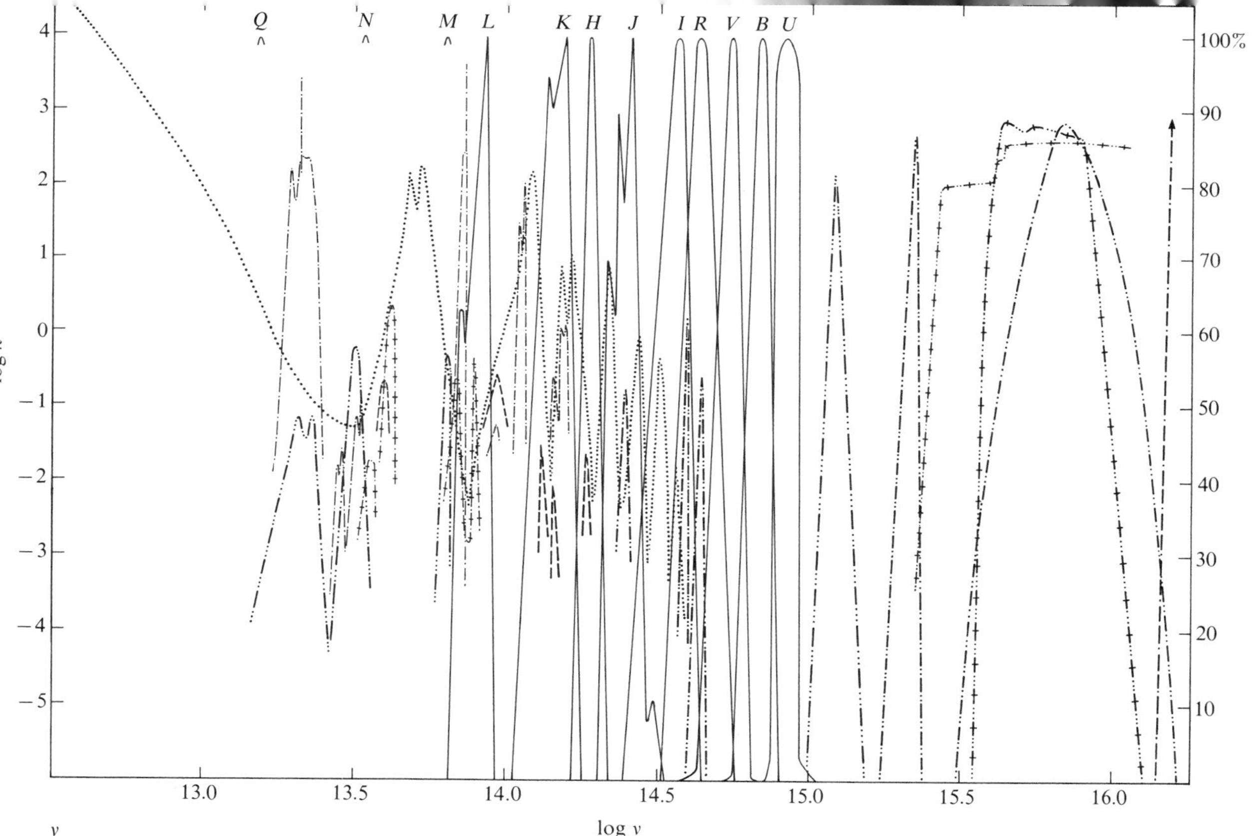

Fig. 1.2B A continuation of Fig. 1.2A, showing also the response curves of the *UBVRIJHKL* photometric system and the maxima (only) of the response curves of the *MNQ* photometric system (right scale).

A radio telescope is a device for receiving and measuring cosmic radio noise. The antenna collects the energy of cosmic radio waves of a determined state of polarization and delivers this energy to the receiver through a suitable transmission line. It also limits the portion of the sky from which radiation is received. The impedances of the antenna, transmission line, and the receiver's input are properly matched to minimize losses. The antenna produces some filtering of frequencies, but it is the receiver that usually determines the frequency bandwidth of a radio telescope. The frequency range of paraboloidal antennas is rather large; it is limited by surface accuracy at high frequencies and by the diameter of paraboloidal mirrors at low frequencies. (Diffraction effects are the cause of very low directivity of paraboloids at long wavelengths.) The feed, normally located in the focus of the paraboloid, is generally much more selective than the paraboloid itself; however, it can usually be interchanged if observations at different wavelengths are to be carried on. Other types of antennas are characterized by narrower frequency bands.

Antennas respond to polarized radiation (the polarization is in general elliptical, in most cases very close to linear). Therefore the antenna responds to one-half of the incident energy flux if the incident radiation is unpolarized. (This statement applies to coherent detectors and not, for example, to a bolometer, which receives both polarizations.) In the receiver the electromagnetic oscillations are filtered, amplified by many orders of magnitude, detected, and finally measured at the receiver's output. Measurements of cosmic radio power are usually determined by comparing the observed power with a known power generated by a calibrating noise generator.

Let us recall the expression (see Appendix 1) relating the intensity of radiation I_ν to the amount of power $dW_\nu d\nu$, or energy $dE_\nu d\nu$, in time dt, flowing across an area in a frequency interval from ν to $\nu + d\nu$ into the directions confined to a solid angle $d\Omega$ around the direction making an angle ϑ with the outward normal $\mathbf{n}$ to $d\sigma$ (this expression is considered to be the definition of the intensity I_ν):

$$dW_\nu d\nu = \frac{dE_\nu}{dt}\, d\nu = I_\nu \cos\vartheta \; d\Omega \; d\sigma \; d\nu. \tag{1.1}$$

The geometry pertinent to this definition is illustrated in Figure 1.3. If $d\sigma$ is identified with a surface element of a transmitting antenna, $dW_\nu d\nu$ will then be the power emitted (within $d\nu$ and within $d\Omega$ around the

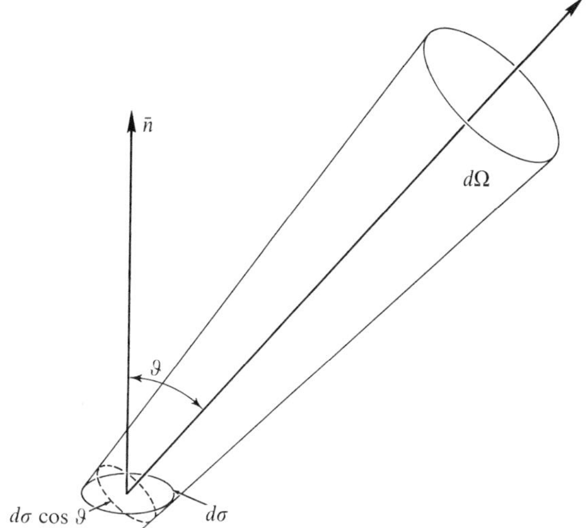

Fig. 1.3 Introducing the definition of the intensity of radiation.

direction within an angle ϑ from the normal $\boldsymbol{n}$) by an element $d\sigma$ of the surface of that antenna. I_ν will be the intensity of this emission. If $d\sigma$ is identified with a surface element of a receiving antenna, the absorption of radiation from the sky by the antenna will be represented by the same equation (1.1), in which $dW_\nu d\nu$ now stands for the power absorbed by the antenna (equal to minus the power emitted by the same antenna when transmitting) and I_ν stands for the brightness† of the radiation received (equal to minus the radiation emitted by the same antenna when transmitting if the same amount of power $dW_\nu d\nu$ was involved).

In general, brightness depends on direction. We can use any two coordinates to characterize this direction—celestial coordinates in the horizon, or equatorial coordinates, or any other system. The response (i.e., the power absorbed) by an element $d\sigma$ of a receiving antenna to radiation coming from within a finite solid angle Ω will depend on the brightness distribution of the radiation in the sky within the region subtended by the solid angle Ω. The actual antenna surface is composed of many elements with normals pointed in different directions (to increase the directivity of the antenna; see the following sections of this chapter). In order to characterize the response of the entire antenna to the incoming

† In radio astronomy brightness is sometimes designated by B instead of I. We will retain I as the designation for brightness in order to avoid confusion with the Planck function, which is usually represented by B.

radiation, we will introduce a function called the *antenna pattern*,† which describes the antenna response as a function of direction. The antenna pattern is the same for receiving and transmitting, as can be shown from the second law of thermodynamics.

If $P_\nu(\vartheta, \varphi)$ is the antenna pattern (normalized in the sense that $P_\nu(0,0) = 1$) and A_e is the effective aperture (effective surface area) of the antenna, we can integrate equation (1.1) over a solid angle Ω and over the surface of the antenna:

$$W_\nu d\nu = \frac{1}{2} A_e \, d\nu \iint_\Omega I_\nu(\vartheta, \varphi) \, P_\nu(\vartheta, \varphi) \, d\Omega, \tag{1.2}$$

where ϑ is the angle between a given direction and the direction of the antenna axis (the direction for which $P_\nu = 1$). The antenna pattern $P_\nu(\vartheta, \varphi)$ replaces the $\cos\vartheta$ response pattern of a flat surface $d\sigma$. The antenna pattern is a dimensionless quantity, and the effective aperture A_e has the dimensions of a surface. Since the antenna responds to radiation of one polarization only, the factor $\frac{1}{2}$ in equation (1.2) is appropriate if the incident radiation is unpolarized. The response of an antenna to polarized radiation will be discussed later.

In the case of constant brightness with respect to direction, equation (1.2) integrated over 4π steradians can be written as

$$W_\nu d\nu = \frac{1}{2} A_e \, d\nu \, I_\nu \, \Omega_A, \tag{1.3}$$

where Ω_A, defined by

$$\Omega_A = \iint_{4\pi} P_\nu(\vartheta, \varphi) \, d\Omega, \tag{1.4}$$

is called the *beam area* of the antenna‡ and its units are steradians. Equation (1.3) can be used when observing an extended source of uniform brightness with dimensions larger than the beam area.

In the case of a localized source, i.e., a source with a brightness dis-

† At small distances from the antenna the pattern is a function of distance *(near-field pattern)*; this dependence on distance becomes unimportant at sufficiently large distances and is entirely negligible in radio astronomy, where the antenna pattern is considered to be a function of direction only *(far-field pattern)*. In this book we will refer to the *power pattern* of an antenna, i.e., to the pattern expressed in terms of the field intensity. The antenna pattern, in general, depends on the frequency.

‡ Ω_A is also called the beam solid angle of an antenna or sometimes the pattern solid angle.

tribution such that most of the radiation comes from a small (but finite) region of the sky,[†] if the brightness I_ν can be considered uniform within Ω_S and zero outside this region, and if the source is much smaller than the antenna beam area (i.e., if $\Omega_S \ll \Omega_A$), equation (1.2) can be written as

$$W_\nu d\nu = \frac{1}{2} A_e \, d\nu \, I_\nu \, \Omega_S \tag{1.5}$$

if that the antenna beam is aligned with the source.

The flux F_ν of a source[‡] is

$$F_\nu = \iint_\Omega I_\nu(\vartheta, \varphi) \cos\vartheta \, d\Omega, \tag{1.6}$$

while the apparent flux (or observed flux) of a source is defined as

$$F_{\nu A} = \iint_\Omega I_\nu(\vartheta, \varphi) \, P_\nu(\vartheta, \varphi) \, d\Omega. \tag{1.7}$$

The apparent (observed) flux will be equal to the "true" flux if $P_\nu(\vartheta, \varphi) = \cos\vartheta$ or if the source is small compared with the antenna beam area, that is, if $P_\nu(\vartheta, \varphi) \approx 1$ and $\cos\vartheta \approx 1$ in the region occupied by the source.

We will define the observed brightness (or apparent brightness) as

$$I_{\nu A} = \frac{F_{\nu A}}{\Omega_A} = \frac{1}{\Omega_A} \iint_\Omega I_\nu(\vartheta, \varphi) \, P(\vartheta, \varphi) \, d\Omega \tag{1.8}$$

and the average brightness of the source as

$$I_{\nu S} = \frac{F_\nu}{\Omega_S} = \frac{1}{\Omega_S} \iint_\Omega I_\nu(\vartheta, \varphi) \cos\vartheta \, d\Omega. \tag{1.9}$$

For a localized source of much smaller extent than the antenna beam area ($\Omega_S \ll \Omega_A$), we have

$$I_{\nu A} = \frac{F_{\nu A}}{\Omega_A} \approx \frac{F_\nu}{\Omega_A} = \frac{\Omega_S}{\Omega_A} I_{\nu S}. \tag{1.10}$$

For an extended source of uniform brightness ($I_\nu = I_{\nu S}$) of much larger

---

† Such sources are sometimes called point sources; however, truly "point" sources (sources subtending infinitesimal solid angles) do not exist. Source components with sizes of the order of 10^{-3} seconds of arc seem to be the closest approximation to point sources.

‡ We are referring here to the flux-per-unit frequency. This quantity is often called "specific flux" or "flux density." For brevity we will call this quantity simply "flux." In referring to the flux integrated over some region of frequencies, we will use the term "total flux."

extent than the antenna beam area ($\Omega_S \gg \Omega_A$), we have

$$I_{\nu A} = \frac{F_{\nu A}}{\Omega_A} \approx \frac{\Omega_A I_{\nu S}}{\Omega_A} = I_{\nu S}. \tag{1.11}$$

As indicated in the Notation, we are using the CGS system of units and the Gaussian system for electromagnetic quantities. In the CGS system the unit of flux is erg sec^{-1} cm^{-2} Hz^{-1}, and the unit of brightness is erg sec^{-1} cm^{-2} Hz^{-1} steradian^{-1}. In observational radio astronomy the MKS system is used, and the units of flux and brightness are W m^{-2} Hz^{-1} and W m^{-2} Hz^{-1} steradian^{-1}, respectively. One W m^{-2} Hz^{-1} is sometimes called one jansky, while 10^{-26} W m^{-2} Hz^{-1} is usually called a flux unit (f.u.) since the flux of the majority of observed radio sources is of that order of magnitude. We will note here that the flux expressed in CGS units is represented by a number 1000 times larger than the number representing the same flux in MKS units. Therefore one flux unit is equal to 10^{-23} erg sec^{-1} cm^{-2} Hz^{-1}.

If we are interested in the total power W within a bandwidth $\Delta\nu$, we have to integrate equation (1.2) from ν to $\nu + \Delta\nu$ over $d\nu$. However, since radioastronomical observations are very monochromatic (compared to optical observations), i.e., the bandwidth is small compared with both the mean frequency ν of observation and the extent of the radio window, we can usually neglect the dependence of I_ν and P_ν on frequency within the bandwidth $\Delta\nu$ and write

$$W = \frac{1}{2} A_e \, \Delta\nu \iint_\Omega I_\nu(\vartheta, \varphi) \, P_\nu(\vartheta, \varphi) \, d\Omega. \tag{1.12}$$

We will delete the subscript ν in all subsequent formulas.

The directional properties of an antenna are characterized by the antenna pattern (Figure 1.4). In order to specify the pattern, a three-dimensional diagram is necessary in principle unless the pattern is symmetrical. The main features of the antenna pattern can be described by specifying the angular width of the main lobe at the half-power level (called the *half-power beam width*, HPBW) or at the level of the first nulls (called the *beam width between the first nulls*, BWFN). The pattern is also often characterized in terms of the following solid angles: *beam solid angle* Ω_A [cf. equation (1.4)], *main-lobe solid angle* Ω_M,

$$\Omega_M = \iint_{\text{main lobe}} P(\vartheta, \varphi) \, d\Omega, \tag{1.13}$$

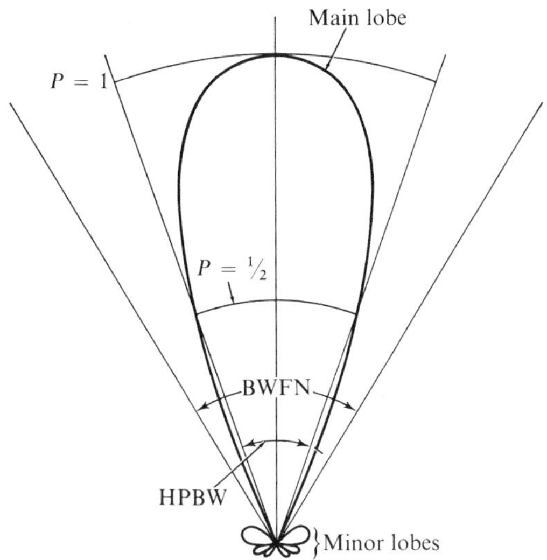

Fig. 1.4 Polar diagram of an antenna pattern.

and *minor-lobes solid angle* Ω_m,

$$\Omega_m = \iint_{\text{minor lobes}} P(\vartheta, \varphi)\ d\Omega\,, \tag{1.14}$$

or by the following ratios of these quantities: *directivity* D,

$$D = \frac{4\pi}{\Omega_A}; \tag{1.15}$$

beam efficiency ϵ_M,

$$\epsilon_M = \frac{\Omega_M}{\Omega_A}; \tag{1.16}$$

and *stray factor* ϵ_m,

$$\epsilon_m = \frac{\Omega_m}{\Omega_A}. \tag{1.17}$$

The directivity of an antenna can also be defined as the ratio of the maximum power radiated by the antenna (in the direction of $P = 1$) to the average power (over all directions). This definition is equivalent to equation (1.15). It is formulated for a transmitting case, but it is a characteristic of the antenna in general because the transmitting and the receiving properties of the antenna are the same.

Frequently the directional properties of an antenna are characterized by the dimensionless function $G(\vartheta, \varphi)$ instead of $P(\vartheta, \varphi)$. This function is called the *directive gain* of the antenna and is simply the product of the directivity D and the pattern function $P(\vartheta, \varphi)$:

$$G(\vartheta, \varphi) = D \cdot P(\vartheta, \varphi). \tag{1.18}$$

Maximum gain, of course, is equal to the directivity D. In other words, the directive gain of an antenna can be described as the ratio of power radiated in a given direction by an antenna to power radiated in the same direction by an isotropic antenna under the same conditions.

We will now consider a lossless antenna enclosed by a blackbody at an absolute temperature T. Suppose that within the blackbody enclosure there is another small blackbody subtending a solid angle $\Delta\Omega_S$ as seen by the antenna. The small blackbody also has the temperature T. The antenna is connected to a matched resistance R of temperature T. The entire system is therefore in thermodynamic equilibrium, and the amount of energy radiated from the antenna to the blackbody is equal to the amount of energy radiated in the opposite direction:

$$kT\,\Delta\nu\, G(\vartheta, \varphi)\frac{\Delta\Omega_S}{4\pi} = 2kT\,\Delta\nu\lambda^{-2} \cdot \frac{1}{2} A_e P(\vartheta, \varphi)\, \Delta\Omega_S. \tag{1.19}$$

On the left-hand side the term $kT\Delta\nu$ is the thermal noise power of a matched resistance at a temperature T. On the right-hand side of the above equation the Rayleigh-Jeans approximation for blackbody radiation is used. The factor $\frac{1}{2}$ accounts for the fact that this radiation is not polarized, while the antenna responds to only one polarization. Equation (1.19) can be simplified to the form,

$$D = \frac{4\pi}{\lambda^2} A_e, \tag{1.20}$$

which gives us a *relationship between the directivity and the effective aperture of the antenna*. It can also be written as follows by the use of equation (1.15)

$$A_e \Omega_A = \lambda^2. \tag{1.21}$$

The main lobe of the antenna pattern corresponds to the primary maximum of a diffraction pattern; side lobes correspond to secondary maxima. The size of the main lobe will therefore determine the *resolving power* of the antenna. A pair of sources with an angular distance much smaller than the width of the main lobe of the antenna pattern cannot be resolved by this antenna. For example, if L is the diameter of a paraboloidal antenna, we have $A_e \approx \pi L^2/4$ (in reality, the effective aperture is smaller than the geometrical aperture of the antenna); and using equations (1.16) and (1.20), we can write

$$\frac{4\lambda^2}{\pi L^2} \approx \frac{\lambda^2}{A_e} = \Omega_A = \frac{\Omega_M}{\epsilon_M} \approx \frac{\vartheta^2{}_{\text{HPBW}}}{\epsilon_M} \tag{1.22}$$

Since $\epsilon_M \approx 0.75$ for most of the large antennas, we have for the half-power beam width in radians

$$\vartheta^2{}_{\text{HPBW}} \approx \frac{\lambda^2}{L^2}. \tag{1.23}$$

Equation (1.23) gives the resolving power of the antenna in terms of its diameter L and the wavelength λ of observation. For a 250 ft paraboloid ϑ_{HPBW} is approximately equal to 50′ of arc at a wavelength of one meter. This much lower resolving power of radio telescopes than that of optical telescopes is a consequence of the much larger wavelength of the radiation received.

The power W delivered to an antenna is often expressed in terms of the *antenna temperature* T_A defined by the expression,

$$\Delta\nu k T_A = W. \tag{1.24}$$

The antenna temperature is related neither to the temperature of the material of the antenna itself nor to that of the surrounding medium. It does depend on the temperature of the bodies whose radiation is being received if the mechanism producing the radiation is thermal. The physical meaning of the antenna temperature becomes apparent from the two following statements: if the antenna is surrounded by a blackbody at a temperature T_A, then the antenna will absorb the power given by equation (1.24) provided that there are no losses in the antenna and in the surrounding medium; furthermore, if a matched impedance at a temperature T_A is connected to the terminals of the antenna, then it will deliver to the antenna the power given by equation (1.24).

A source of radio radiation is often characterized by the *brightness temperature* T_B instead of by the brightness I. The brightness temperature, introduced through the Rayleigh-Jeans approximation for the blackbody law, is defined by

$$T_B = \frac{\lambda^2}{2k} I, \tag{1.25}$$

The physical meaning of the brightness temperature is very limited, because the brightness temperature is the temperature of a blackbody whose radiant intensity in the range of frequencies from ν to $\nu + d\nu$ is the same as that of the observed source, and the vast majority of cosmic radio sources are not even thermal. The brightness temperature of a given source may vary widely with frequency.

Both the antenna and brightness temperatures are related to the incoming radiation from a source. Brightness temperature characterizes the intensity of this radiation, and antenna temperature characterizes the power received by a particular antenna absorbing this radiation. The relationship between brightness and antenna temperatures can be obtained from equation (1.2) by the use of equations (1.21), (1.24), and (1.25):

$$T_A \iint P(\vartheta, \varphi)\, d\Omega = \iint T_B(\vartheta, \varphi)\, P(\vartheta, \varphi)\, d\Omega. \tag{1.26}$$

This relation can be simplified in the two limiting cases for an extended source (T_B constant within the antenna beam solid angle),

$$T_A = T_B, \tag{1.27}$$

and for a compact source ($\Omega_S \ll \Omega_A$),

$$T_A = T_B \frac{\Omega_S}{\Omega_A}. \tag{1.28}$$

When an antenna is scanning a source with a brightness distribution, $T_B(x)$, the observed antenna temperature in the one-dimensional case is

$$T_A(x) \int_{-\infty}^{+\infty} P(\xi)\, d\xi = \int_{-\infty}^{+\infty} P(\xi - x)\, T_B(\xi)\, d\xi, \tag{1.29}$$

where $P(\xi)$ is the (one-dimensional) antenna directional diagram. Equation (1.29) describes the smoothing process of the temperature distribution $T_B(x)$ by an antenna with a pattern $P(\xi)$. The smoothing process filters out all the (spatial) frequencies in the brightness distribution $T_B(x)$ higher than a cutoff frequency $S = L/\lambda$, where L is the length of the aperture and λ is the wavelength of observation. The observed antenna temperature distribution $T_A(x)$ is therefore not sufficient for a unique determination of the brightness distribution $T_B(x)$ since it does not contain information on frequencies higher than S.

1.3 Response of an Antenna to Polarized Radiation

We can describe the receiving properties of an antenna in a given direction by the voltages $\tilde{E}_1$ and $\tilde{E}_2$,

$$\begin{aligned} \tilde{E}_1 &= \tilde{E}^0 \cos \tilde{\alpha}, \\ \tilde{E}_2 &= \tilde{E}^0 \sin \tilde{\alpha}\, e^{-i\tilde{\delta}}, \end{aligned} \tag{1.30}$$

induced, respectively, by horizontal and vertical waves of unit amplitude and polarization.† When a plane wave of arbitrary amplitude and polarization,

$$E_1 = E^0 \cos\alpha\,,$$
$$E_2 = E^0 \sin\alpha\, e^{i\delta}\,, \tag{1.31}$$

is received by an antenna with properties described by equation (1.30), its response will be a voltage proportional to

$$V = |E_1\tilde{E}_1 + E_2\tilde{E}_2| = E^0\tilde{E}^0\,|\cos\alpha\cos\tilde{\alpha} + \sin\alpha\sin\tilde{\alpha}\, e^{i(\delta-\tilde{\delta})}|$$
$$= E^0\tilde{E}^0\cos\gamma\,. \tag{1.32}$$

The last equality is the definition of the angle $\gamma (0 \leq \gamma \leq \pi/2)$. We can compute $\cos^2\gamma$ from the definition of γ. If we remember that the absolute value of a complex number $|a + ib|$ is equal to $\sqrt{(a^2 + b^2)}$, then we can introduce $\cos^2\gamma$ into the trigonometric identity $\cos 2\gamma = 2\cos^2\gamma - 1$ in order to obtain

$$\cos 2\gamma = \cos 2\alpha \cos 2\tilde{\alpha} + \sin 2\alpha \sin 2\tilde{\alpha} \cos(\delta - \tilde{\delta})\,. \tag{1.33}$$

The physical meaning of the angle γ becomes apparent if one recalls the representation of the polarization state on the Poincaré sphere (see Appendix 1). If P represents the state of polarization of the incident wave (equation 1.31) and $\tilde{P}$ the polarization state of the antenna (equation 1.30), then by equation (1.33) 2γ is the angular distance between the points P and $\tilde{P}$. The factor $\cos\gamma$ appearing in equation (1.32) is therefore a consequence of the polarization mismatching between the antenna and the wave. The polarization of the antenna and of the wave will be matched ($\cos\gamma = 1$) if the polarization ellipses of the wave transmitted by the antenna and the wave incident on the antenna have the same ellipticity and orientation, but the opposite sense of rotation.

In equation (1.32) $\tilde{E}^0$ has the dimension of length (*effective height* of the antenna); and, of course, $(\tilde{E}^0)^2$ has the dimension of area. The power available from the antenna, per unit bandwidth, due to an elliptically polarized wave equation (1.31) coming from a point source is therefore

$$W = FA_e\cos^2\gamma, \tag{1.34}$$

where $A_e = (\tilde{E}^0)^2$ and F is the flux of the incident wave.

---

† The minus sign in the phase shift is connected with the reversal of time which transforms a transmitting antenna into a receiving antenna. An antenna transmitting, for example, left-handed elliptically polarized waves will receive right-handed elliptically polarized waves.

As shown in Appendix 1, the completely polarized incident wave can be represented in terms of the Stokes parameters Q, U, and V or by the parameters I, β, and φ,

$$\begin{aligned} Q &= I \cos 2\beta \cos 2\varphi, \\ U &= I \cos 2\beta \sin 2\varphi, \\ V &= I \sin 2\beta, \end{aligned} \tag{1.35}$$

instead of by equation (1.31). Similarly, the properties of the antenna can be described by a set of "Stokes parameters":

$$\begin{aligned} \tilde{Q} &= \tilde{I} \cos 2\tilde{\beta} \cos 2\tilde{\varphi}, \\ \tilde{U} &= \tilde{I} \cos 2\tilde{\beta} \sin 2\tilde{\varphi}, \\ \tilde{V} &= \tilde{I} \sin 2\tilde{\beta}. \end{aligned} \tag{1.36}$$

If, for the point source, the Stokes parameters representing the wave are expressed in flux units (i.e., $I \to F$), and the ones representing the properties of the antenna are expressed in the units of the effective area of the antenna (i.e., $I \to A_e$), then we can show that,† per unit bandwidth,

$$W = FA_e \cos^2 \gamma = \frac{1}{2} (I\tilde{I} + Q\tilde{Q} + U\tilde{U} + V\tilde{V}). \tag{1.37}$$

The incident wave can be decomposed into one wave having the state of polarization matching that of the antenna and another having the opposite polarization. The antenna will respond only to the polarization-matched wave and will not extract any energy from the oppositely polarized wave. This is why only one-half of the energy can be extracted by the antenna from an unpolarized wave.

A general, partially polarized wave F can be represented as a sum of two independent waves: an unpolarized wave, F_N, and a completely (elliptically) polarized wave, F_P. The antenna response per unit bandwidth described by equation (1.34) can then be written in the form,

$$W = \frac{1}{2} A_e F_N + \cos^2 \gamma \, A_e F_P, \tag{1.38}$$

or, if we introduce the degree of polarization Π of the incident wave,

$$\Pi = \frac{F_P}{F} = \frac{\sqrt{Q^2 + U^2 + V^2}}{I}, \tag{1.39}$$

† By applying the relation $\cos 2\gamma = \sin 2\beta \sin 2\tilde{\beta} + \cos 2\beta \cos 2\tilde{\beta} \cos 2(\varphi - \tilde{\varphi})$ (which follows from the cosine theorem of Albategnius in spherical trigonometry) to the spherical triangle formed by the vertices at the north pole, P, and $\tilde{P}$ on the Poincaré sphere in Figure 1.5.

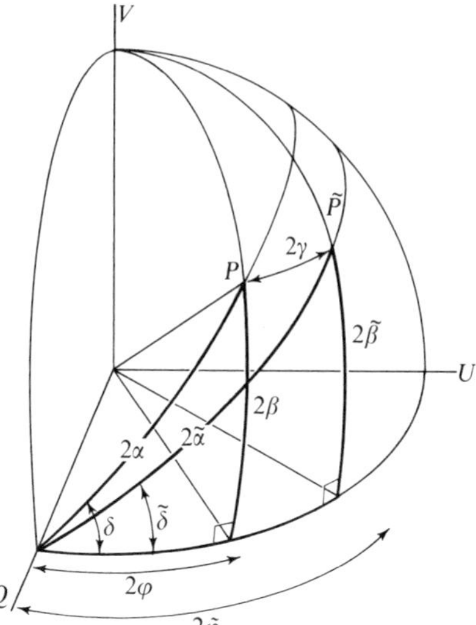

Fig. 1.5 Poincaré sphere representation of the state of polarization of the antenna ($\tilde{P}$) and of the incoming wave (P).

then we have

$$W = \frac{1}{2} A_e \; F(1 + \Pi \cos 2\gamma). \tag{1.40}$$

In the case of an extended radio source, the antenna response per unit bandwidth is given by

$$W = \frac{1}{2} A_e \iint_\Omega I_N(\vartheta, \varphi) \; P(\vartheta, \varphi) \; d\Omega + \cos^2 \gamma \, A_e \iint_\Omega I_P(\vartheta, \varphi) \; P(\vartheta, \varphi) \; d\Omega, \tag{1.41}$$

where I_N and I_P are the intensities of the unpolarized and of the completely polarized components of the incident radiation, respectively.

1.4 Systems of Antennas; Interferometers

We will consider the response to a plane wave of a set of two identical and similarly oriented antennas that are joined by a transmission line to a single receiver (Figure 1.6). Such a system of antennas is called a simple (adding) interferometer. We will assume that the wave front of a plane wave makes an angle ϑ with the line connecting the two antennas (the baseline). The phase difference $\Delta\varphi$ between signals from the two antennas (we will assume that no difference in phase is introduced by

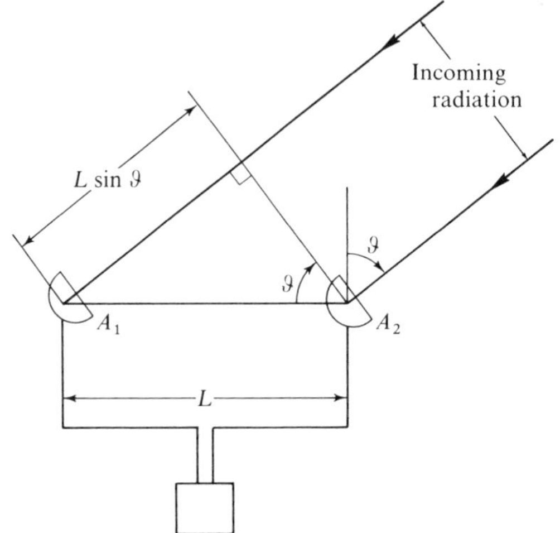

Fig. 1.6 A two-element interferometer.

the equipment) is equal to

$$\Delta\varphi = 2\pi S \sin\vartheta \approx 2\pi S\vartheta \tag{1.42}$$

for small ϑ, where $S = L/\lambda$ is the base-line length measured in wavelenths. The power W_I delivered from both antennas of an interferometer averaged over a period is

$$W_I = W_A(1 + \cos 2\pi S\vartheta), \tag{1.43}$$

where W_A is the power delivered by a single antenna.†

The power received by an interferometer as a function of the direction of incoming radiation will attain maxima at angles $\vartheta = n/S$ and minima at angles $\vartheta = (n + 1/2)/S$ (Figure 1.7), where n is an integer and $S = L/\lambda$. The maxima and minima of the interferometer pattern are therefore equally spaced in the vicinity of the zenith (i.e., for small ϑ), and the pattern diagram consists of equal lobes with the maxima separated by an angle $S^{-1} = \lambda/L$ radians. If the baseline is located in an east-west direction, then the diurnal motion of the source over the sky will cause the record to exhibit interference fringes. The lobes of the interferometer

† The power delivered from both antennas will be proportional to the square of the sum of the voltages induced in each antenna. If those voltages are $E_1 \sin(\omega t + \varphi_1)$ and $E_2 \sin(\omega t + \varphi_2)$, then $E^2 = E_1^2 + E_2^2 + 2E_1E_2\cos(\varphi_2 - \varphi_1)$. If the two antennas are identical, then E_1 is equal to E_2, and equation (1.43) follows, since $\Delta\varphi$ is by definition equal to $\varphi_2 - \varphi_1$. Since the two antennas are connected in parallel to the receiver, the matched impedence is halved; and this cancels a factor of two, which would otherwise appear in equation (1.43).

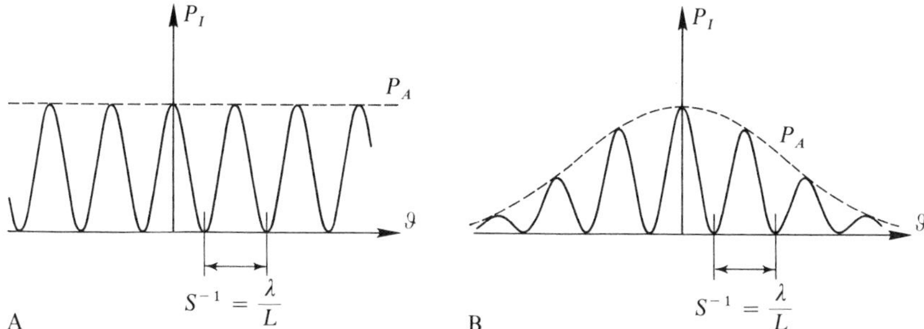

Fig. 1.7 Pattern P_I (ϑ) of a two-element interferometer, (A) with isotropic elements, and (B) with directional elements (solid curve). P_A (ϑ) is the pattern of an individual element of the interferometer (broken curve).

pattern will have the same amplitude if the elements of the interferometer are isotropic, i.e., if W_A does not depend on ϑ. However, if W_A does depend on ϑ, then the single pattern W_A is superimposed on the interferometer pattern (Figure 1.7).

The response of an interferometer to an extended source can be visualized in terms of the response to many point sources located all over the region corresponding to the extended source. If the extent of the source is comparable to, but smaller than, the interferometer lobe spacing, the resulting fringes are less pronounced than when a point source is observed. If the region occupied by the source is larger than the interferometer lobe spacing, the fringe pattern is absent (Figure 1.8).

We will consider in more detail the response of an interferometer to an extended source. Let (x, y) be rectangular coordinates along and across a circle of declination on the sky (assuming that the observation is made sufficiently far away from the pole), and let S_x and S_y be the effective length (expressed in wavelength units) of the interferometer baseline in the x and y directions, respectively. If $I(x - \Omega t, y)$ is the source brightness distribution and Ω is the velocity of the celestial sphere (the origin of the coordinate system is on the axis of the interferometer), then the available power will be

$$W_I = \frac{1}{2} A_e \Delta\nu \iint I(x - \Omega t, y)\, P(x, y) \{1 + \cos [2\pi(S_x x + S_y y)]\}\, dx\, dy. \quad (1.44)$$

Changing the coordinate system into one fixed on the sky and assuming that the individual antennas are tracking the source, we can write equation

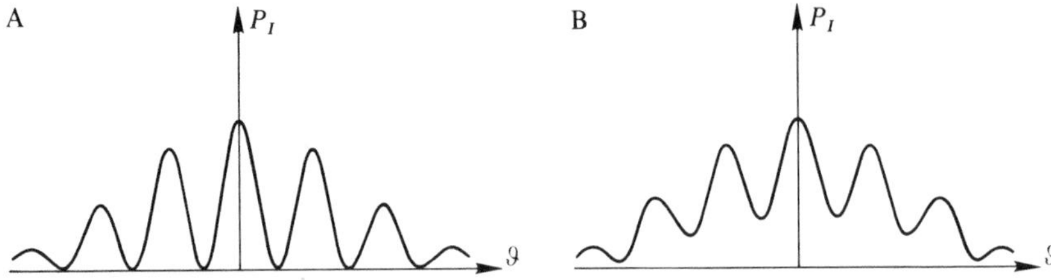

Fig. 1.8 Response of an interferometer to a point source (A) and to an extended source with the same flux (B).

(1.44) in the form,

$$W_I = \frac{1}{2} A_e \, \Delta\nu \, P(x_1 + \Omega\tau, y_1)$$

$$\iint I(x, y) \{1 + \cos 2\pi[S_x(x + \Omega t) + S_y y]\} \, dx \, dy$$

$$= \frac{1}{2} A_e \, \Delta\nu \, P(x_1 + \Omega t, y_1) \; [1 + V \cos (2\pi S_x \Omega t - \sigma)]$$

where

$$\mathscr{V} = V e^{i\sigma} = \frac{\iint \exp\,[-2\pi i(S_x x + S_y y)] \; I(x, y) \; dx \; dy}{\iint I(x, y) \; dx \; dy} \tag{1.46}$$

is the complex *visibility function*. V is called the *visibility amplitude*, and σ is the *visibility phase*. We can see that the complex visibility function is no more than the normalized two-dimensional Fourier transform of the source brightness distribution $I(x, y)$ with respect to the variables S_x and S_y. An interferometer record obtained at one baseline length, as on Figure 1.7, yields one value of the visibility function for the value of S corresponding to the baseline length. The visibility amplitude is the ratio of the range of variation of available power to twice the average available power:

$$V = \frac{W_{\max} - W_{\min}}{W_{\max} + W_{\min}} \tag{1.47}$$

The phase of the visibility function can be obtained from the record if the time interval Δt at which the envelope maximum follows an interference maximum and the time difference τ between successive maxima on the record are known:

$$\delta = \frac{2\pi\Delta t}{\tau}. \tag{1.48}$$

In practice the measurement of the visibility phase is more difficult than the measurement of the visibility amplitude. Any change in phase length of the two transmission lines (for example, due to temperature changes at the time of observation) may introduce errors in the determination of the phase of the visibility function. Measurements of fringe patterns obtained at different baseline lengths permit the plotting of the visibility amplitude and phase as a function of the baseline length expressed in wavelength units. From the visibility function the brightness distribution of the source can be partially reconstructed. Usually it is done by fitting to the observed visibility function a visibility function computed for an assumed brightness distribution of the source. From the properties of Fourier transforms and the fact that the brightness distribution is real, it follows that the brightness distribution of a source confined within $x = \pm x_0$ and $y = \pm y_0$ is completely determined by an (infinite) set of measurements giving the complex visibility function made at discrete spacings such that S_x and S_y are integral multiples of $(2x_0)^{-1}$ and $(2y_0)^{-1}$, respectively (Bracewell's theorem). Of course, measurements at any smaller intervals of the spacing will also completely determine the brightness distribution of the source, but they will contain some redundancy. Figure 1.9 presents the amplitudes and phases of the visibility function for some simple models of the brightness distribution.

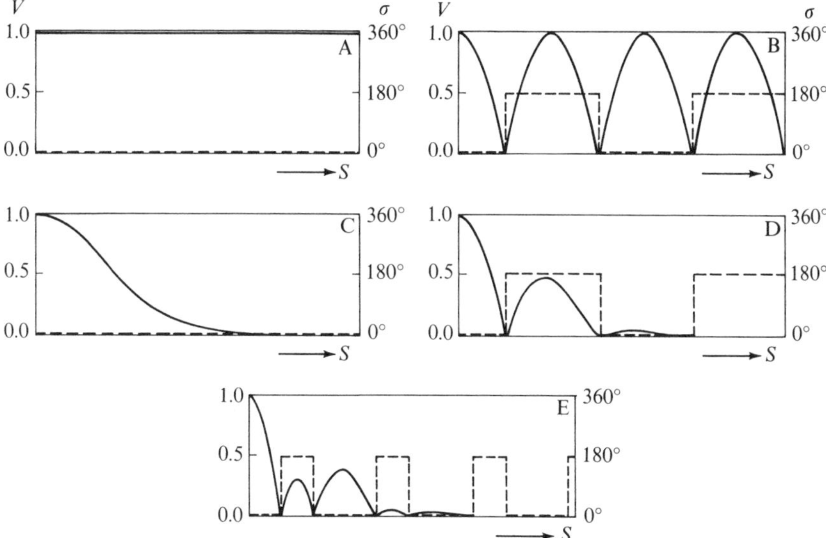

Fig. 1.9 Visibility amplitude $V(S)$ (continuous line) and phase $\sigma(S)$ (broken line) for several one-dimensional models of the brightness distribution in radio sources: (A) Single point-source. (B) Double point-source. (C) Single source with Gaussian brightness distribution. (D) Double source with Gaussian brightness distribution. (E) Triple source with Gaussian brightness distribution. All the components of multiple sources are equal.

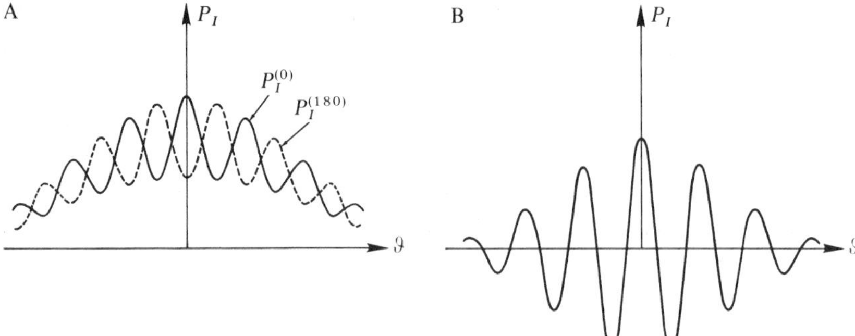

Fig. 1.10 Fringe pattern of a two-element interferometer (A) when both elements are in phase $P_I^{(0)}$ and in opposite phases $P_I^{(180)}$; and a fringe pattern of a phase-switching interferometer (B).

The process of measurement with an inteferometer can be greatly accelerated if the phase change necessary to obtain the interference pattern is done not by the diurnal motion of the source but electronically inside the system. This type of interferometer, called a *swept-lobe interferometer*, is used especially for observations of phenomena of short duration, such as solar bursts.

In a *phase-switching interferometer* the phase of one of the elements is periodically reversed synchronously with the reversal of polarity at the output. The output record of a phase-switching interferometer is shown in Figure 1.10. A phase-switching interferometer has a few advantages over a simple adding interferometer. It reduces the effect of the fluctuation of receiver gain as in the Dicke system (see the next section). It also eliminates variations in the background brightness of the sky and is able to suppress certain types of interference, particularly when the interference is picked up by one aerial only.

An increase in the number of elements spaced in multiples of S narrows the lobes. The HPBW of such grating lobes is equal to the reciprocal of nS where n is the number of elements. The separation between these grating lobes is, of course, equal to S^{-1}. Between these grating lobes, however, we have the whole system of minor lobes (Figure 1.11). Increasing the aperture of the elements of such a multi-element interferometer will suppress the grating lobes relative to the center lobe. If the aperture of each element is of the order of S, then all of the grating lobes are effectively suppressed except for the center lobe. The resolving properties of such an interferometer are practically equivalent to those of a continuous aperture of the same size as the length of the entire inter-

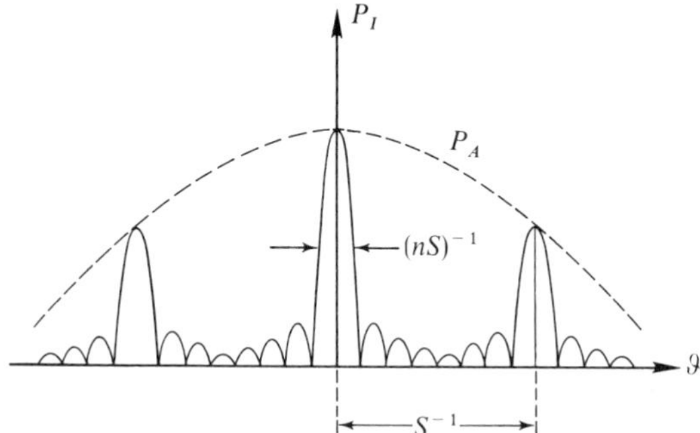

Fig. 1.11 Response pattern of a multi-element interferometer. S is the baseline length (in wavelengths) between two neighboring elements (each of which is characterized by the pattern P_A); n is the number of elements.

ferometric system. However, the sensitivity of such a system is much smaller than the sensitivity of a continuous aperture of that size, because the effective aperture of this interferometer is equal only to the sum of the effective apertures of its elements.

A multi-element interferometer working along an east-west line together with a similar system working in a north-south line is called a *Mills cross*. The sensitivity pattern of a Mills cross has a cross-shaped view on the celestial sphere (Figure 1.12). If the record obtained when both lines of the antennas are connected in opposite phases is subtracted from the record obtained when both lines of the antennas are connected in phase, the result is a record that corresponds to the signals coming from the center area of the cross (shaded area of Fig. 1.12). Therefore the Mills cross actually has a *pencil beam* response pattern. By introducing a successive phase shift to either or both arms of the Mills cross, one can direct the pencil beam at a desired point on the celestial sphere.

Very high resolution interferometry can be carried out with two elements of an interferometer which are not directly connected. The local oscillators at each element are locked in phase with an atomic frequency standard, and the signals from each element, together with precise time information, are independently recorded on magnetic tape and later reduced together at a data-processing center. This method of very long baseline interferometric measurements can be used at any baseline length.

A large aperture S can be synthesized by the use of an interferometer with a variable baseline. Measurements are made at different positions of

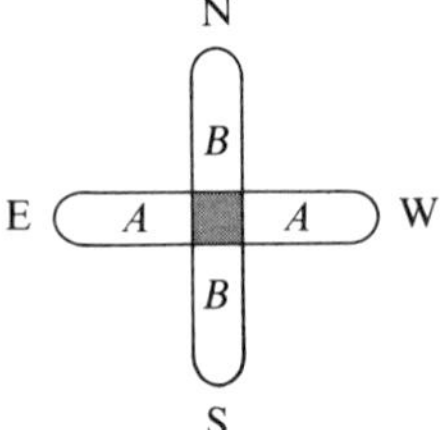

Fig. 1.12 Reception pattern of a Mills cross. AA is the region on the sky viewed by the north-south line of the antennas and BB is the region on the sky viewed by the east-west line of the antennas. The shaded area is the pencil beam resulting from combining the outputs from the two lines of antennas with appropriate phases.

the element of the interferometer corresponding to different baselines of length between zero and S and different directions (this can be achieved, for example, if the elements move along tracks forming a letter T). By adding the results of measurements at different baselines with appropriate weights (in the filled aperture certain spacings of the elements occur more frequently than others), one can obtain results equivalent, in principle, to a measurement with a completely filled aperture S; however, this process will take correspondingly more time. If progressive phase gradients are introduced into the contributions from different spacings, different positions on the sky can be measured. This method of observation is called *aperture synthesis*.

High-resolution investigations of the brightness distribution of some radio sources can be made by studying the diffraction fringes during a *lunar occultation* of the source. Observations of lunar occultations can also give precise positions of such radio sources.

1.5 Receivers

Superheterodyne receivers are most often used in radio astronomy, because they overcome the technical difficulties in amplifying high-frequency signals. In a superheterodyne receiver a radio-frequency signal ν_{RF} from the antenna is combined in a mixer with a signal produced by a local oscillator ν_{LO}. The resulting intermediate-frequency signal, $\nu_{IF} = \nu_{LO} - \nu_{RF}$, is then amplified. The power of the intermediate frequency signal is directly proportional to the power of the radio-frequency signal delivered by the antenna; its frequency is much lower, however, and can therefore be conveniently amplified in subsequent amplifying stages of the receiver. In receivers working at longer wavelengths the radio-frequency signal goes to a radio-frequency amplifier before it is mixed with the local oscillator signal. In these receivers the radio-frequency amplifier sometimes determines the band-pass of the receiver and therefore performs the principal filtering of frequencies of radio noise. In receivers working at millimeter and centimeter wavelengths the radio-frequency amplifying stage is sometimes omitted, and the band-pass of the receiver is determined by the intermediate frequency-amplifying stage. The radio-frequency signal is received in two channels centered on the frequencies equal to the sum and the difference of the local oscillator frequency and the intermediate frequency.

The process of filtering of frequencies by the amplifying stage corresponds to the mathematical operation of deriving Fourier coefficients,

$$A_\tau(\nu) = \int_0^\tau \varphi(t)\, e^{2\pi i \nu t}\, dt, \tag{1.49}$$

of the cosmic noise $\varphi(t)$. The intermediate frequency-amplifying stage is followed by a detector, which obtains the squares of the moduli, $|A_\tau(\nu)|^2$, of the Fourier coefficients. τ is the integration time of the recording device located at the output of the receiver. An infinitely long integration time τ would yield the flux density

$$F_\nu = \lim_{\tau=\infty} \frac{1}{\tau} |A_\tau(\nu)|^2, \tag{1.50}$$

with a total flux of

$$\int F_\nu\, d\nu = F = \langle [\varphi(t)]^2 \rangle. \tag{1.51}$$

However, the integration time usually ranges in practice from a few seconds to a hundred, and the fluxes obtained for different pulses of duration τ will not be exactly the same. The output will therefore exhibit fluctuations, which can be decreased by increasing the integration time τ.

The sensitivity of a radio telescope is limited by fluctuations in the receiver output due to the statistical character of the noise generated within the receiver. The noise power per unit bandwidth, $W_R = kT_R$, generated in the system with noise temperature T_R, will be recorded with fluctuations such that the standard deviation ΔW_R of the reading W_R is inversely proportional to the square root of the number of pulses averaged by the recording device within the time τ. The duration of one pulse amplified within the frequency interval $\Delta\nu$ will be of the order of $1/\Delta\nu$. Therefore the number of such pulses recorded by the recording device having the time constant τ will be $\tau \cdot \Delta\nu$, and

$$\Delta W_R = \gamma \frac{W_R}{\sqrt{\tau \cdot \Delta\nu}}, \tag{1.52}$$

where γ is a coefficient of proportionality of the order of unity and depends on the construction of the system. The power per unit bandwidth of the signal W_A must not be smaller then ΔW_R because it would be confused with the fluctuations of the noise generated in the system. Therefore, the minimum detectable flux will be

$$F_{\min} = 2\gamma \frac{kT_R}{A_e\sqrt{\tau \cdot \Delta\nu}}. \tag{1.53}$$

For a radio telescope with a given effective aperture A_e and a given noise temperature T_R, the threshold of a detectable signal can be decreased by increasing either the bandpass $\Delta\nu$ or the integration time constant τ. However, the increase of the bandpass is limited by the fact that wide-band amplifiers have a relatively small gain at each stage and therefore require many stages. When interferometer techniques are used, clarity of the interference pattern requires a relatively narrow bandpass. An increase of the integration time is, on the other hand, limited by technical problems, which are associated mainly with the stability of the system. For typical values of $\tau = 100$ sec and $\Delta\nu = 1$ MHz, the factor $\sqrt{(\tau \cdot \Delta\nu)}$ is equal to 0.01%.

It is therefore possible to measure signal-to-noise ratios of the order of 10^{-8}, provided that the gain G of the system is absolutely stable. Otherwise a variation ΔG in the receiver's gain can be confused with a change ΔW_A in the signal W_A such that

$$\frac{\Delta W_A}{W_A} = \frac{\Delta G}{G}\left(1 + \frac{W_R}{W_A}\right). \tag{1.54}$$

In equation (1.54) the factor in parentheses can be very large for weak sources. For example, when W_R/W_A is of the order of 1000, a change of 0.1% in gain will cause a 100% error in the measurement of W_A. Since stabilization of the gain is a rather difficult problem, the so-called switched systems are generally used.

In a Dicke system the input of the receiver is switched between the antenna and a comparison noise source. The switching frequency is high enough to eliminate any appreciable change in the gain during one cycle. The difference between the power delivered by the antenna and the power generated by the comparison noise source is then amplified, detected, and recorded. If the power W_C generated by the comparison source is made equal to the power delivered by the antenna when the antenna is not pointing at the source, then the output reading is directly proportional to the signal from the observed source; and if no signal is present there is no output reading. If W_A is the power of the signal from the source, than in a Dicke system a variation ΔG in the gain G produces an error ΔW_A in the signal power W_A given by

$$\frac{\Delta W_A}{W_A} = \frac{\Delta G}{G}, \tag{1.55}$$

rather than by equation (1.54). We can see, therefore, that the effect of gain variations in a Dicke system is $(1 + W_R/W_A)$ times smaller than in the case of an unswitched system. Instead of switching between the antenna and the comparison source, sometimes the input of the receiver is switched between the two horns, with one horn pointed at the source while the other receives radiation from the background sky. The sensitivity of a Dicke receiver is lower by a factor of two than an unswitched receiver because the signal is connected to the receiver only half of the time. For such a receiver we therefore have to increase by a factor of two the minimum detectable flux given by equation (1.53).

In a Dicke receiver strong signals can be substantially affected by gain variations, but there are several ways of stabilizing the gain. In the null-balancing method, for example, the noise power generated by the comparison source is regulated by the receiver's integrator output in such a way that the output of the receiver is zero at all times. The regulating signal is therefore the actual output signal.

At low frequencies, observations with a given radio telescope are resolution limited. The number of sources observable at these frequencies is determined by the beamwidth; the neighboring sources are very likely to be confused unless there is no more than one detectable source [in the sense of equation (1.53)] in an area twenty to eighty times the beam area. At sufficiently high frequencies, observations are sensitivity limited since the minimum detectable flux is high, and resolution is no longer a problem. There is a region of frequencies between the resolution-limited and the sensitivity-limited domains of the spectrum which is optimal for radio source counts.

Bibliographical Notes to Chapter 1

1.1 The observations of cosmic objects through the radio window are relatively recent, although Edison and Lodge suggested many years ago that the sun might emit detectable radio waves. The first astronomical radio observations were made in 1932 by Karl G. Jansky at the Bell Telephone Laboratories in Homedel, New Jersey, when he detected a steady noise coming from the direction of the galactic center. Investigating the interference in radio reception at 14.7 cm, Jansky detected a variable source of radiation having a period of 23 hours and 56 minutes. This value of the period suggested an extraterrestrial origin of the source.

1. K. G. Jansky, "Directional Studies of Atmospherics at High Frequencies," *Proc. IRE* **20**, 1920–1932 (1932).

Subsequent research associated the source of radiation with the galactic center.

2. K. G. Jansky, "Electrical Disturbances Apparently of Extraterrestrial Origin," *Proc. IRE* **21**, 1387–1398 (1933).
3. K. G. Jansky, "A Note on the Source of Interstellar Interference," *Proc. IRE* **23**, 1158–1163 (1935).

G. Reber was the first to use a paraboloidal reflector in radioastronomical observation. His telescope with a diameter of 32 ft. had a fixed mounting. It operated at a frequency of 160 MHz (1.85 m) and had a directional diagram of $10° \times 12°$. The telescope's minimum detectable intensity was 7.10^{-22} W/m^2 Hz sterad.

4. G. Reber, "Cosmic Static," *Astrophys. J.* **91**, 621–624 (1940).
5. G. Reber, "Cosmic Static," *Astrophys. J.* **100**, 279–287 (1944).

Among the first astronomers to extend the range of observations into the intermediate infrared (approximately 1–4 microns) were Pettit and Nicholson.

6. E. Pettit and S. B. Nicholson, "Stellar Radiation Measurements," *Astrophys. J.* **68**, 279–308 (1928).

The far infrared observations of stars through the 8–14 micron and 4.4–5.5 micron windows were first done by the authors of the next two papers.

7. B. C. Murray and R. L. Wildey, "Stellar and Planetary Observations at 10 Microns," *Astrophys. J.* **137**, 692–693 (1963).
8. H. L. Johnson and R. I. Mitchell, "Stellar Photometry at 5 Microns," *Astrophys. J.* **138**, 302–303 (1963).

The first observations of stars through the farthest 20 micron window were made, and new sensitive detectors were developed, by Johnson and his students.

9. H. L. Johnson, F. J. Low, and D. Steinmetz, "Infrared Observations of the Neugebauer-Martz-Leighton 'Infrared Star' in Cygnus," *Astrophys. J.* **142**, 808–810 (1965).

The influence of the Earth's atmosphere on radiation from cosmic sources is described in some detail, in Ref. 10, which contains an extensive bibliography of the subject, and in Ref. 11.

10. J. L. Pawsey and R. N. Bracewell, *Radio Astronomy*, Chap. XI, Clarendon Press, Oxford, 1955.
11. J. C. Pecker and E. Schatzman, *Astrophysique Generale*, Part II, Chap. I, Masson et Cie., Paris, 1959.

For bibliographies on interplanetary scintillation, see the following.

12. E. E. Salpeter, "Interplanetary Scintillations. I: Theory," *Astrophys. J.* **147**, 433–448 (1967).
13. M. H. Cohen, E. J. Gundermann, H. E. Hardebeck, and L. E. Sharp, "Interplanetary Scintillations. II: Observations," *Astrophys. J.* **147**, 449–466 (1967).
14. M. H. Cohen, E. J. Gundermann, and D. E. Harris, "New Limits on the Diameters of Radio Sources," *Astrophys. J.* **150**, 767–782 (1967).

Fig. 1.1 was adapted from:

15. A. D. Code, "Stellar Astronomy from a Space Vehicle," *Astron. J.* **65**, 278–284 (1960).

Fig. 1.2 is based on Fig. 9 in Ref. 11 and on figures in the following references.

16. C. W. Allen, *Astrophysical Quantities*, University of London, The Athlone Press, 1963.
17. H. L. Johnson and R. I. Mitchell, "A Completely Digitized Multicolor Photometer," *Comm. Lunar and Planet. Lab.* No. 14, 73–81 (1962).
18. R. W. Hobbs, "Millimeter Wave Radio Astronomy at NRL," *Report of NRL Progress*, 8–15 (Jan. 1967).

1.2 The response of an antenna to incoming radiation is treated in detail by Kraus. Refs. 19 and 20 contain extensive bibliographies of the subject.

19. J. D. Kraus, *Antennas*, McGraw-Hill, New York, 1950.
20. J. D. Kraus, *Radio Astronomy*, Chaps. 3 and 6, McGraw-Hill, New York, 1966.

The subject is also covered in Chapter II of Ref. 10, and in the following:

21. J. L. Steinberg and J. Lequex, *Radioastronomie*, Chap. 3, Dunod, Paris, 1960. (*Radio Astronomy*. Mc Graw-Hill, New York, 1963).
22. R. N. Bracewell, "Radio Astronomy Techniques," *in* S. Flugge, ed., *Handbuch der Physik*, Vol. 53, pp. 42–129, Springer, Berlin, 1962.
23. J. G. Bolton, "Radio Telescopes," *in* G. P. Kuiper and B. M. Middlehurst, eds., *Telescopes*, Chap. 11, Univ. of Chicago Press, 1960.

1.3. For the response of an antenna to polarized radiation see the following:

24. H. C. Ko, "On the Response of a Radio Antenna to Complex Radio Waves," *Proc. Natl. Electronics Conf.* **17**, 500–508 (1961).
25. H. C. Ko, "On the Reception of Quasi-Monochromatic Partially Polarized Radio Waves," *Proc. IRE* **50**, 1950–1957 (1962).
26. G. A. Deschamps, "Geometrical Representation of the Polarization of a Plane Electromagnetic Wave," *Proc. IRE* **39**, 540–544 (1951).

1.4. Radio interferometry is considered in Chapter 6 of Ref. 20, Chapter 4 of Ref. 21, and Ref. 22. See also

27. R. N. Bracewell, "Radio Interferometry of Discrete Sources," *Proc. IRE* **46**, 97–105 (1958).

See bibliography in Chapter 6 of Ref. 20 for further references. Aperture synthesis is treated in the following two papers:

28. M. Ryle and A. Hewish, "The Synthesis of Large Radio Telescopes," *Monthly Notices Roy. Astron. Soc.* **120**, 220–230 (1960).
29. M. Ryle, "Aperture Synthesis," *in* H. P. Palmer, R. D. Davies and M. I. Large, eds., *Radio Astronomy Today*, pp. 76–80, Harvard University Press, Cambridge, 1963.

The techniques of lunar occultation observations are described in:

30. P. A. G. Scheuer, "On the Use of Lunar Occultations for Investigating the Angular Structure of Radio Sources," *Australian J. Phys.* **15**, 333–343 (1962).
31. S. van Hoerner, "Lunar Occultations of Radio Sources," *Astrophys. J.* **140**, 65–79 (1964).

1.5. A review of radio telescope receivers is given by

32. M. E. Tiuri, "Radio Telescope Receivers," Chap. 7 of Ref. 20.

See also Chap. II of Ref. 10; Chap. III of Ref. 21; Ref. 22; and the following two sources:

33. I. Shklovsky, *Cosmic Radio Waves*, Chap. II, Gostechizdat, Moscow, 1965; and Harvard University Press, Cambridge, 1960.
34. F. D. Drake, "Radio Astronomy Radiometers and Their Calibration," *in* G. P. Kuiper and B. M. Middlehurst, eds., *Telescopes*, Chap. 12, University of Chicago Press, 1960.

2

Plasma in a Magnetic Field

2.1 Introduction

A gas is composed of neutral particles, and its behavior is determined by interaction between these neutral particles. At large distances the particles interact with each other as a result of attracting Van der Waals forces, which result from the instantaneous dipole of one of the molecules inducing a dipole moment in the other molecules. The potential of Van der Waals forces is inversely proportional to the sixth power of the distance between interacting molecules. If the average kinetic energy per particle exceeds the ionizing potential of atoms, the gas will become ionized and will be composed of positive ions, negative ions, and some neutral particles. If such a system consists of a nearly equal number of positive and negative charges, it is called a plasma.

Besides interactions between neutral particles in a plasma, there are interactions between neutral and charged particles and, most important, interactions between the charged particles themselves. The interaction between a neutral and a charged particle will depend, in general, on the nature of the neutral particle and on its distance from a charged particle. At large distances the charged particle induces a dipole moment in the neutral molecule, and the interaction is an electrostatic interaction between that induced dipole and the charged particle. The potential of the dipole is proportional to the dipole moment and inversely proportional to the square of the distance. The induced dipole moment is proportional to the electric field of the charged particle, which in turn is proportional to the inverse square of the distance. Therefore, the potential of the interaction between a charged particle and a neutral molecule is inversely proportional to the fourth power of the distance between those two particles. The interactions between charged particles themselves are characterized by a Coulomb potential which is inversely proportional to the distance. Of the three types of interactions described here the Coulomb interaction has the longest range. This is the reason why in most cases, even at a relatively low degree of ionization of the medium, the Coulomb interactions will be more important than the other interactions. It is only under the conditions of weak discharges in gases that the interactions between neutral particles and charged particles are important; and in this case we have a so-called Lorentz gas which is described mainly in terms of collisions between electrons and neutral molecules.

Most of the matter in the universe is ionized, and therefore the physics of plasmas is of particular importance for astrophysics. In what follows we will therefore consider the behavior of an electrically neutral (on the average) system of charged and neutral particles interacting with each other and eventually interacting with an external magnetic field. We will consider mainly the Coulomb interactions and will neglect all the quantum effects, which are important at small distances between interacting particles. These quantum effects are important in degenerate gases and in the electron theory of metals.†

It is useful to characterize the condition of a plasma by specifying four parameters having the dimension of length. The trajectories of two particles interacting by means of Coulomb forces are represented by hyperbolas in the center of the mass reference system. The deviation of the particles' trajectories depends on the impact parameter. We can introduce here a particular value λ_i of the *impact parameter* defined by the requirement that a deviation of the direction of the velocity of a particle by an angle of 90° from the original direction of particle velocity results from the collision characterized by that value of the impact parameter. This critical impact parameter is

† If the average kinetic energy per particle is very high (larger than a few million electron volts) we would have a gas composed of free electrons, nucleons, and eventually free mesons; in the description of the behavior of such a gas the important short-range internuclear forces should be taken into account.

$$\lambda_i = \frac{e^2}{mv^2} = \frac{e^2}{3kT}, \tag{2.1}$$

where e is the charge; m, the mass of the particles; v, their relative velocity; T, the kinetic temperature of the gas; and k the Boltzmann constant. The last equation holds if we replace the average value of the square of the particle velocity by $3kT/m$. The second parameter characterizing the plasma will be a certain *mean free path* λ_0, defined as the mean path of a particle between the two successive collisions which deviate its trajectory by an angle of the order of 90°. The volume that a sphere of radius λ_i sweeps out in one second when it is moving at an average speed v is equal to $\pi\lambda_i^2 v$. Since in this volume there are $N\pi\lambda_i^2 v$ molecules, the collision frequency will be

$$\nu_C = \pi\lambda_i^2 v N; \tag{2.2}$$

and the mean free path will then be

$$\lambda_0 = \frac{v}{\nu} = \frac{1}{\pi\lambda_i^2 N} = \frac{9k^2T^2}{\pi N e^4}. \tag{2.3}$$

In the above considerations we used the concept of molecules as billiard balls of diameter λ_i. We did, in fact, replace the Coulomb interaction potential between charged particles by the potential of a billiard ball having a sharp cutoff at λ_i. Our next plasma parameter will be the *average distance λ_P between two particles*. If we divide the volume of the plasma into cubes of volume λ_P in such a way that in every cube there will be only one particle, then we will see that the average distance between two particles is

$$\lambda_P = N^{-1/3}, \tag{2.4}$$

where N is the particle density. The fourth parameter characterizing the plasma is the *Debye length* λ_D. The Debye length is a measure of charge separation, which results from thermal motions in a plasma. As already mentioned, a plasma is a system of particles which is electrically neutral at large scale, and deviation from neutrality will be eliminated immediately by the flow of charge. In the absence of external sources of energy, local deviations from neutrality can be caused by the thermal energy of the plasma itself. We will calculate the dimensions of a region in which this is possible, and this dimension will be the Debye length. Suppose that at the expense of thermal energy $\mathscr{E}_T$ of a plasma contained in the volume of radius R_1,

$$\mathscr{E}_T = \frac{4}{3}\pi R_1^{\,3}\cdot\frac{1}{2}NkT, \tag{2.5}$$

the negative charge was expelled from this volume and located in the shell $R_2 - R_1$ surrounding the sphere R_1. The volume of the shell, which is approximately equal to that of the sphere, has an outer radius

$$R_2 \approx \frac{5}{4}R_1.$$

The electric field inside the sphere is

$$E_1 = \frac{4}{3}\pi r^3\cdot\frac{Ne}{r^2} = \frac{4}{3}\pi Ner, \tag{2.6}$$

where r is a running distance from the center of the sphere. The electric field in the shell is

$$\begin{aligned} E_2 &= \left(\frac{4}{3}\pi r^3 - \frac{4}{3}\pi R_1^{\,3}\right)N(-e)\frac{1}{r^2} + \frac{4}{3}\pi R_1^{\,3}\frac{Ne}{r^2} \\ &= \frac{4}{3}\pi Ner\left(\frac{2R_1^{\,3}}{r^3} - 1\right). \end{aligned} \tag{2.7}$$

The electrostatic energy associated with this shift of charge is

$$\begin{aligned} \mathscr{E}_E &= \frac{1}{8\pi}\int_0^{R_2} E^2 4\pi r^2\,dr \\ &= \frac{1}{2}\int_0^{R_1} E_1^{\,2}r^2\,dr + \frac{1}{2}\int_{R_1}^{R_2} E_2^{\,2}r^2\,dr \approx \frac{1}{4}\pi^2N^2e^2R_1^{\,5}. \end{aligned} \tag{2.8}$$

Putting $\mathscr{E}_T$ equal to $\mathscr{E}_E$, we obtain the maximum value of R_1, which we will call λ_D,

$$\lambda_D = \sqrt{\frac{8kT}{3\pi Ne^2}} \approx 20\sqrt{\frac{T}{N}}.$$

This maximum value of the radius R_1 equal to λ_D is called the Debye radius. For a plane disturbance (we considered here a spherical disturbance) the Debye length is equal to

$$\lambda_D = \sqrt{\frac{kT}{4\pi Ne^2}} \approx 7\sqrt{\frac{T}{N}}. \tag{2.9}$$

If a plasma is macroscopically neutral, the Debye length must be much smaller than the characteristic dimensions of the system and much smaller than the scale of macroscopic fluctuations of density, temperature, and so on. This condition is fulfilled in astrophysics.

Equations (2.1), (2.3), (2.4), and (2.9) give the four parameters, λ_i, λ_0,

λ_P, and λ_D, as functions of the kinetic temperature of the plasma and its number density. Of course only two of the four parameters are independent, since they all depend only on T and N. Figure 2.1 represents the $\log N$-$\log T$ plane for plasmas. On this plane six lines with a slope of one third are drawn; along those lines, two of the four parameters are equal for each line. The lines lie very close together and they divide the $\log N$-$\log T$ plane into two regions: a region for which $\lambda_i \ll \lambda_P \ll \lambda_D \ll \lambda_0$ and the region for which an opposite inequality holds. The first region is called the region of individual plasma behavior, and the second one is called the region of collective plasma behavior for reasons which will be clarified below. In fact the ratio $X_{T/E}$ of the parameters λ_P and λ_i,

$$X_{T/E} = \frac{\lambda_P}{\lambda_i} = \frac{3kT}{e^2 N^{1/3}}, \tag{2.10}$$

is sufficient to distinguish between the individual and collective behavior of a plasma. $X_{T/E}$ is essentially the ratio of the thermal and Coulomb energies of a particle. In terms of $X_{T/E}$ we have $\lambda_i \propto \lambda_i X_{T/E}{}^0$, $\lambda_P \propto \lambda_i X_{T/E}$, $\lambda_D \propto \lambda_i X_{T/E}{}^{3/2}$ and $\lambda_0 \propto \lambda_i X_{T/E}{}^3$; and therefore $X_{T/E} \gg 1$ implies $\lambda_i \ll \lambda_P \ll \lambda_D \ll \lambda_0$, while $X_{T/E} \ll 1$ implies $\lambda_i \gg \lambda_P \gg \lambda_D \gg \lambda_0$.

In the region of individual plasma close encounters can be well approximated by binary collisions because of the condition $\lambda_i \ll \lambda_P$. Distant encounters are very numerous; however, since the electric field of a charged particle is effective only up to a distance equal to the Debye length λ_D, the great majority of distant collisions are not very efficient (λ_D is much smaller than λ_0) and cause only small wiggles in the electron's trajectory, while the close encounters cause the trajectory to deviate substantially. The critical impact parameter is much smaller than the distance between the ions. At the same time this distance is smaller than the Debye length, and the mean free path is the largest of these quantities. In the region of collective plasma, in which $\lambda_i \gg \lambda_P \gg \lambda_D \gg \lambda_0$, we cannot describe encounters as binary collisions; we have to consider the simultaneous action of many ions.

On the same diagram (Figure 2.1) the line parallel to the abscissa axis is determined by the condition $X_{T/R} \approx 1$, where

$$X_{T/R} = \frac{kT}{mc^2} \tag{2.11}$$

is essentially the ratio of the thermal and rest energies of a particle; it divides the region in which the classical approach is appropriate (the region below the line, $X_{T/R} \ll 1$) from the region in which a relativistic

Table 1 Characteristics of several astrophysical plasmas (CGS)

Plasma	Log																
	N	T	H	λ_i	λ_P	λ_D	λ_0	ν_C	ν_0	ω_H	r_H	$X_{T/E}$	$X_{T/R}$	$X_{T/F}$	$X_{F/R}$	$X_{H/R}$	$X_{T/H}$
1. Neutral interstellar hydrogen (H I)	−2	2	−6	−5.3	0.7	2.8	12.0	−6.7	3.0	1.3	5.5	5.9	−7.8	13.7	−21.5	−5.3	−2.3
2. Region of ionized hydrogen (H II)	0	4	−6	−7.3	0.0	2.8	14.0	−4.3	4.0	1.3	6.5	7.3	−5.8	14.4	−20.2	−7.3	1.7
3. Ionosphere (F-layer)	6	3.5	−0.3	−6.8	−2.0	−0.4	7.0	2.4	7.0	7.0	0.5	4.8	−6.3	9.9	−16.2	−1.9	−4.2
4. Solar chromosphere	12	4	3	−7.3	−4.0	−3.2	2.0	7.3	10.0	10.3	−2.5	3.3	−5.8	6.4	−12.2	−1.3	−4.3
5. Solar corona	7	6	−4	−9.3	−2.3	0.3	11.0	−0.1	7.5	3.3	5.5	6.9	−3.8	11.7	−15.5	−10.3	6.7
6. Stellar interiors	27	7.5		−10.8	−9.0	−9.0	−6.0	17.7	17.5	—	—	1.8	−2.3	−0.1	−2.2	—	—
7. White dwarfs	32	7		−10.3	−10.7	−11.7	−12.0	23.4	20.0	—	—	−0.4	−2.8	−4.0	1.2	—	—

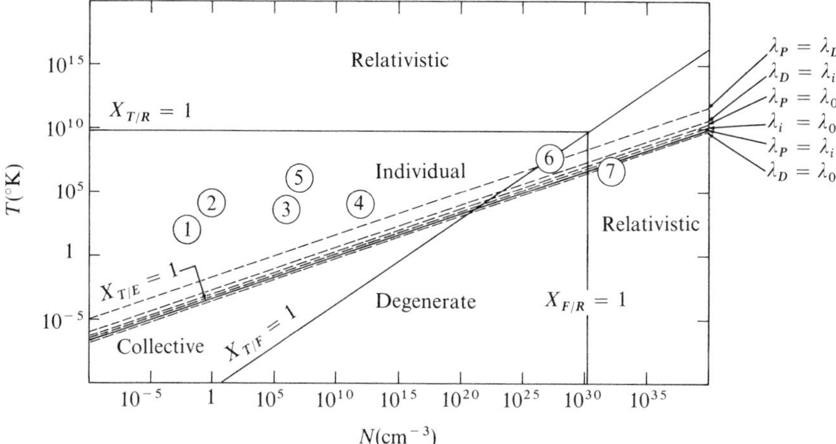

Fig. 2.1 The log N–log T plane for plasmas. Numbers identify the regions corresponding to entries in Table 1.

treatment is necessary (above the line, $X_{T/R} > 1$). The line of slope 2/3, determined by the condition of quantum degeneracy $X_{T/F} \approx 1$, where

$$X_{T/F} = \frac{kT}{\dfrac{\hbar^2}{2m}(3\pi^2 N)^{2/3}} \tag{2.12}$$

is essentially the ratio of the thermal and Fermi threshold energies, divides the region in which the classical treatment is appropriate (the region well above that line, $X_{T/F} \gg 1$) from the region in which the plasma is degenerate and the quantum treatment is necessary (below the line, $X_{T/F} < 1$). However, when the Fermi threshold energy becomes comparable to or larger than the rest energy, $X_{F/R} \gtrsim 1$,

$$X_{F/R} = \frac{\hbar^2 (3\pi^2 N)^{2/3}}{2m^2 c^2}, \tag{2.13}$$

the relativistic quantum treatment is appropriate; this takes place even at very low temperatures if the densities are sufficiently large. The line $X_{F/R} = 1$, independent of temperature, is also plotted in Figure 2.1. Table 1 gives the values of the parameters described above for several astrophysical plasmas.

2.2 Boltzmann Equation; Fluid Description of Plasmas

It is impossible to describe the great majority of plasmas by specifying the trajectories of individual particles. Usually the best description of the behavior of a plasma is the statistical one, which specifies the distribution function for the various kinds of particles in the system. The statistical approach is meaningful only when applied to systems which contain a large number of particles in an element of space which is small in comparison with the scale of change of the macroscopic parameters characterizing the system. The *particle distribution function*, $f(\mathfrak{q}_i, \mathfrak{p}_i, t)\, d\mathfrak{q}_i\, d\mathfrak{p}_i$, is defined as the total number of particles contained in an elementary volume $d\mathfrak{q}_1\, d\mathfrak{q}_2\, d\mathfrak{q}_3\, d\mathfrak{p}_1\, d\mathfrak{p}_2\, d\mathfrak{p}_3$ in the phase space $(\mathfrak{q}_i, \mathfrak{p}_i)$ at a given instant of time t. The distribution function, in general, depends on time. This dependence is due to the motion of particles in the geometric space and to the change of the velocities of these particles caused by the forces acting on them. This change of velocities can be visualized as motion in the velocity space. There are two kinds of forces in a plasma that act on the particles—forces which arise from the interaction between neighboring particles, and body forces which arise from the system as a whole, like the Lorentz force due to the electromagnetic field induced by the currents in the plasma. There may also be external forces, such as gravitation, or Lorentz force deriving from an external magnetic field.

The distribution function itself is not a measurable quantity; but the moments of the distribution function in velocity space are measurable. Because these moments are related to such quantities as the mass density of the plasma, the mean velocity of the particles, the pressure, the thermal energy density, and so on, we will first derive the equation for the distribution function called the transport equation, and will then compute the velocity moments of this equation. In this way we will arrive at a set of equations comprising only macroscopic quantities that are directly measurable. This set of equations constitutes the fluid description of plasma.

If there are no interactions between particles which change their momentum abruptly, we can assume the validity of the continuity equation for the distribution function in phase space. This continuity equation is

$$\frac{\partial f}{\partial t} + \nabla \cdot (f\boldsymbol{U}) = \frac{\partial f}{\partial t} + f\nabla \cdot \boldsymbol{U} + (\boldsymbol{U} \cdot \nabla) f = 0, \tag{2.14}$$

where ∇ is the operator in the phase space $(\mathfrak{q}_i, \mathfrak{p}_i)$, and

$$\boldsymbol{U}(\mathfrak{q}_1, \mathfrak{q}_2, \mathfrak{q}_3, \mathfrak{p}_1, \mathfrak{p}_2, \mathfrak{p}_3, t) = \left[\frac{d\mathfrak{q}_1}{dt}, \frac{d\mathfrak{q}_2}{dt}, \frac{d\mathfrak{q}_3}{dt}, \frac{d\mathfrak{p}_1}{dt}, \frac{d\mathfrak{p}_2}{dt}, \frac{d\mathfrak{p}_3}{dt}\right] \tag{2.15}$$

is the velocity of particles in the phase space. Without interactions the changes of the coordinates and the momenta of particles are continuous. When interactions (collisions) are taken into account, we must add to the continuity equation (2.14) the term $(\partial f/\partial t)_{\text{coll}}$, which describes the changes in the distribution function caused by abrupt momentum changes by collisions. In a collisionless system, using the summation convention and remembering that $\boldsymbol{U}$ is a six-vector in a six-dimensional phase space, we find

$$\nabla \cdot \boldsymbol{U} = \frac{\partial}{\partial \mathfrak{q}_i}\frac{d\mathfrak{q}_i}{dt} + \frac{\partial}{\partial \mathfrak{p}_i}\frac{d\mathfrak{p}_i}{dt} = \frac{\partial^2 \mathscr{H}}{\partial \mathfrak{q}_i \partial \mathfrak{p}_i} - \frac{\partial^2 \mathscr{H}}{\partial \mathfrak{p}_i \partial \mathfrak{q}_i} = 0, \tag{2.16}$$

where $\mathscr{H}$ is the Hamiltonian; and therefore

$$\frac{\partial f}{\partial t} + (\boldsymbol{U} \cdot \nabla) f = 0, \tag{2.17}$$

or Df/Dt is equal to zero. In other terms,

$$\frac{\partial f}{\partial t} + \left\{ \frac{d\mathfrak{q}_i}{dt}\frac{\partial f}{\partial \mathfrak{q}_i} + \frac{d\mathfrak{p}_i}{dt}\frac{\partial f}{\partial \mathfrak{p}_i} \right\} = 0; \tag{2.18}$$

or using Hamilton's equations,

$$\frac{\partial f}{\partial t} + \left\{ \frac{\partial \mathscr{H}}{\partial \mathfrak{p}_i}\frac{\partial f}{\partial \mathfrak{q}_i} - \frac{\partial \mathscr{H}}{\partial \mathfrak{q}_i}\frac{\partial f}{\partial \mathfrak{p}_i} \right\} = 0. \tag{2.19}$$

Equation (2.18) [or its equivalent form, equation (2.19)] is called the *Liouville equation.* It describes the flow of particles in the phase space by means of a differential equation† for the distribution function f if there are no interactions between particles.

The canonical variables for a particle in a magnetic field in the non-relativistic approximation are

$$\mathfrak{q}_i = x_i,$$

$$\mathfrak{p}_i = mv_i + \frac{e}{c} A_i; \tag{2.20}$$

and the Hamiltonian is

$$\mathscr{H} = \frac{1}{2m}\left(\mathfrak{p}_i - \frac{e}{c} A_i\right)^2 + e\varphi, \tag{2.21}$$

† In the general case, which is not being considered here, the Hamiltonian $\mathscr{H}$ may contain integrals over $\mathfrak{q}_i$ and $\mathfrak{p}_i$ involving the distribution function f, and the Liouville equation is then an integro-differential equation.

where A_i and φ are the vector and scalar potentials of the field, respectively. In this case we can transform the Liouville equation into an equation in the (x_i, v_i) space.† The result of the transformation is

$$\frac{\partial f}{\partial t} + v_k \frac{\partial f}{\partial x_k} + \frac{F_k}{m} \frac{\partial f}{\partial v_k} = 0. \tag{2.22}$$

In this equation F_k stands for the Lorentz force,

$$F_k = -e \frac{\partial \varphi}{\partial x_k} - \frac{e}{c} \frac{\partial A_k}{\partial t} + \frac{e}{c} [v \times (\nabla \times A)]_k, \tag{2.23}$$

or

$$\boldsymbol{F} = e\boldsymbol{E} + \frac{e}{c} \boldsymbol{v} \times \boldsymbol{H}, \tag{2.24}$$

if, instead of the vector and scalar potentials, we use the electric and magnetic field intensities,

$$\boldsymbol{E} = -\frac{1}{c} \frac{\partial \boldsymbol{A}}{\partial t} - \nabla \varphi,$$

$$\boldsymbol{H} = \nabla \times \boldsymbol{A}. \tag{2.25}$$

The Liouville equation written in the (x_k, v_k) space is called the collisionless *Boltzmann equation* or Vlasov equation. In general the Boltzmann equation, called also the transport equation, contains a collisional term if interactions between particles are taken into account:

$$\frac{\partial f}{\partial t} + v_k \frac{\partial f}{\partial x_k} + \frac{F_k}{m} \frac{\partial f}{\partial v_k} = \left(\frac{\partial f}{\partial t}\right)_{\text{coll}}. \tag{2.26}$$

We are interested in macroscopic properties of the plasma, i.e., in average quantities. We will consider first a single fluid, i.e., we will assume all the particles are identical. To obtain equations containing the average quantities characterizing the fluid, we will form moments (in velocity v) of the Boltzmann equation (2.26) by multiplying this equation by a power of

†To obtain this transformation start with the Liouville equation in the form of equation (2.19). The terms $\partial\mathscr{H}/\partial\mathfrak{p}_i$ and $\partial\mathscr{H}/\partial\mathfrak{q}_i$ can then be easily calculated with the aid of equation (2.21). The results must be expressed in terms of the coordinates x_i and v_i. The first term, $\partial\mathscr{H}/\partial\mathfrak{p}_i$, is simply equal to v_i, and the $\partial\mathscr{H}/\partial\mathfrak{q}_i$ term is equal to $-v_k e/c\ (\partial A_k/\partial x_i) + e(\partial\varphi/\partial x_i)$. In the new space (x_i, v_i) the distribution function f is a function of $v_k(\mathfrak{q}_i, \mathfrak{p}_i)$, x_k, and t. This should be remembered when computing the terms $\partial f/\partial\mathfrak{q}_i$, $\partial f/\partial\mathfrak{p}_i$, and $\partial f/\partial t$. In computing the terms of the type $\partial f/\partial y$, where y is $\mathfrak{q}_i$ or $\mathfrak{p}_i$ or t, this derivative may be represented as a sum of three terms, $(\partial f/\partial v_k)\cdot(\partial v_k/\partial y)$, $(\partial f/\partial x_k)\cdot(\partial x_k/\partial y)$, and $(\partial f/\partial t)\cdot(\partial t/\partial y)$, and then each term may be expressed as a function of x_k, v_k, and t. Introducing these results into the Liouville equation gives equation (2.22).

v and integrating it over the velocity space. The result will depend on the ordinary coordinates x_1, x_2, x_3, and on time, and it will be expressed in terms of the following average quantities: mass density, mean velocity, pressure tensor, force density, thermal energy density, and the heat flow vector. The *mass density* and the *mean velocity* of the fluid are, respectively,

$$\rho = \int mfd^3v \tag{2.27}$$

$$\boldsymbol{V} = \frac{1}{\rho}\int m\boldsymbol{v}fd^3v \tag{2.28}$$

We will refer the *peculiar velocities* $\boldsymbol{u}$ of the particles to the average velocity defined above,

$$u_i = v_i - V_i(x_1, x_2, x_3, t); \tag{2.29}$$

i.e., we will introduce the new independent variable $\boldsymbol{u}$ instead of $\boldsymbol{v}$ (the variables $\boldsymbol{x}$, $\boldsymbol{u}$, and t are considered independent). Since $du_i = dv_i$, we can simply interchange du_i and dv_i wherever convenient. In the new variables, $f(x_1, x_2, x_3, v_1, v_2, v_3, t) \to f(x_1, x_2, x_3, u_1, u_2, u_3, t)$. By the definition of u_i, we have

$$\int m\boldsymbol{u}f\, d^3u = 0. \tag{2.30}$$

We will define the *total pressure tensor*, as

$$\Pi_{ij} = \int mv_iv_jfd^3v = \pi_{ij} + V_iV_j\rho, \tag{2.31}$$

where the *kinetic pressure tensor* is

$$\pi_{ij} = \int mu_iu_jf\, d^3u. \tag{2.32}$$

The pressure tensor describes the transport of the jth component of the momentum in the ith direction. As a symmetric tensor it has six independent components. The *force density* is

$$\mathscr{F} = \int \boldsymbol{F}f\, d^3v; \tag{2.33}$$

the *thermal energy density* is

$$\epsilon = \int \frac{1}{2}\, mu^2f\, d^3u; \tag{2.34}$$

and the *heat flow vector* is

$$\boldsymbol{q} = \int \frac{1}{2}\, m u^2 \boldsymbol{u} f\, d^3u. \tag{2.35}$$

The distribution function f is normalized to N (the number of particles in a unit coordinate volume):

$$\int f\, d^3v = N. \tag{2.36}$$

We will consider the following moments:

$$m, \qquad m\boldsymbol{v}, \qquad \frac{1}{2}\, m v^2. \tag{2.37}$$

Since the change in total mass, momentum, and kinetic energy produced by binary collisions between particles in zero if the potential energy of interaction is negligible, the right-hand side term in equation (2.26) does not give any contribution to the moments (2.37):

$$\begin{aligned}\int m\left(\frac{\partial f}{\partial t}\right)_{\text{coll}} d^3v &= \int m v\left(\frac{\partial f}{\partial t}\right)_{\text{coll}} d^3v \\ &= \int \frac{1}{2}\, m v^2 \left(\frac{\partial f}{\partial t}\right)_{\text{coll}} d^3v = 0. \end{aligned} \tag{2.38}$$

The quantities ρ and $\boldsymbol{V}$ are functions of $\boldsymbol{x}$ and t, and we are here treating $\boldsymbol{x}$, $\boldsymbol{v}$, and t as independent variables. We have assumed that F_i does not depend on v_i (that is true, e.g., for gravitational forces and for the Lorentz force, which is always perpendicular to the velocity vector).

The zero-order moment of the Boltzmann equation gives an *equation of mass conservation* known from ordinary hydrodynamics:†

$$\int m\left(\frac{\partial f}{\partial t} + v_i\, \frac{\partial f}{\partial x_i} + \frac{F_i}{m}\frac{\partial f}{\partial v_i}\right) d^3v = \frac{\partial \rho}{\partial t} + \frac{\partial}{\partial x_i}\, (\rho V_i) = 0,$$

or in vector notation,

$$\frac{\partial \rho}{\partial t} + \nabla \cdot (\rho \boldsymbol{V}) = 0. \tag{2.39}$$

First-order moments of the Boltzmann equation give three *momentum conservation equations*:

---

† This integration is straightforward. We assume that the distribution function vanishes at the boundary of the region occupied by the fluid, or at infinity, and therefore that the expression $F_j f$ vanishes at the limits of integration.

$$\int mv_j\left(\frac{\partial f}{\partial t}+v_i\,\frac{\partial f}{\partial x_i}+\frac{F_i}{m}\frac{\partial f}{\partial v_i}\right)d^3v$$

$$=\rho\left(\frac{\partial V_j}{\partial t}+V_i\,\frac{\partial V_j}{\partial x_i}\right)+\frac{\partial}{\partial x_i}\,\pi_{ij}-\mathscr{F}_j=0,$$

or

$$\rho\,\frac{DV}{Dt}+\nabla\cdot\overline{\overline{\pi}}-\mathscr{F}=0.^{\dagger} \tag{2.40}$$

The second-order moment of the Boltzmann equation gives the *energy conservation equation*:

$$\int\frac{1}{2}mv^2\left(\frac{\partial f}{\partial t}+v_i\,\frac{\partial f}{\partial x_i}+\frac{F_i}{m}\frac{\partial f}{\partial v_i}\right)d^3v$$

$$=\frac{\partial \epsilon}{\partial t}+V_i\,\frac{\partial \epsilon}{\partial x_i}+\epsilon\,\frac{\partial V_i}{\partial x_i}+\pi_{ij}\,\frac{\partial V_j}{\partial x_i}+\frac{\partial q_i}{\partial x_i}=0,$$

or

$$\frac{D\epsilon}{Dt}+\epsilon\nabla\cdot V+\overline{\overline{\pi}}:\nabla V+\nabla\cdot q=0.^{\ddagger} \tag{2.41}$$

Specification of all the moments of the distribution function is equivalent to the knowledge of the distribution function itself. However, in practice we cannot specify an infinite number of moments; therefore we will consider only a few moments of the distribution function—i.e., the moments of zero, first, and second order. The number of unknown moments of the distribution function will, however, always be larger

† The calculations here are a little more complex than those for the zero-order moment. The first term in the integral of equation (2.40) can be transformed with the help of equations (2.28) and (2.29). The second term should be developed with the aid of equations (2.29), (2.27), and (2.31). The third term, after integration by parts, can be simplified under the assumptions that v_jF_if vanishes at the limits of integration, since, according to our assumptions, the distribution function decreases more rapidly than F_i or v_j at the boundary. Furthermore, in our case F_i does not depend on v_i. This term with the use of equation (2.33) becomes equal to $-\mathscr{F}_j$.

‡ The first term in equation (2.41) can be evaluated with the help of equations (2.29), (2.30), and (2.34). The evaluation of the second term involves the use of equations (2.29), (2.30), (2.34), and (2.31). The third term in equation (2.41) should be integrated by parts, and again we will use our assumption that the distribution function decreases at the boundary of the system faster than v^2F_i, as well as the assumption that F_i does not depend on v_i. Then with the use of equations (2.30) and (2.33) it is easy to show that the third term is equal to $-V_iF_i$. The sum of all three terms is equal to the second part of equation (2.41) if the continuity equation and the momentum equation are used to reduce the number of terms.

than the number of equations which we can obtain by averaging the Boltzmann equation. This is related to the presence of a term explicitly containing v_i in the Boltzmann equation. Therefore, to solve the system of equations, some assumption must be made about the highest moment of the distribution function. In ordinary hydrodynamics, for example, such an assumption is that the pressure is a scalar and is given by an equation of state in terms of two thermodynamic variables, e.g., density ρ and temperature T. The assumption that the pressure is a scalar will reduce equation (2.40) to the form

$$\rho \frac{DV}{Dt} = -\nabla p + \mathscr{F}. \tag{2.42}$$

The energy equation for an adiabatic process ($\boldsymbol{q} = 0$) will degenerate to the equation of state for a monatomic gas†,

$$\frac{D}{Dt}\{p\rho^{-5/3}\} = 0. \tag{2.43}$$

In plasma physics we generally have to deal with three distinct types of particles (electrons, ions, and neutral particles), and in some cases we must use three sets of equations for the three distinct distribution functions (f^- for electrons, f^+ for ions, and f^0 for neutral particles). This kind of approach is known as three-fluid hydrodynamics. If the plasma is completely ionized, the two-fluid approach is appropriate. In this case, which we will consider now, we have two Boltzmann equations, one for electrons and one for ions, but the right-hand sides must have additional collisional terms in order to describe the collisions between electrons and ions. In the electron and the ion equations (upper and lower sets of superscripts refer to electron and ion equations, respectively)

---

† If the rate of collisions between particles is as large as it is in gases under ordinary conditions, the collisions cause the distribution function to be Maxwellian or very nearly Maxweillian; i.e.,

$$f(\boldsymbol{x}, \boldsymbol{v}) = N\left(\frac{m}{2\pi kT}\right)^{3/2} \exp\left[-\frac{m(\boldsymbol{u}-V)^2}{2kT}\right].$$

For the Maxwellian distribution function the π tensor is diagonal: $\pi_{ij} = p\delta_{ij}$.

$$p = NkT = \rho kT/m = \frac{2}{3} c_v T,$$

$$\epsilon = c_v T = \frac{3}{2} p,$$

where c_v is the specific heat.

$$\left(\frac{\partial f^{\mp}}{\partial t}\right)_{\text{coll}} = \left(\frac{\partial f^{\mp\mp}}{\partial t}\right)_{\text{coll}} + \left(\frac{\partial f^{\mp\pm}}{\partial t}\right)_{\text{coll}} \tag{2.44}$$

Now the conservation laws apply only to the first collisional term in each equation. The second term represents the exchange of the quantity described by the conservation law (momentum or energy) between the two fluids because of electron-ion interactions. If we denote the exchange of momentum between the electrons and the ions by $\Delta \boldsymbol{p}^{-+}$, and between the ions and the electrons by $\Delta \boldsymbol{p}^{+-}$, and the exchange of energy by $\Delta \mathscr{E}^{-+}$ and $\Delta \mathscr{E}^{+-}$, respectively,† we can form the moments of the transport equation for each fluid:

$$\begin{gathered}
\frac{\partial \rho^{\mp}}{\partial t} + \nabla \cdot (\rho^{\mp} \boldsymbol{V}^{\mp}) = 0, \\
m^{\mp} n^{\mp} \left(\frac{\partial}{\partial t} + \boldsymbol{V}^{\mp} \cdot \nabla\right) \boldsymbol{V}^{\mp} + \nabla \cdot \overline{\overline{\pi}}^{\mp} - n^{\mp} e^{\mp} \left(\boldsymbol{E} + \frac{\boldsymbol{V}^{\mp}}{c} \times \boldsymbol{H}\right) = \Delta \boldsymbol{p}^{\mp\pm}, \\
\left(\frac{\partial}{\partial t} + \boldsymbol{V}^{\mp} \cdot \nabla\right) c_v^{\mp}\, T^{\mp} + c_v^{\mp}\, T^{\mp} \nabla \cdot \boldsymbol{V}^{\mp} + \pi^{\mp} : \nabla \boldsymbol{V}^{\mp} + \nabla \cdot \boldsymbol{q}^{\mp} = \Delta \mathscr{E}^{\mp\pm}.
\end{gathered} \tag{2.45}$$

In the next section we will use equation (2.45) for the discussion of the propagation of high-frequency waves in a plasma. However, we should first consider the average hydrodynamic quantities for a two-fluid plasma and look briefly at the generalized form of Ohm's law for a plasma. Instead of the variables n^+, n^- (or ρ^+, ρ^-) and $\boldsymbol{V}^+$, $\boldsymbol{V}^-$ (referring to the individual fluids), let us introduce the following variables referring to the system as a whole:

matter density,

$$\rho = \rho^+ + \rho^- = n^+ m^+ + n^- m^-; \tag{2.46}$$

charge density,

$$Q = n^+ e^+ + n^- e^-; \tag{2.47}$$

average velocity,

$$\boldsymbol{V} = \frac{\rho^+ \boldsymbol{V}^+ + \rho^- \boldsymbol{V}^-}{\rho^+ + \rho^-} = \frac{1}{\rho}\,(n^+ m^+ \boldsymbol{V}^+ + n^- m^- \boldsymbol{V}^-); \tag{2.48}$$

---

† Note that by the conservation of total momentum and energy, we have

$$\Delta \boldsymbol{p}^{-+} + \Delta \boldsymbol{p}^{+-} = \Delta \mathscr{E}^{-+} + \Delta \mathscr{E}^{+-} = 0.$$

and *net current density*,

$$j = J - J_{\text{conv}} = n^+ e^+ (V^+ - V) + n^- e^- (V^- - V). \tag{2.49}$$

The convective current density,

$$J_{\text{conv}} = QV = (n^+ e^+ + n^- e^-)\, V \tag{2.50}$$

and the total current density,

$$J = n^+ e^+ V^+ + n^- e^- V^-, \tag{2.51}$$

can be used to replace the charge density and the net current density wherever convenient. Since we have one independent continuity equation for each fluid [equation (2.45)], two linear combinations of the continuity equations for ions and electrons will be independent (the corresponding statement, of course, also applies to the momentum and energy equations). We will let one linear combination be simply the sum of the equations and the second one be the sum of the products of $e^\pm/m^\pm$ times the appropriate equation. We therefore obtain from the continuity equations the equation of continuity of mass,

$$\frac{\partial \rho}{\partial t} + \nabla \cdot (\rho V) = 0, \tag{2.52}$$

and the equation of continuity of charge,

$$\frac{\partial Q}{\partial t} + \nabla \cdot J = 0. \tag{2.53}$$

The sum of the momentum equations gives

$$\rho \frac{DV}{Dt} + \nabla \cdot \overline{\overline{\pi}} - QE - \frac{1}{c} J \times H = 0, \tag{2.54}$$

where†

$$\overline{\overline{\pi}} = \overline{\overline{\pi}}^+ + \overline{\overline{\pi}}^-, \tag{2.55}$$

---

† In the first form of the momentum equation the kinetic pressure tensor has the form

$$\pi_{ij}^\pm = \int m^\pm (v_i^\pm - V_i^\pm)(v_j^\pm - V_j^\pm)\, d^3v.$$

since the peculiar velocities $u_i^\pm$ are defined with respect to $V_i^\pm$, while in equations (2.54) and (2.63) this tensor has the form

$$\pi_{ij}^\pm = \int m^\pm (v_i^\pm - V_i)(v_j^\pm - V_j)\, d^3v,$$

since the peculiar velocities $u_i^\pm$ are referred to the average velocity V_i given by equation (2.48).

if we describe random velocities with respect to V, not to V^+ and V^-.

If we multiply the momentum equation for electrons by e^-/m^- and the one for ions by e^+/m^+, and if we add the results together, we can obtain an equation for the electric current in a plasma under the assumptions that the concentrations of ions and electrons do not change with time, that the ions are much heavier than electrons and therefore practically immobile (m^-/m^+ is negligible compared with unity), and that the pressure is a scalar:†

$$\frac{\partial \boldsymbol{J}}{\partial t} + \omega_G \boldsymbol{J} \times \frac{\boldsymbol{H}}{H} - \frac{e^-}{m^-} \Delta \boldsymbol{p}^{-+} = \frac{n^-(e^-)^2}{m^-}\left(\boldsymbol{E} + \frac{\boldsymbol{V}}{c} \times \boldsymbol{H} - \frac{1}{n^- e^-} \nabla p^-\right) - n^- e^-(\boldsymbol{V}^- \cdot \nabla)\boldsymbol{V}^- + n^+ e^+(\boldsymbol{V}^+ \cdot \nabla)\boldsymbol{V}^+ \quad (2.56)$$

where ω_G is the Larmor frequency and is given by

$$\omega_G = -\frac{e^- H}{m^- c} = 1.8 \times 10^7\, H. \quad (2.57)$$

We will approximate the interaction term contained in equation (2.56) by assuming that the exchange of momentum between ions and electrons is roughly proportional to the relative velocity of the particles. The average momentum gained by an electron in each collision is $m^-(\boldsymbol{V}^+ - \boldsymbol{V}^-)$ and is approximately equal to $-m^-(\boldsymbol{V}^- - \boldsymbol{V})$ if the peculiar velocities of the ions are negligible compared with the peculiar velocities of the electrons. Since the number of such collisions per cubic centimeter is equal to $\nu_C n^-$, where ν_C is the collision frequency, the average momentum exchange is

$$\Delta \boldsymbol{p}^{-+} = -m^-(\boldsymbol{V}^- - \boldsymbol{V})\nu_C n^-. \quad (2.58)$$

† The derivation of equation (2.56) is somewhat cumbersome. The term containing the time derivative of the electric current and the nonlinear term containing the velocities of the electrons and ions in equation (2.56) arise from the terms containing the convective derivatives of the velocities in the equations of momentum for ions and electrons. The terms containing the divergence of the pressure tensor in the momentum equation yield the term with the pressure gradient in equation (2.56) under the assumptions that the mass of the ions is much larger than the mass of the electrons and that the pressure is a scalar. The terms in the momentum equations containing the Lorentz forces can be transformed to give the terms containing the magnetic and electric fields in equation (2.56) under the assumptions that the mass of an electron is negligible compared with the mass of an ion, that the peculiar velocities of the ions are negligible compared with the peculiar velocities of the electrons, and that the plasma is neutral on the average.

Eliminating $V^- - V$ between the above equation and the equation giving the net current density (with the same approximations),

$$j = n^+ e^+ (V^+ - V) + n^- e^- (V^- - V) \approx n^- e^- (V^- - V), \quad (2.59)$$

we have the following relation between Δp^{-+} and j:

$$\Delta p^{-+} = - \frac{m^- \nu_C}{e^-} j. \quad (2.60)$$

For a homogeneous medium (if ∇p^- is negligible or no thermoelectric currents are present), we can write equation (2.56) with the aid of equation (2.60) in a linear approximation (second-order terms in velocity are neglected) in the form

$$\frac{\partial J}{\partial t} + \omega_G J \times \frac{H}{H} + \nu_C j = \frac{n^-(e^-)^2}{m^-} \left(E + \frac{V}{c} \times H \right). \quad (2.61)$$

Equations (2.56) and (2.61) are generalized forms of *Ohm's law*. If (as an order of magnitude approximation $\nu \approx \partial/\partial t$ is the characteristic frequency of the problem (e.g., the frequency of electromagnetic waves in a plasma, if wave propagation is the problem considered), we can write equation (2.61) as

$$\nu J + \omega_G J \times \frac{H}{H} + \nu_C j = \frac{n^-(e^-)^2}{m^-} \left(E + \frac{V}{c} \times H \right). \quad (2.62)$$

It is customary to define the electrical conductivity σ as the coefficient of proportionality between j and E in equation (2.62). σ is, in general, a tensor and depends on ν, ω_G, ν_C, and on the direction of the magnetic field; the electrical conductivity of a plasma differs in the direction of the magnetic field from that in the direction perpendicular to it. Depending on the type of problem considered, it is usually possible to neglect one or two of the frequencies ν, ν_C, or ω_G compared with the remaining ones and in this way to simplify Ohm's law.

The sum of the energy equations (2.46, 2.47) gives

$$\frac{D}{Dt}(c_v T) + c_v T \nabla \cdot V + \overline{\overline{\pi}} : \nabla V + \nabla \cdot q - j \cdot \left(E + \frac{V}{c} \times H \right) = 0, \quad (2.63)$$

where $\overline{\overline{\pi}}$ is the kinetic pressure tensor (see footnote, page 00), and the last term represents the Joule heating.

Since in plasma physics we explicitly describe charges and currents in vacuum, we can use two *Maxwell equations* in the form

$$\nabla \times \boldsymbol{H} = \frac{4\pi}{c} \boldsymbol{J} + \frac{1}{c} \frac{\partial \boldsymbol{E}}{\partial t}, \tag{2.64}$$

$$\nabla \times \boldsymbol{E} = -\frac{1}{c} \frac{\partial \boldsymbol{H}}{\partial t},$$

with the conditions

$$\nabla \cdot \boldsymbol{E} = 4\pi Q, \tag{2.65}$$

$$\nabla \cdot \boldsymbol{H} = 0.$$

If we take the divergence of the first Maxwell equation of equation (2.64), then we find, with the help of the equation of continuity of charge [equation (2.53)], that

$$0 \equiv \nabla \cdot (\nabla \times \boldsymbol{H}) = \frac{1}{c} \frac{\partial}{\partial t} (\nabla \cdot \boldsymbol{E} - 4\pi Q);$$

that is, if $\nabla \cdot \boldsymbol{E} = 4\pi Q$ is satisfied at one time (an initial condition only), it is satisfied at all times. Conversely, from the first Maxwell equation and from the condition that $\nabla \cdot \boldsymbol{E} = 4\pi Q$ at all times, the equation of continuity of charge follows. By the same procedure we find from the second Maxwell equation (2.64), with no other relation assumed, that

$$0 \equiv \nabla \cdot (\nabla \times \boldsymbol{E}) = -\frac{1}{c} \frac{\partial}{\partial t} (\nabla \cdot \boldsymbol{H});$$

that is, if $\nabla \cdot \boldsymbol{H} = 0$ is satisfied at one time (an initial condition only), then it is satisfied at all times. We see then that the usual set of four Maxwell equations follows from just two of the Maxwell equations and the equation of continuity of charge if the other two equations are given only as initial conditions.

2.3 Propagation of Waves in a Plasma

We will now discuss the propagation of electromagnetic waves in a plasma imbedded in a magnetic field $\boldsymbol{H}_0$ generated by an external source. We will adopt the two-fluid model with the formalism developed in the preceding section, and in addition we will assume that the plasma in the state when it is unperturbed by the wave is neutral ($Q = 0$) and stationary ($\boldsymbol{V}^- = \boldsymbol{V}^+ = 0$). We will also assume that the kinetic pressure tensors $\pi_{ik}{}^-$ and $\pi_{ik}{}^+$ are reduced to the scalars p^+ and p^- representing isotropic pressures, and that the pressures are functions of the temperatures T^+

and T^- of the electron and ion gases: $p^+ = n^+ kT^+$ and $p^- = n^- kT^-$. The temperatures T^+ and T^- are equal when the electron and ion gases are in thermodynamic equilibrium.

The propagation of waves of small amplitude will be discussed in the linear approximation; the perturbed (by the wave) state of a plasma can be represented in this approximation by the following set of equations:

the field equations,

$$\nabla \times \delta \boldsymbol{E} = -\frac{1}{c}\frac{\partial \boldsymbol{H}}{\partial t},$$

$$\nabla \times \boldsymbol{H} = \frac{4\pi}{c}\boldsymbol{j} + \frac{1}{c}\frac{\partial \delta \boldsymbol{E}}{\partial t},$$

$$\nabla \cdot \delta \boldsymbol{E} = 4\pi \delta Q,$$

$$\nabla \cdot \boldsymbol{H} = 0; \tag{2.66}$$

the equations of continuity,

$$\frac{\partial \delta n^\pm}{\partial t} + \nabla \cdot (n^\pm \delta \boldsymbol{V}^\pm) = 0; \tag{2.67}$$

and the equations of momentum conservation,

$$n^\pm m^\pm \frac{\partial \delta \boldsymbol{V}^\pm}{\partial t} = n^\pm e^\pm \left(\delta \boldsymbol{E} + \frac{\partial \boldsymbol{V}^\pm}{c} \times \boldsymbol{H}_0 \right) - \nabla p^\pm$$

$$- n^\pm m^\pm \nu_C (\delta \boldsymbol{V}^\pm - \delta \boldsymbol{V}). \tag{2.68}$$

In the above equations resulting from equations (2.45), (2.58), (2.64), and (2.65), under the assumptions specified here, the perturbed state of the plasma is described with the use of the following variables:

electron density	$n^- + \delta n^-$
ion density	$n^+ + \delta n^+$
electron mean velocity	$0 + \delta \boldsymbol{V}^-$
ion mean velocity	$0 + \delta \boldsymbol{V}^+$
electron pressure	$p^- + \delta p^-$
ion pressure	$p^+ + \delta p^+$
electric field	$0 + \delta \boldsymbol{E}$
magnetic field	$\boldsymbol{H}_0 + \delta \boldsymbol{H}$
charge density	$0 + \delta Q$,

where the increments describe the perturbation identified with a wave of small amplitude; the powers of increments higher than first are neglected. The charge density and the current density in equation (2.66) can be expressed in terms of the remaining variables through the following (linearized) equations:

$$\delta Q = \delta n^- e^- + \delta n^+ e^+,$$
$$j = n^- e^- \delta V^- + n^+ e^+ \delta V^+. \tag{2.69}$$

We will further assume that the plasma is uniform, the external magnetic field $\boldsymbol{H}_0$ is homogeneous, and the perturbations are adiabatic; i.e.,

$$\delta p^{\pm} = m^{\pm} (v_T^{\pm})^2 \, \delta n^{\pm}.$$

The appropriate expressions for $(v_T^{\pm})^2$, the mean square velocities, when the compression is in only one direction are

$$(v_T^{\pm})^2 = 3kT^{\pm}/m^{\pm}.$$

We will look for the solution of the linearized system of equations of a plasma in the form (plane waves propagating in the z-direction)

$$\boldsymbol{A} = \boldsymbol{A}_0 \exp\,[-i(\tilde{\omega}t + \tilde{k}z)],$$

where $\tilde{\omega}$ and $\tilde{k}$ are in general complex, or in an equivalent form,

$$\boldsymbol{A} = \boldsymbol{A}_0 \exp\,(\omega' t + k' z) \exp\,[-i(\omega t + kz)]. \tag{2.70}$$

The imaginary part of the frequency and wave number, ω' and k', are responsible for damping (absorption) of waves. In the collisionless case $\nu \gg \nu_C \to 0$ there is no damping (except for Landau damping, see below) and the wave propagates with the phase velocity,

$$V_{\text{ph}} = \frac{\omega}{k},$$

and the group velocity,

$$V_{\text{gr}} = \frac{d\omega}{dk}.$$

We will assume first that $\nu_C = 0$ in order to discuss the propagation of waves without damping (later we will return to the case $\nu_C \neq 0$ in order to consider the absorption of waves in a plasma). Under this assumption we can reduce the system of linear differential equations (2.66)–(2.68), having solutions of the type given in equation (2.70), to a system of linear homogeneous algebraic equations by using $\partial/\partial t = i\omega$ and $\partial/\partial z = ik$. This set of equations will have a nonzero solution if its determinant vanishes. By setting this determinant equal to zero, we obtain the dispersion equation relating the propagation constant (wave number), $k = 2\pi/\lambda$, to the frequency ω. In general, this dispersion equation is of the fourth order in k^2; i.e., it gives four modes of wave propagation (each mode having two identical waves propagating along z in opposite directions): the ordinary wave, the extraordinary wave, the electron wave, and the ion wave. If there is no transverse component of the external magnetic field, the ordinary and extraordinary modes are transverse electromagnetic waves, and the electron and ion waves are longitudinal waves. Coupling between the longitudinal and transverse waves appears when the transverse component of the external magnetic field is nonzero. We will omit the algebraic procedure leading to the dispersion equation and use this equation in a simpler form resulting from the additional assumption of a fully ionized hydrogen plasma ($n^- = n^+ = N$) with infinitely heavy (and therefore immobile) ions, $m^+/m^- = 1836 \rightarrow \infty$. In this way we will lose the *ion mode* in our dispersion equation, and the dispersion relation will become a third-order equation in k^2,

$$\{\omega^2 [1 - \beta_T^2 n^2] - \omega_0^2\} \cdot \{[\omega^2 (1 - n^2) - \omega_0^2]^2 - \omega^2 \omega_G^2 \cos^2 \vartheta \, (1 - n^2)^2\} - \omega^2 \omega_G^2 \sin^2 \vartheta \, (1 - n^2)[\omega^2 (1 - n^2) - \omega_0^2] = 0. \tag{2.71}$$

In this equation $\beta_T = v_T/c \equiv v_T^-/c$, n is the (real part of the) refractive index $n = kc/\omega$, ϑ is the angle between the direction of the wave propagation and of the external magnetic field, and ω_0 is the plasma frequency,

$$\omega_0 = \sqrt{\frac{4\pi (e^-)^2 n^-}{m^-}} = 5.6 \times 10^4 \, N^{1/2}. \tag{2.72}$$

If there is no transverse magnetic field ($\vartheta = 0$), we have longitudinal propagation. The dispersion equation (2.71) splits into the two equations

$$\omega^2 (1 - \beta_T^2 n^2) - \omega_0^2 = 0,$$

$$[\omega^2 (1 - n^2) - \omega_0^2]^2 - \omega^2 \omega_G^2 (1 - n^2)^2 = 0; \tag{2.73}$$

the first describes the electron mode, and the second gives both the ordinary and extraordinary modes. The *electron mode* (or p-mode) is a longitudinal wave with the frequency

$$\omega = \sqrt{k^2 v_T^2 + \omega_0^2}; \tag{2.74}$$

the plasma takes part in the wave motion, just as a neutral gas takes part in the motion associated with sound waves, and this longitudinal wave cannot exist outside of a plasma. In a sound wave propagating in a neutral medium, a particle acquires an average momentum parallel to the motion of the ensemble of the particles through many short-range, nearly incoherent interactions, the range being smaller than the interparticle distance λ_P. In plasma oscillations the momentum is transferred to a particle through long-range interactions with particles up to the distance of the order of the Debye length λ_D, and usually $\lambda_D \gg \lambda_P$. The electric field provides a coupling between these interactions which causes a coherent disturbance. In a cold plasma ($\beta_T = 0$) the electron oscillations are non-dispersive ($\omega = \omega_0$); oscillations of frequency ω_0 can occur in a plasma, but their group velocity is zero. If $\beta_T \neq 0$, the refractive index of the electron plasma wave,

$$n^2 = \beta_T^{-2}\left(1 - \frac{\omega_0^2}{\omega^2}\right) \tag{2.75}$$

becomes imaginary for $\omega < \omega_0$; the plasma frequency ω_0 is therefore a lower limit on the frequency of plasma oscillations. The phase and group velocities of electron plasma waves are

$$V_{\text{ph}} = \frac{\omega}{k} = \frac{v_T}{\sqrt{1 - \dfrac{\omega_0^2}{\omega^2}}} = v_T\sqrt{1 + \frac{\lambda^2}{\lambda_E^2}},$$

$$V_{\text{gr}} = \frac{d\omega}{dk} = v_T\sqrt{1 - \frac{\omega_0^2}{\omega^2}} = \frac{v_T}{\sqrt{1 + \dfrac{\lambda^2}{\lambda_E^2}}},$$

where λ_E is the characteristic length for electron waves defined as

$$\lambda_E = 2\pi\frac{v_T}{\omega_0} \approx 10\,\lambda_D, \tag{2.76}$$

and λ is the wavelength. The inequalities $V_{\text{ph}} > V_{\text{gr}}$, $V_{\text{ph}} > v_T$, and $V_{\text{gr}} < v_T$ always hold, while V_{ph} and V_{gr} are related by $V_{\text{gr}} \cdot V_{\text{ph}} = v_T^2$. The electrons with thermal velocities close to the phase velocity of the wave are unable to pass through the minima of the potential of the wave and are trapped in the maxima, thus reducing the amplitude of the electron wave. This effect is often referred to as *Landau damping*. It becomes important when V_{ph} approaches v_T, because the number of trapped electrons becomes large and completely disorganizes the wave. Therefore only waves with V_{ph} substantially larger than v_T, say $V_{\text{ph}} > \sqrt{2}\,v_T$ (that is, $\omega < \sqrt{2}\,\omega_0$, $\lambda > \lambda_E$), can propagate without appreciable Landau damping.

The second equation of (2.73) describes the *ordinary wave*,

$$n^2 = 1 - \frac{\omega_0^2}{\omega(\omega + \omega_G)}, \tag{2.77}$$

which is a transverse left-handed circularly polarized wave, and the *extraordinary wave*,

$$n^2 = 1 - \frac{\omega_0^2}{\omega(\omega - \omega_G)}, \tag{2.78}$$

which is a transverse right-handed circularly polarized wave. The ordinary wave can propagate in a plasma only if its frequency is larger than

$$\omega_{\min} = \sqrt{\omega_0^2 + \frac{1}{4}\omega_G^2} - \frac{1}{2}\omega_G,$$

and the limiting frequency for the extraordinary wave is

$$\omega_{\min} = \sqrt{\omega_0^2 + \frac{1}{4}\omega_G^2} + \frac{1}{2}\omega_G;$$

at frequencies lower than $\omega_{\min}$ the refractive indices become imaginary.

In the absence of the longitudinal component of the applied magnetic field ($\vartheta = \pi/2$, transverse propagation), only the ordinary mode can be factored from equation (2.71). This mode is linearly polarized with the electric vector parallel to the magnetic field. However, if $\beta_T = 0$, then, in addition to a somewhat simplified ordinary mode, the other mode can be obtained from equation (2.71) with the following simple dispersion relation:

$$n^2 = 1 - \frac{\omega_0^2/\omega^2}{1 - \omega_G^2/(\omega^2 - \omega_0^2)}.$$

In the general case of an arbitrary angle ϑ, the dispersion equation (2.71) cannot be factored except for a cold plasma ($\beta_T = 0$), when one gets a quadratic equation which readily yields the Appleton-Hartree formula often used in atmospheric physics.

In galactic and extragalactic astronomy ω_G^2/ω^2 is very small (e.g., for $H = 10^{-5}$ gauss, $\omega_G = 200$ Hz), and ω_0^2/ω^2 is also small because of the low electron densities. Under these circumstances the condition

$$\left(\frac{\omega_G}{\omega}\right)^2 \frac{\sin^4\vartheta}{4\cos^2\vartheta} \ll \left(1 - \frac{\omega_0^2}{\omega^2}\right)^2 \tag{2.79}$$

is satisfied for a cold plasma for a wide range of angles ϑ. It can be shown that when the inequality (2.79) holds (quasi-longitudinal propagation), the modes can be approximated by the ordinary and extraordinary modes for the longitudinal propagation. Moreover, since ω_G is negligible in comparison with ω, there is no need to differentiate between the ordinary and extraordinary modes; the dispersion equation for either of these modes [equations (2.77) and (2.78)] becomes

$$n^2 = 1 - \frac{\omega_0^2}{\omega^2}. \tag{2.80}$$

The plasma can therefore be treated as isotropic except in problems involving the computation of the phase difference between the ordinary and extraordinary rays. An example of this exception is the problem of the Faraday rotation of the plane of polarization of an electromagnetic wave passing through a slab of plasma. The difference of phase φ, $(\omega/c) \cdot (n_{\text{ord}} - n_{\text{ext}})s$, is proportional to the path length s through the plasma, which in astronomical conditions is very large and thus offsets the very small difference in the refractive indices. The Faraday rotation angle χ_F in radians is

$$\begin{aligned}\chi_F &= \frac{1}{2}\varphi = \frac{1}{2}\frac{\omega}{c}\,(n_{\text{ord}} - n_{\text{ext}})\,s \\ &= \frac{1}{2}\frac{\omega_0^2}{c}\frac{\omega_G}{\omega^2 - \omega_G^2}s \approx \frac{1}{2}\frac{\omega_0^2\,\omega_G}{c\,\omega^2}s \\ &= 0.93 \times 10^6\,\frac{NH_{\|}s}{\omega^2}\end{aligned} \tag{2.81}$$

When $NH_{\|}$ varies along the path, $NH_{\|}s$ should be replaced by $\int NH_{\|}ds$.

Let us return to the general case of propagation of electromagnetic waves in a collisionless plasma (the ions are not assumed to be immobile). The four modes of propagation are illustrated in Figure 2.2. In this figure $\omega_G^{\pm}$ are the Larmor frequencies $(e^{\pm}H/m^{\pm}c)$; V_S is the velocity of sound,

$$V_S^2 = \frac{1}{\rho}\,[\rho^+(v_T^+)^2 + \rho^-(v_T^-)^2];$$

V_A is the Alfvén velocity,

$$V_A = \frac{H_0}{\sqrt{4\pi\rho}}; \tag{2.82}$$

and ϑ is the angle between the magnetic field and the direction of propagation of waves. For low frequencies there are three modes of propagation, called magnetosonic modes: slow, Alfvén, and fast. These modes are nondispersive; for sufficiently low frequencies their velocities are independent of frequency. The magnetosonic waves can easily be derived from the system of macroscopic hydromagnetic equations describing the behavior of a conducting fluid in a magnetic field. The hydromagnetic equations can be derived from the plasma equations by adding together the equations for the electron and ion gases and working with the approximation that $\nu_C \gg \omega_G \gg \omega$, which considerably simplifies Ohm's law.

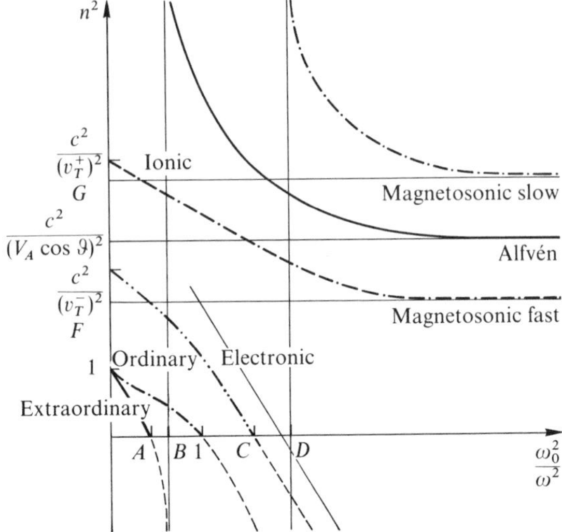

Fig. 2.2 The modes of propagation of electromagnetic waves in a plasma. The following are values of the ordinates and abscissae A, B, C, D, F, G:

$$A = 4\omega_0{}^2[\sqrt{(\omega_G^-)^2 + (\omega_G^+)^2 + 4\omega_0{}^2} + (\omega_G^- - \omega_G^+)]^{-2},$$

$$B = \omega_0{}^2(\omega_G^- \cos \vartheta)^{-2}$$

$$C = 4\omega_0{}^2[\sqrt{(\omega_G^-)^2 + (\omega_G^+)^2 + 4\omega_0{}^2} - (\omega_G^- - \omega_G^+)]^{-2},$$

$$D = \omega_0{}^2(\omega_G^+ \cos \vartheta)^{-2}$$

$$F = \frac{c^2}{2\cos^2 \vartheta}\left[\frac{1}{V_A{}^2} + \frac{1}{V_S{}^2} - \frac{\sin^2 \vartheta}{c^2} + \sqrt{\left(\frac{1}{V_A{}^2} + \frac{1}{V_S{}^2} - \frac{1+\cos^2 \vartheta}{c^2}\right)^2 - 4\cos^2 \vartheta\left(\frac{1}{V_A{}^2} - \frac{1}{c^2}\right)\left(\frac{1}{V_S{}^2} - \frac{1}{c^2}\right)}\right],$$

$$G = \frac{c^2}{2\cos^2 \vartheta}\left[\frac{1}{V_A{}^2} + \frac{1}{V_S{}^2} - \frac{\sin^2 \vartheta}{c^2} - \sqrt{\left(\frac{1}{V_A{}^2} + \frac{1}{V_S{}^2} - \frac{1+\cos^2 \vartheta}{c^2}\right)^2 - 4\cos^2 \vartheta\left(\frac{1}{V_A{}^2} - \frac{1}{c^2}\right)\left(\frac{1}{V_S{}^2} - \frac{1}{c^2}\right)}\right].$$

An analysis of the dispersion relations shows that if $\omega_0 \ll \omega_G$, the refraction index for the transverse waves is always close to unity except in the immediate neighborhood of the Larmor frequencies. If the opposite inequality holds, the refractive index is always different from unity, and the plasma strongly affects the propagation of the electromagnetic wave. Introducing a parameter

$$X_{H/R} = \frac{H^2}{8\pi mc^2 N}, \tag{2.83}$$

which is the ratio of the magnetic to rest energy densities, we can say that for $X_{H/R} \gg 1$, $n \approx 1$ and for $X_{H/R} \ll 1$, $n \neq 1$. A plasma characterized by large values of the parameter $X_{H/R}$ is called a rarefied plasma, and one characterized by small values of the same parameter is referred to as a dense plasma. Figure 2.3 represents a $\log T - \log N/H^2$ plane for plasmas. In Figure 2.3, besides the $X_{H/R} = 1$ and $X_{T/R} = 1$ lines, we have also plotted an $X_{T/H} = 1$ line;

$$X_{T/H} = \frac{12\pi NkT}{H^2} \tag{2.84}$$

is the ratio of the thermal to magnetic energy densities in a plasma (or the ratio of sound and Alfvén velocities). For large values of $X_{T/H}$ the plasma cannot be confined to a limited portion of space by the magnetic field.

We discussed the propagation of electromagnetic waves in a collisionless plasma, i.e., assuming that $\nu_C = 0$. If $\nu_C \neq 0$, a certain amount of energy will be absorbed from the wave and dissipated through collisions into heat—the wave will be damped. The damping (absorption) is described by the first exponential factor in equation (2.70). The absorption coefficient defined by equation (A.22) can be written as

$$\kappa_\nu = -\frac{1}{I}\frac{dI}{ds} = -2\kappa'.$$

For $\omega \gg \nu_C \gg \omega_G$ and $\omega \gg \omega_0$, it can be shown that

$$\kappa' = -\frac{\nu_C}{2cn} \cdot \frac{\omega_0{}^2}{\omega^2}.$$

In the process of absorption (or emission) of electromagnetic energy the collisions between electrons and protons are much more important than the electron-electron collisions, because in the latter case only quadrupole effects are involved. The calculation of the collision frequency ν_C is rather involved, and the result depends on certain assumptions concerning, for example, screening of the field of the ions by electrons and other ions. For a Maxwellian distribution of electron velocities the frequency of electron-ion encounters is given by an approximation sufficient for many radio astronomical applications:

$$\begin{aligned} \nu_C &= \frac{4\sqrt{2\pi}}{3}\,\frac{e^4}{\sqrt{m}}\,\frac{N}{(kT)^{3/2}}\ln\left[1.32\,\frac{(kT)^{3/2}}{e^2\sqrt{m}\,\omega}\right] \\ &= 3.6\,\frac{N}{T^{3/2}}\left(17.7 + \ln\frac{T^{3/2}}{\nu}\right), \end{aligned} \tag{2.85}$$

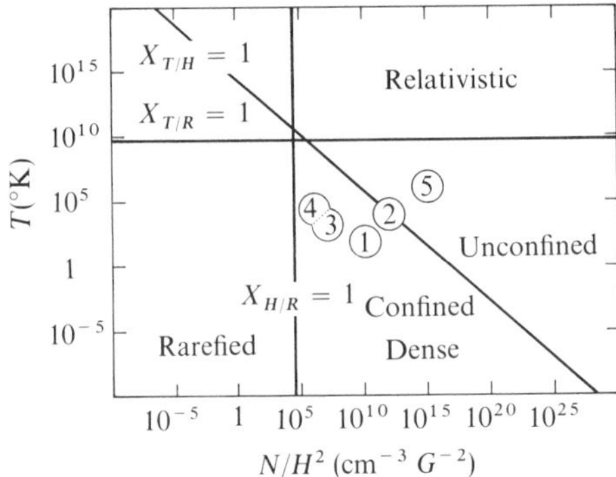

Fig. 2.3 The log N/H^2 – log T plane for plasmas. Numbers identify the regions corresponding to some of the entries in Table 1.

which depends weakly on the frequency of the wave since a given interaction between a proton and an electron may be efficient in absorbing (or emitting) radiation at low frequencies (and therefore be counted as a collision at these frequencies), but may not be efficient at higher frequencies. Combining the above three equations and assuming $n \approx 1$, we have for a rarefied plasma

$$\begin{aligned}\kappa_\nu &= \frac{32\pi^{3/2}}{3\sqrt{2}}\frac{e^6}{cm^{3/2}}\frac{N^2}{(kT)^{3/2}\,\omega^2}\ln\left[1.32\frac{(kT)^{3/2}}{e^2\sqrt{m}\,\omega}\right]\\ &= 9.8\times10^{-3}\frac{N^2}{T^{3/2}\,\nu^2}\left(17.7+\ln\frac{T^{3/2}}{\nu}\right).\end{aligned} \tag{2.86}$$

Absorption of the energy of an electromagnetic wave in a plasma by a proton-electron system accelerates the electron moving in the electromagnetic field of a proton. The inverse process is, of course, also possible and involves the deceleration of an electron in the Coulomb field of a proton accompanied by the emission of radiation. This emission is called bremsstrahlung or free-free emission. Since the energy emitted in bremsstrahlung is of thermal origin and the distribution of electron velocities is Maxwellian, the source function is Planckian, or

$$\frac{\varepsilon_\nu}{\kappa_\nu} = B_\nu(T), \tag{2.87}$$

and the emission coefficient at radio frequencies is given by

$$\begin{aligned}\varepsilon_\nu &= \frac{16}{3\sqrt{2\pi}}\frac{e^6}{c^3 m^{3/2}}\frac{N^2}{\sqrt{kT}}\ln\left[1.32\frac{(kT)^{3/2}}{e^2\sqrt{m}\,\omega}\right]\\ &= 3.0\times10^{-39}\frac{N^2}{T^{1/2}}\left(17.7+\ln\frac{T^{3/2}}{\nu}\right),\end{aligned} \tag{2.88}$$

where $B_\nu(T) \approx 2kT\nu^2/c^2$.

2.4. Motion of Charged Particles in a Magnetic Field

Until now we have described the behavior of an ensemble of particles in a magnetic field in terms of average quantities like density, mean velocity, pressure, electrical conductivity, and so forth, without regard to the motion of individual particles. In this and the following section we will investigate the behavior of individual relativistic charged particles in a magnetic field.

The motion of a charged particle in an electromagnetic field is described by the Lorentz equation

$$\frac{d\boldsymbol{p}}{dt} = e\boldsymbol{E} + \frac{e}{c}\,\boldsymbol{v} \times \boldsymbol{H}, \tag{2.89}$$

where $\boldsymbol{p}$ is the particle's momentum, $\boldsymbol{v}$ its velocity, and e its charge. The electrostatic force $e\boldsymbol{E}$ is directed along the electric field lines; the magnetic force, $(e/c)\,\boldsymbol{v} \times \boldsymbol{H}$, is always perpendicular to the particle's velocity and therefore does not do any work. In a uniform magnetic field equation (2.89) reduces to

$$\frac{\mathscr{E}}{ec}\,\frac{d\boldsymbol{v}}{dt} = \boldsymbol{v} \times \boldsymbol{H}, \tag{2.90}$$

where a relativistic relation between the momentum $\boldsymbol{p}$ and the energy $\mathscr{E}$,

$$\boldsymbol{p} = \frac{\mathscr{E}\boldsymbol{v}}{c^2}, \tag{2.91}$$

is used to eliminate $\boldsymbol{p}$. Since there is no work associated with the action of the Lorentz force, the particle's energy $\mathscr{E}$ remains constant during the entire motion described by equation (2.90).† Let us assume that the magnetic field is directed along the z axis. Multiplying the second Cartesian component of the vector equation (2.90) by $i = \sqrt{-1}$ and adding it to the first, we have

$$\frac{d}{dt}\,(v_x + iv_y) = -i\omega_H(v_x + iv_y),$$

which yields after integration

$$v_x + iv_y = v_{0\perp} \exp\,[-i(\omega_H t + \alpha)\,], \tag{2.92}$$

† As shown in the next chapter, a particle moving in a magnetic field emits radiation; the radiative losses, of course, cause the particle's energy to decrease with time. Equation (2.89) should therefore contain a radiative loss term; however, this term is very small compared with the Lorentz force and will be neglected in our considerations.

or

$$v_x = v_{0\perp} \cos (\omega_H t + \alpha),$$

$$v_y = -v_{0\perp} \sin (\omega_H t + \alpha),$$

where $v_{0\perp}$ and α are constants to be determined from the initial conditions, and ω_H is the electron gyrofrequency,

$$\omega_H = \frac{ecH}{\mathscr{E}} = \frac{eH}{\gamma mc} = \frac{\omega_G}{\gamma} \tag{2.93}$$

with

$$\gamma = (1 - \beta^2)^{-1/2}, \ \beta = \frac{v}{c}.$$

When the velocity of a particle is small, $\gamma \approx 1$ and $\omega_H = \omega_G = eH/mc$. Integrating equation (2.92) we have

$$x = x_0 + r_H \sin (\omega_H t + \alpha),$$

$$y = y_0 + r_H \cos (\omega_H t + \alpha),$$

where

$$r_H = \frac{v_{0\perp}}{\omega_H} = |\boldsymbol{r}_H|,$$

is the radius of gyration, and

$$\boldsymbol{r}_H = \frac{c}{eH^2} \boldsymbol{p} \times \boldsymbol{H}. \tag{2.94}$$

The third component of equation (2.90) is $dv_z/dt = 0$ and yields

$$z = z_0 + v_{0\|} t,$$

which indicates that the motion of a particle along the magnetic field is uniform; it is unaffected by the field. The motion of the particle is therefore a superposition of a uniform motion along the field and a circular motion with the radius r_H and circular frequency ω_H in the plane perpendicular to the field; the resulting trajectory is a helix. In vector notation we can write (where $\boldsymbol{r}$ is the radius vector; initial position along $\boldsymbol{i}$)

$$\boldsymbol{r}(t) = \frac{c\beta \sin \theta}{\omega_H} (-\boldsymbol{i} \cos \omega_H t + \boldsymbol{i}_2 \sin \omega_H t) + \boldsymbol{i}_3 \, t \, c \, \beta \cos \theta \tag{2.96}$$

and

$$\boldsymbol{\beta}(t) = \beta \sin \theta \, (\boldsymbol{i} \sin \omega_H t + \boldsymbol{i}_2 \cos \omega_H t) + \boldsymbol{i}_3 \, \beta \cos \theta, \tag{2.97}$$

where θ is the angle between $\boldsymbol{v}$ and $\boldsymbol{H}$. If we look along the magnetic field (with the magnetic vector directed away from us), a negative particle gyrates clockwise and a positive particle moves counterclockwise. The stronger the field, the smaller the radius r_H of curvature of the circular motion.

When discussing the motion of a particle under the action of other forces in addition to the Lorentz force, it is convenient to consider the motion of the so-called guiding center $\boldsymbol{r}_C$, defined as

$$\boldsymbol{r}_C = \boldsymbol{r} + \boldsymbol{r}_H, \tag{2.98}$$

where $\boldsymbol{r}$ is the position vector of a particle and is given by equation (2.96) if the motion is caused by the magnetic force only (arising from a uniform field), and $\boldsymbol{r}_H$, given by equation (2.94), points toward the center of gyration. These two centers coincide if the particle is under the influence of the Lorentz force only; when the velocity of motion of the guiding center (and of the center of gyration) due to other forces is small compared with the velocity of circular motion due to the Lorentz force, we do not need to distinguish between the two centers. We will not consider in detail the motion of particles in a magnetic field under the action of various other forces, but will point out that the center of gyration will experience a drift in the direction perpendicular to the directions of the field and the external force. In addition a small inhomogeneity in the magnetic field will cause a drift in the direction perpendicular to both the field and its gradient. The drifts of charged particles in a magnetic field are represented in Figure 2.4.

Let us consider now the motion of charged particles in a slowly changing field. It can be shown (see, for example, Ref. 3 in the Preliminary Reading List) that for a system in motion periodic with respect to the canonical coordinate $\mathfrak{q}_i$ with an associated canonical momentum $\mathfrak{p}_i$, the so-called phase integral, defined as

$$\mathscr{I}_i = \oint \mathfrak{p}_i \, d\mathfrak{q}_i, \tag{2.99}$$

where the integration is carried out over the full cycle of the coordinate $\mathfrak{q}_i$, remains constant during adiabatic changes of the properties of the system, i.e., changes that are slow compared with, and not related to, the relevant periods of the motion. If the gyration period of a charged particle moving in a magnetic field is small compared with the time scale

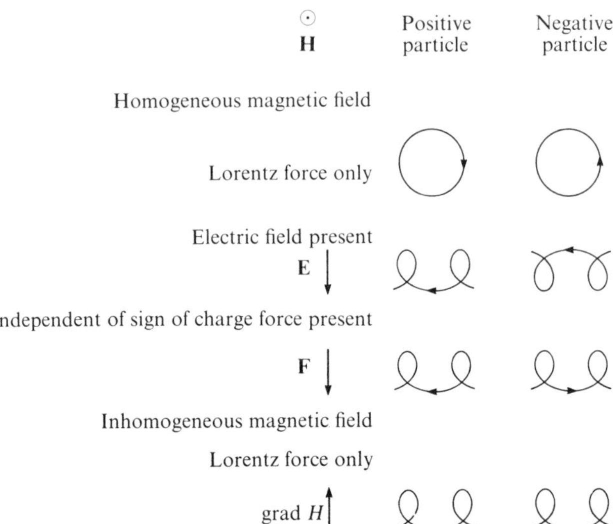

Fig. 2.4 Drifts of a charged particle in a magnetic field due to the electric field E, to a force F independent of the sign of the particle's charge, and to the presence of a small gradient of the magnetic field. The magnetic field is perpendicular to the plane of the figure and directed toward the reader.

of changes of magnetic field,

$$\frac{2\pi}{\omega_H} \ll \frac{H}{\left|\frac{\partial H}{\partial t}\right|}, \tag{2.100}$$

then the changes are adiabatic; and we have from the phase integral for the transverse component of the motion

$$\oint \mathbf{p}_\perp \, d\boldsymbol{l} = \oint \left(\gamma m \boldsymbol{v}_\perp + \frac{e}{c} \boldsymbol{A}\right) \cdot d\boldsymbol{l} = \text{const}, \tag{2.101}$$

where $\boldsymbol{A}$ is the vector potential of the electromagnetic field and $d\boldsymbol{l}$ is the line element along the circular path of the particle. Using equations (2.25), (2.94), and (2.98) and Stokes theorem, we can write equation (2.101) as

$$\oint \gamma m r_H{}^2 \omega_H \, d\vartheta + \frac{e}{c} \int (\nabla \times \boldsymbol{A}) \cdot \boldsymbol{n} \, d\sigma$$

$$= 2\pi\gamma m r_H{}^2 \omega_H + \frac{e}{c} \int \boldsymbol{H} \cdot \boldsymbol{n} \, d\sigma = \pi r_H{}^2 \boldsymbol{H} \frac{e}{c} = \text{const}, \tag{2.102}$$

where $\boldsymbol{n}$ is the normal to the surface enclosed by the circular path of the particle (antiparallel to $\boldsymbol{H}$), $d\sigma$ is the surface element and $dl = r_H\, d\vartheta$. Equation (2.102) implies that the magnetic flux ϕ through the particle's orbit is an adiabatic invariant of the motion

$$\phi = \pi r_H^2 H = \text{const}, \qquad (2.103)$$

or, in other words, that

$$\frac{p_\perp^2}{H} = \text{const} \qquad (2.104)$$

during the adiabatic motion of a charged particle in a magnetic field.

2.5 Electromagnetic Acceleration of Charged Particles

Two basic electromagnetic acceleration processes can be distinguished: the betatron process, in which the energy of charged particles is changed by magnetic fields changing in time; and the Fermi process, in which the energy of charged particles is changed when they encounter regions of higher magnetic field moving in space. In both types of processes the energy change (in the observer's frame) can be positive or negative—in the betatron process this depends on whether the magnetic field is increasing or decreasing; and in the Fermi process, on whether the component velocity of the region of higher magnetic field along the particle's path has the opposite sign to the particle's velocity or the same sign. If the magnetic field in some region of space is systematically increasing until all the particles are by some means able to leave the region, the betatron process is called the systematic betatron process. Similarly, if particles are trapped between two regions of higher magnetic field approaching each other, the Fermi process of the change of a particle's energy is called the systematic Fermi acceleration. In cosmic conditions both the Fermi and betatron systematic accelerations are expected to be rather rare; we expect particles to move through fluctuating magnetic fields and to collide with randomly moving regions of a higher magnetic field. However, if certain additional conditions, which we will discuss later, are fulfilled, then the gains of energy will exceed the losses, and particles will be accelerated on the average. In this case we call the acceleration process a (betatron or Fermi) statistical acceleration.

In the betatron process an (adiabatic) change of the magnetic field in which a particle is gyrating produces a change in the component of the particle's momentum which is perpendicular to the field. This follows from the adiabatic invariant of equation (2.104). The longitudinal component of the momentum $p_{\|}$ is unaffected by changes of the field. The betatron process is fully reversible—an increase of the field produces an increase of the transverse momentum, and a decrease of the transverse momentum follows a decrease of the field. An increase of the field is equivalent to a transverse compression of the gas because it decreases the radius of gyration. Since in a transverse compression, the volume $\tau \propto r_H^2$, then it follows that $p_{\perp} \propto r_H^{-1}$. For nonrelativistic and ultrarelativistic particles, $\mathscr{E} \propto p^2$ and $\mathscr{E} \propto p$, respectively, and therefore for a magnetic transverse compression of a gas, the index Γ defined in the kinetic theory as $\mathscr{E}_k = \tau^{1-\Gamma}$ will have the values $\Gamma = 2$ and $\Gamma = 3/2$ for nonrelativistic and ultrarelativistic particles, respectively. If the magnetic field is far from homogeneous, the compression can be considered isotropic on the average. In this case $\tau \propto r_H^3$ and $\Gamma = 5/3$ and $\Gamma = 4/3$ for nonrelativistic and ultrarelativistic particles, respectively.

As we have said before, the betatron process is a reversible one. Therefore, if the particles in a fluctuating field are to acquire a certain amount of energy on the average, there must be present some additional process—for example, one that would repeatedly remove the transverse momentum of particles and convert it into the form of parallel momentum, which is not affected by the betatron process. Collisions with other particles provide such a mechanism and redistribute the particle energy among all the degrees of freedom. We can assume that after each collision we have

$$p_{\|}^2 = \frac{1}{3}\, p^2_{\text{total}},$$

$$p_{\perp}^2 = \frac{2}{3}\, p^2_{\text{total}}.$$

Let us consider here a simple model of a statistical betatron mechanism with collisions in which the full cycle of changes of the magnetic field is twice as large as the time between collisions (Figure 2.5). Immediately after the first collision of the cycle we have

$$p_{\|}^2 = \frac{1}{3}\, p_1^2,$$

$$p_{\perp}^2 = \frac{2}{3}\, p_1^2,$$

$$p^2_{\text{total}} = p_1^2.$$

Just before the second collision of the cycle we have, as a result of the

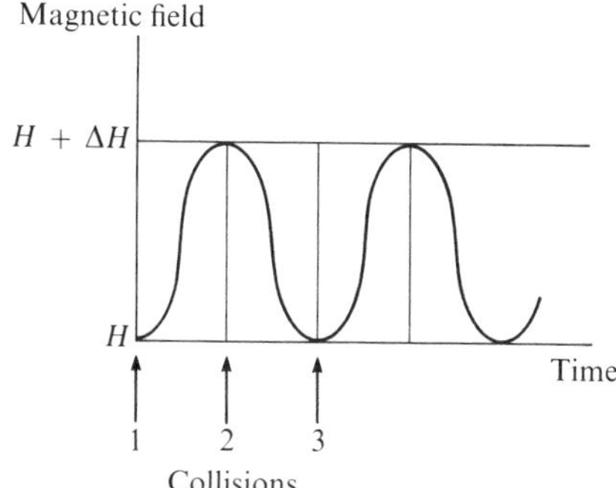

Fig. 2.5 A model of the statistical betatron acceleration mechanism.

betatron acceleration in an increasing field,

$$p_{\parallel}{}^2 = \frac{1}{3}\, p_1{}^2 \qquad \text{(unchanged)},$$

$$p_{\perp}{}^2 = \frac{2}{3}\, p_1{}^2\, \frac{H + \Delta H}{H} \qquad \text{(increased)},$$

$$p^2{}_{\text{total}} = p_2{}^2 = \frac{1}{3}\, p_1{}^2 \left(1 + 2\,\frac{H + \Delta H}{H}\right) \qquad \text{(increased)}.$$

The collision redistributes the momentum, and therefore immediately after the collision we have

$$p_{\parallel}{}^2 = \frac{1}{3}\, p_2{}^2 = \frac{1}{9}\, p_1{}^2 \left(1 + 2\,\frac{H + \Delta H}{H}\right) \qquad \text{(increased)},$$

$$p_{\perp}{}^2 = \frac{2}{3}\, p_2{}^2 = \frac{2}{9}\, p_1{}^2 \left(1 + 2\,\frac{H + \Delta H}{H}\right) \qquad \text{(decreased)},$$

$$p^2{}_{\text{total}} = p_2{}^2 = \frac{1}{3}\, p_1{}^2 \left(1 + 2\,\frac{H + \Delta H}{H}\right) \qquad \text{(unchanged)}.$$

Now the betatron deceleration affects only the perpendicular component of the momentum, and at the end of our cycle (immediately before the third collision) we have

$$p_{\parallel}{}^2 = \frac{1}{9}\, p_1{}^2 \left(1 + 2\,\frac{H + \Delta H}{H}\right) \qquad \text{(unchanged)},$$

$$p_{\perp}{}^2 = \frac{2}{9}\, p_1{}^2 \left(1 + 2\,\frac{H + \Delta H}{H}\right) \frac{H}{H + \Delta H} \qquad \text{(decreased)},$$

$$p^2{}_{\text{total}} = p_3{}^2 = \frac{1}{9}\, p_1{}^2 \left(1 + 2\,\frac{H + \Delta H}{H}\right)\left(1 + 2\,\frac{H}{H + \Delta H}\right) \qquad \text{(decreased)}.$$

The total change of the particle's momentum in the entire cycle of the change of the magnetic field is therefore

$$\Delta p^2 = p_3^2 - p_1^2 \cong \frac{2}{9}\, p^2 \left(\frac{\Delta H}{H}\right)^2,$$

which indicates a net gain of second order in $\Delta H/H$. We discussed here a simple example of equally (and favorably) spaced collisions (one can easily think of a model which will not produce a net acceleration). However, on the average in cosmic fluctuating fields the statistical betatron process gives

$$\langle \Delta p^2 \rangle \approx \alpha_B\, p^2 \left(\frac{\Delta H}{H}\right)^2, \tag{2.105}$$

where α_B is a small coefficient.

The Fermi process consists of changes of the particle energy as a result of encounters ("collisions") of particles with regions of a higher magnetic field. The adiabatic invariant prohibits the particle from entering a region of sufficiently high magnetic field; i.e., the particle motion is reversed, and thus the phenomenon has the aspect of a collision. To see it more clearly, let us consider the motion of a particle along the z-axis into a region of converging magnetic lines of force $H(z)$. Since the energy of the particle and its total momentum are constant during the motion,

$$v^2 = v_\perp{}^2 + v_\parallel{}^2 = v_{0\perp}{}^2 + v_{0\parallel}{}^2 = v_0{}^2 = \text{const.}$$

The adiabatic invariant of equation (2.104) is in the form,

$$v_\perp{}^2 = v_{0\perp}{}^2\, \frac{H(z)}{H_0},$$

where H_0 is the magnetic field away from the region of convergence (away from the bottleneck), and

$$v_\parallel{}^2 = v_0{}^2 - v_{\perp 0}{}^2\, \frac{H(z)}{H_0}. \tag{2.106}$$

Equation (2.106) states that if the particle enters a region where $H(z)$ is large enough for the right-hand side of equation (2.106) to be zero, the particle cannot propagate any further in the direction $+z$ ($v_\parallel = 0$), and can only be reflected back in the $-z$ direction.

To examine the change of energy experienced by a particle in a collision with a region of high magnetic field (we will call such a region a "magnetic mirror"), let us consider the motion of a particle between two magnetic mirrors adiabatically approaching each other. The particle motion will be periodic with respect to the coordinate (z) parallel to the magnetic lines of force because of reflections from the magnetic mirrors (we assume that the motion of the mirrors is very slow compared with the particle motion). We can therefore apply the theorem of the invariance of the phase integral of equation (2.99) for the longitudinal motion:

$$\oint \mathfrak{p}_{\parallel}\, d\mathfrak{q}_{\parallel} = \oint \gamma\, m v_{\parallel}\, dz = \text{const} \tag{2.107}$$

during the motion. If θ is the angle between the (instantaneous) velocity of the particle and the magnetic field (the field is considered homogeneous and is parallel to the z-axis except in the very small regions around $\pm z_0$ where an abrupt increase of the field sufficient to reflect the particle takes place), we can write $v_{\perp 0} = v_0 \sin\theta$ and, neglecting the contributions to the phase integral from the small regions around $\pm z$, i.e., assuming $H(z) = H_0$, we can insert equation (2.106) in the form,

$$v_{\parallel}^2 = v_0^2\,(1 - \sin^2\theta) = v_{0\parallel}^2,$$

into equation (2.107) and obtain the result

$$\oint \gamma\, m v_{\parallel}\, dz = \oint \gamma\, m v_{0\parallel}\, dz = \oint p_{0\parallel}\, dz = 4z_0\, p_{0\parallel} = \text{const},$$

where $p_{0\parallel}$ is the parallel momentum of the particle before entering the bottleneck, which is assumed to be infinitesimally short (a magnetic mirror). We therefore have the parallel adiabatic invariant.

$$p_{\parallel} z = \text{const},$$

omitting zero subscripts. If the mirrors, which are slowly approaching each other are shifted at some later time by Δz from their original position, the change of the particle's parallel momentum is

$$\frac{\Delta p_{\parallel}}{p_{\parallel}} = -\frac{\Delta z}{z}, \tag{2.108}$$

where z is the later position of the magnetic mirrors. If w is the velocity of the mirrors (by the assumptions of adiabaticity $w \ll v$), then during the time t, each mirror moves a distance $\Delta z = wt$, and the particle experiences $n = v_{\parallel} t/2z$ reflections from the mirrors. Therefore the change of the (parallel) momentum in one collision with a magnetic mirror is

$$\left(\frac{\Delta p_{\parallel}}{p_{\parallel}}\right) = -\frac{\Delta z}{nz} = -2\frac{w}{v_{\parallel}},$$

or

$$\Delta p_{\parallel} = -2\gamma m w.$$

In terms of energy $[\mathscr{E}^2 = c^2(p^2 + m^2c^2), \boldsymbol{p} = \mathscr{E}\boldsymbol{v}/c^2]$ for one collision of a relativistic particle with a magnetic mirror we have

$$\Delta\mathscr{E} = -2\mathscr{E}\frac{\boldsymbol{w}\cdot\boldsymbol{v}_{||}}{c^2}. \tag{2.109}$$

If the velocities $\boldsymbol{v}_{||}$ and $\boldsymbol{w}$ are parallel before a collision, the particle will experience an energy loss during a collision. These collisions with moving magnetic mirrors are called type A collisions (Figure 2.6A). The change of a particle's energy can also occur as a result of a type B collision, in which a particle moves along a curved tube of force which in turn is moving (Figure 2.6B).

The motion of converging parallel magnetic mirrors is equivalent to a one-dimensional compression of a gas of trapped particles. The index Γ is equal to 3 or 2 for nonrelativistic or highly relativistic particles, respectively. If the magnetic mirrors are not exactly parallel, the particles will be scattered off the mirrors, and on the average all the velocity components will be equal after a certain time. In this case the compression can be considered three-dimensional with Γ equal to 5/3 and 4/3 for nonrelativistic and ultrarelativistic particles, respectively. The compression of the particle gas cannot be carried out without limits. When a volume determined by r_H is achieved, the adiabaticity condition is no longer fulfilled, and a further compression is impossible. This puts an upper limit on the energy acquired by particles as a result of a Fermi systematic acceleration. There can be various geometries of a systematic Fermi acceleration of particles under cosmic conditions; Figure 2.7 presents an example in which particles moving around a curved line of force are trapped by an advancing shock front.

In astrophysical conditions the statistical Fermi process is more important than the systematic process. Statistical acceleration results from the greater probability of a head-on collision of a particle with randomly moving magnetic clouds (acting like magnetic mirrors) than of an overtaking collision, as the first is proportional to the sum of the particle and cloud velocities, $v + w$, and the second to their difference, $v - w$. Since an energy gain is associated with a head-on collision and an energy loss with an overtaking collision, we will have on the average a net gain of energy, which for a perpendicular collision with the mirrors is

$$\langle\Delta\mathscr{E}\rangle = \frac{v+w}{2v}\Delta\mathscr{E} - \frac{v-w}{2v}\Delta\mathscr{E} = 2\frac{w^2}{c^2}\mathscr{E}.$$

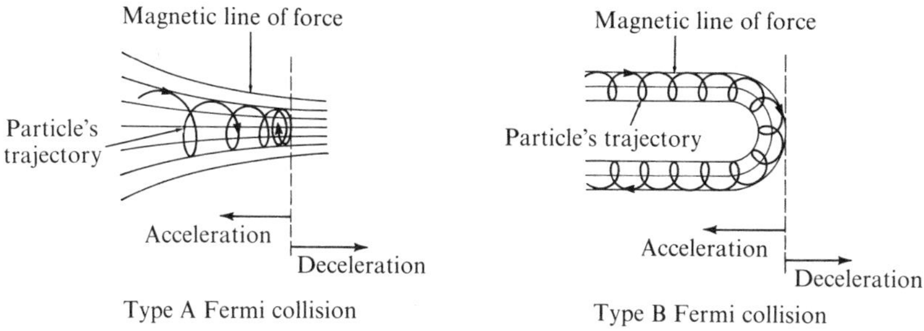

Fig. 2.6 Two types of collisions leading to acceleration or deceleration of charged particles by the Fermi process.

In general, when the collisions are not necessarily perpendicular, we have

$$\langle \Delta \mathscr{E} \rangle = \alpha_F \frac{w^2}{c^2} \mathscr{E}, \tag{2.110}$$

where the coefficient α_F is of the order of unity. If λ_F is a mean free path and t_F is the mean time between collisions, we can write the average rate of energy gain as

$$\frac{d\mathscr{E}}{dt} = \eta_F \mathscr{E}, \tag{2.111}$$

where

$$\eta_F = \alpha_F \frac{vw^2}{\lambda_F c^2} = \alpha_F \frac{w^2}{t_F c^2}. \tag{2.112}$$

The statistical Fermi acceleration is a second-order process in w/c. However, it acts during the entire lifetime of a particle in the accelerating region, and it is able to supply an unlimited acceleration for individual particles as long as the total energy of all accelerated particles is substantially less than the total kinetic energy of the magnetized clouds in the region.

The statistical Fermi acceleration process is effective, however, only for particles with energies larger than a certain threshold energy $\mathscr{E}_1$; below the threshold the rate of energy losses suffered by a particle as a result of its iteraction with the medium is greater than the rate of energy gained by the Fermi process. However, for heavy particles and large α_F the threshold energy $\mathscr{E}_1$ can be equal to zero under favorable conditions. If the probability $P(t)$ that a particle will be accelerated by the Fermi

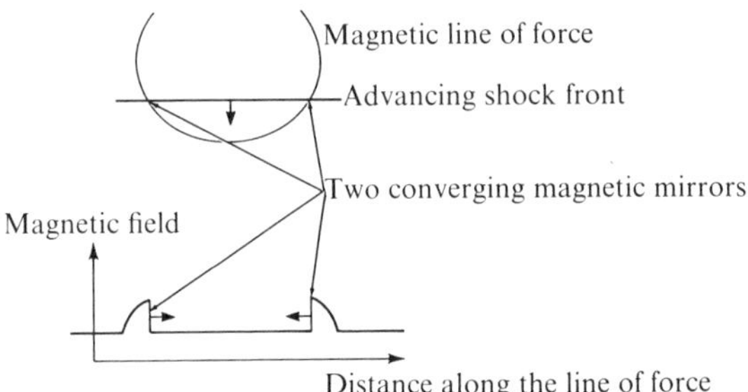

Fig. 2.7 Systematic Fermi acceleration of charged particles trapped by an advancing shock front.

statistical process for a time from $t = 0$ to some time between t and $t + dt$ is

$$P(t)\; dt = \frac{1}{\tau}\, e^{-(t/\tau)}\, dt, \qquad (2.113)$$

where τ is an average acceleration time, then the number of particles $N(\mathscr{E})\, d\mathscr{E}$ with energies between $\mathscr{E}$ and $\mathscr{E} + d\mathscr{E}$, proportional to $P(t)\, dt$, can be obtained from equation (2.113) by inserting into it the following expression obtained from equation (2.111):

$$dt = \frac{d\mathscr{E}}{\eta_F \mathscr{E}},$$

together with its integral,

$$t = \frac{1}{\eta_F} \ln\left(\frac{\mathscr{E}}{mc^2}\right).$$

The result is a power-law energy distribution,

$$N(\mathscr{E}) \propto \mathscr{E}^{-\gamma}, \qquad (2.114)$$

with the index

$$\gamma = 1 + \frac{1}{\eta_F \tau}. \qquad (2.115)$$

Although the Fermi statistical acceleration leads to a power-law distribution of energy among accelerated particles like that observed in many sources of cosmic radio emission as well as in cosmic rays, the process does not seem to be an efficient accelerator in astrophysical conditions (in the interstellar medium $\eta_F \approx 10^{-17}$) except perhaps in supernovae shells ($\eta_F \approx 10^{10}$). Moreover, the index of the energy distribution equation (2.115) ought to be very different for different radio sources (because of expected differences in η_F and τ), but this is not the case (see Chapter 6). Increased attention is currently being paid to processes of acceleration of particles by waves in a turbulent plasma, but the origin of energetic particles whose effects (like synchrotron radiation) are observed in radio sources remains one of the major questions of radio astronomy.

Bibliographical Notes to Chapter 2

2.1-2.2 Some general references to plasma physics are the following:

1. C. L. Longmire, *Elementary Plasma Physics*, Interscience, New York, 1963.
2. J. L. Delcroix, *Theory of Ionized Gases*, Interscience, New York, 1960.
3. L. Spitzer, *Physics of Fully Ionized Gases*, Interscience, New York, 1962.
4. S. Gartenhaus, *Elements of Plasma Physics*, Holt, Rinehart and Winston, New York, 1964.
5. J. L. Delcroix, *Plasma Physics*, Wiley and Sons, London, 1965.
6. S. Chandrasekhar, *Plasma Physics*, University of Chicago Press, 1962.
7. W. B. Thompson, *An Introduction to Plasma Physics*, Addison-Wesley, Reading, Mass., 1964.

Fig. 2.1 follows Fig. 33 in Ref. 2.

2.3. An excellent and compact summary of the theory of propagation of electromagnetic waves in a collisionless plasma is given by Ref. 8, and a short review can be found in Ref. 9. More comprehensive treatments can be found in Refs. 10 and 11.

8. J. F. Denisse and J. L. Delcroix, *Theorie des Ondes Dans Les Plasmas*, Dunod, Paris, 1961.
9. J. P. Wild, S. F. Smerd, and A. A. Weiss, "Solar Bursts," *Ann. Rev. Astron. Astrophys.* **1**, 291–366 (1963).
10. V. L. Ginzburg, *Propagation of Electromagnetic Waves in Plasma*, Fizmatgiz, Moscow, 1960.
11. J. A. Ratcliffe, *The Magnetoionic Theory and its Applications to the Ionosphere*, Cambridge University Press, 1959, 1962.

Excitation of plasma waves and subsequent conversion of part of the energy of the waves into electromagnetic radiation was not discussed in Chapter 2. The reader is referred to the following papers:

12. D. Bohm and E. P. Gross, "Theory of Plasma Oscillations. A. Origin of Mediumlike Behavior," *Phys. Rev.* **75**, 1851–1864 (1949).

13. D. Bohm and E. P. Gross, "Theory of Plasma Oscillations. B. Excitation and Damping of Oscillations," *Phys. Rev.* **75**, 1864–1876 (1949).
14. G. B. Field, "Radiation by Plasma Oscillations," *Astrophys. J.* **124**, 555–570 (1956).
15. M. H. Cohen, "Radiation in a Plasma. I. Čerenkov Effect," *Phys. Rev.* **123**, 711–721 (1961).
16. M. H. Cohen, "Radiation in a Plasma. II. Equivalent Sources," *Phys. Rev.* **126**, 289–397 (1962).
17. M. H. Cohen, "Radiation in a Plasma. III. Metal Boundaries," *Phys. Rev.* **126**, 398–404 (1962).
18. V. L. Ginzburg and V. V. Zheleznyakov, "On the Possible Mechanisms of Sporadic Solar Radio Emission (Radiation in an Isotropic Plasma)," *Astron. Zh.* **35**, 694–712 (1958).
19. V. L. Ginzburg and V. V. Zheleznyakov, "On the Propagation of Electromagnetic Waves in the Solar Corona, Taking Into Account the Influence of the Magnetic Field," *Astron. Zh.* **36**, 233–246 (1959).
20. V. L. Ginzburg and V. V. Zheleznyakov, "Noncoherent Mechanisms of Sporadic Solar Radio Emission in the Case of a Magnetoactive Coronal Plasma," *Astron. Zh.* **38**, 3–20 (1961).

The free-free absorption coefficient at radio frequencies is computed in Ref. 10 and in the following five papers.

21. G. Elwert, "Der Absorptionkoeffizient an der langwelligen Grenze des Kontinuierlichen Röntgenspektrums," *Z. Naturforsch.* **3a**, 477–481 (1948).
22. L. Oster, "Der kontinuierliche Absorptionskoeffizient für Frei-Frei-Strahlung im radiofrequenten Spektralgebiet," *Z. Astrophys.* **47**, 169–190 (1959).
23. S. F. Smerd and K. C. Westfold, "The Characteristics of Radio-Frequency Radiation in an Ionized Gas, with Applications to the Transfer of Radiation in the Solar Atmosphere," *Phil. Mag.* **40**, 831–848 (1949).
24. P. A. G. Scheuer, "The Absorption Coefficient of a Plasma at Radio Frequencies," *Monthly Notices Roy. Astron. Soc.* **120**, 231–241 (1960).
25. L. Oster, "Emission, Absorption, and Conductivity of a Fully Ionized Gas at Radio Frequencies," *Rev. Mod. Phys.* **33**, 525–543 (1961).

Fig. 2.2 follows Fig. VI, 4 in Ref. 8, and Fig. 2.3 follows Fig. V, 1 in the same reference.

2.4. Motion of charged particles in magnetic fields is reviewed, for example, in the following books.

26. H. Alfvén and C. G. Falthammar, *Cosmical Electrodynamics—Fundamental Principles*, Oxford University Press, 1963.
27. J. D. Jáckson, *Classical Electrodynamics*, Wiley and Sons, New York, 1963.

Fig. 2.4 taken from Fig. 2.5 of Ref. 26.

2.5. The two classical papers on the Fermi acceleration mechanism are:

28. E. Fermi, "On the Origin of Cosmic Radiation," *Phys. Rev.* **75**, 1169–1174 (1949).
29. E. Fermi, "Galactic Magnetic Fields and the Origin of Cosmic Radiation," *Astrophys. J.* **119**, 1–6 (1954).

Further discussions of the Fermi mechanism can be found in these papers:

30. P. Morrison, S. Olbert, and B. Rossi, "The Origin of Cosmic Rays," *Phys. Rev.* **94**, 440–453 (1954).
31. E. N. Parker, "Hydromagnetic Waves and the Acceleration of Cosmic Rays," *Phys. Rev.* **99**, 241–253 (1955).
32. L. Davis Jr., "Modified Fermi Mechanism for the Acceleration of Cosmic Rays," *Phys. Rev.* **101**, 351–358 (1956).
33. G. R. Burbidge, "Acceleration of Cosmic-Ray Particles Among Extragalactic Nebulae," *Phys. Rev.* **107**, 269–271 (1957).
34. D. G. Wentzel, "Fermi Acceleration of Charged Particles," *Astrophys. J.* **137**, 135–146 (1963).
35. D. G. Wentzel, "Motion Across Magnetic Discontinuities and Fermi Acceleration of Charged Particles," *Astrophys. J.* **140**, 1013–1024 (1964).

Electromagnetic acceleration processes were reviewed by Ginzburg and Syrovatsky.

36. V. L. Ginzburg and S. I. Syrovatsky, *The Origin of Cosmic Rays*, Pergamon Press, New York, 1964.

Processes leading to acceleration of particles in a turbulent plasma were reviewed by Tsitovich, whose paper also contains an extensive bibliography of the subject.

37. V. N. Tsitovich, "Statistical Acceleration of Particles in a Turbulent Plasma," *Usp. Fiz. Nauk* **89**, 89–146 (1966).

Fig. 2.7 follows Fig. 1 in Ref. 34. The presentation in Section 2.5 loosely follows that in Ref. 36.

3

Radiation of Relativistic Electrons in Magnetic Fields in Vacuum (Synchrotron Radiation)

3.1 Introduction

This chapter discusses the theory and properties of the radiation emitted by relativistic electrons gyrating in a magnetic field. This radiation, often called synchrotron radiation (and sometimes referred to as magnetic bremsstrahlung), seems to play an essential role in many cosmic sources of radio radiation. First we will discuss the electromagnetic field associated with an accelerated charge, and then we will specifically consider the properties of the radiation of a charge moving with a relativistic velocity on a helical orbit in a magnetic field at a large distance from the charge. Finally, we will discuss the radiation emitted by an ensemble of relativistic electrons gyrating in a magnetic field; "in vacuum" means that the interaction between electrons will be neglected except for absorption of the synchrotron radiation. Chapter 4 deals with synchrotron radiation in a plasma.

3.2 The Electromagnetic Field of an Accelerated Charge

The retarded vector and scalar potentials $\boldsymbol{A}$, φ, given by

$$\boldsymbol{A}(\boldsymbol{R}, t) = \frac{1}{c} \int R_0^{-1} \boldsymbol{j}(\boldsymbol{r}', t')\ \delta\left(t' - t + \frac{R_0(t')}{c}\right) d\tau'\ dt',$$

$$\varphi(\boldsymbol{R}, t) = \int R_0^{-1}\, Q(\boldsymbol{r}', t')\, \delta\!\left(t' - t + \frac{R_0(t')}{c}\right) d\tau'\, dt', \tag{3.1}$$

are solutions of Maxwell's equations, which describe the electromagnetic field due to distributions of current and charge specified by their densities j and Q. R_0 is the distance from the observer to the element of volume containing some charge or current, the integration is carried out over the volume containing either charges or currents (the volume of the source), or both, and the presence of the delta function indicates that the charge and current densities have to be taken at the retarded time,

$$t' = t - \frac{R_0(t')}{c}. \tag{3.2}$$

We are interested in discussing the field deriving from a point charge moving at high velocity. We can therefore write the current and charge densities in the form

$$\begin{aligned} \boldsymbol{j}(\boldsymbol{R}, t) &= ec\boldsymbol{\beta}(t)\, \delta(\boldsymbol{R} - \boldsymbol{r}(t)), \\ Q(\boldsymbol{R}, t) &= e\delta(\boldsymbol{R} - \boldsymbol{r}(t)) \end{aligned} \tag{3.3}$$

and introduce these expressions into equation (3.1). Since†

$$\int f(x)\, \delta(g(x) - y)\, dx = \left[\frac{f(x)}{\dfrac{dg(x)}{dx}}\right]_{g(x)=y},$$

and‡

$$\frac{\partial t}{\partial t'} = 1 - \boldsymbol{\beta}' \cdot \boldsymbol{R}_0'^{*}, \tag{3.4}$$

we obtain

$$\begin{aligned} \boldsymbol{A}(R, t) &= \frac{e\boldsymbol{\beta}'}{R_0'(1 - \boldsymbol{\beta}' \cdot \boldsymbol{R}_0'^{*})}, \\ \varphi(R, t) &= \frac{e}{R_0'(1 - \boldsymbol{\beta}' \cdot \boldsymbol{R}_0'^{*})}, \end{aligned} \tag{3.5}$$

† See, for example, M. J. Lighthill, *Introduction to Fourier Analysis and Generalized Functions*, Cambridge University Press, 1958.

‡ If we differentiate $\boldsymbol{R}_0(t') = R - r'$ with respect to the retarded time t' and multiply the result by $\boldsymbol{R}_0'^{*}$, we find that $\partial R_0(t')/\partial t' = -c\boldsymbol{\beta}' \cdot \boldsymbol{R}_0'^{*}$. Then differentiating equation (3.2) with respect to the retarded time t' and using the above result, we obtain equation (3.4).

where all the quantities on the right-hand side of the equations are evaluated at the retarded time, and $\boldsymbol{R}_0(t')$ is now the distance between the observer and the point charge.

The intensities of the electric and magnetic fields can be computed from the Lienard–Wiechert potentials by differentiation with respect to the observer's coordinates and time:

$$\boldsymbol{E} = -\frac{1}{c}\frac{\partial \boldsymbol{A}}{\partial t} - \nabla\varphi,$$

$$\boldsymbol{H} = \nabla \times \boldsymbol{A}. \tag{3.6}$$

Since the potentials are given in equation (3.5) as functions of the retarded time and then, through equation (3.4), as functions of $\boldsymbol{R}_0$ and t, we must differentiate first with respect to t' and then use equation (3.4) and

$$\nabla t' = -\frac{\boldsymbol{R}_0'{}^*}{c(1-\boldsymbol{\beta}'\cdot\boldsymbol{R}_0'{}^*)}.\dagger \tag{3.7}$$

At a large distance from the moving charge the result is

$$\boldsymbol{E} = \frac{e}{R_0'}\frac{\boldsymbol{R}_0'{}^* \times [(\boldsymbol{R}_0'{}^* - \boldsymbol{\beta}') \times \dot{\boldsymbol{\beta}}']}{c(1-\boldsymbol{\beta}'\cdot\boldsymbol{R}_0'{}^*)^3},$$

$$\boldsymbol{H} = \boldsymbol{R}_0'{}^* \times \boldsymbol{E}. \tag{3.8}$$

The radiation $\tilde{p}_\Omega$ of the moving particle is therefore

$$\tilde{p}_\Omega = \frac{c}{4\pi}E^2R_0^2$$

$$= \frac{e^2}{4\pi c}\left\{\frac{(\dot{\boldsymbol{\beta}}')^2}{(1-\boldsymbol{\beta}'\cdot\boldsymbol{R}_0'{}^*)^4} + \frac{2(\boldsymbol{R}_0'{}^*\cdot\dot{\boldsymbol{\beta}}')(\boldsymbol{\beta}'\cdot\dot{\boldsymbol{\beta}}')}{(1-\boldsymbol{\beta}'\cdot\boldsymbol{R}_0'{}^*)^5} - \frac{(\boldsymbol{R}_0'{}^*\cdot\dot{\boldsymbol{\beta}}')^2}{\gamma^2(1-\boldsymbol{\beta}'\cdot\boldsymbol{R}_0'{}^*)^6}\right\}. \tag{3.9}$$

If we consider a relativistic particle moving with high velocity ($\beta \approx 1$), then in the direction where $1-\boldsymbol{\beta}'\cdot\boldsymbol{R}_0'{}^*$ is small, the amount of radiation emitted is large compared with the amount emitted in directions where $1-\boldsymbol{\beta}'\cdot\boldsymbol{R}_0'{}^*$ is of the order of unity. This is described by the presence of high powers of $1-\boldsymbol{\beta}'\cdot\boldsymbol{R}_0'{}^*$ in the denominators in equation (3.9). Expanding $1-\boldsymbol{\beta}'\cdot\boldsymbol{R}_0'{}^*$ in powers of ψ,

† This result is found by taking the gradient of the retarded time [equation (3.2)] while noting that $\nabla = \boldsymbol{R}_0^*\,(\partial/\partial R_0)$ and $\nabla R_0(t') = [\nabla R_0(t')]_{t'} + [\partial R_0(t')]/(\partial t')\;\nabla t'$, since $R_0(t')$ is also an implicit function of the coordinates through t'. We then obtain equation (3.7) with the aid of the expression for $\partial R_0(t')/\partial t'$ found in the preceding footnote.

$$1 - \boldsymbol{\beta}' \cdot \boldsymbol{R}_0'^* = 1 - \beta \cos \psi \approx 1 - \beta + \frac{\psi^2}{2}, \tag{3.10}$$

we see that equation (3.10) is of the order of $1 - \beta$ only for $\psi \approx \sqrt{1 - \beta}$ or

$$\psi \approx \frac{1}{\gamma}. \tag{3.11}$$

Therefore most of the radiation is confined within a small angle ψ around the direction of instantaneous velocity.

3.3 Spectral Distribution of Synchrotron Radiation of a Single Electron in Vacuum

As stated in Section 3.1, synchrotron radiation is the radiation emitted by a relativistic electron moving along a helical orbit in a magnetic field. The spectral distribution of energy of this radiation can be investigated by means of a Fourier analysis of the electric vector of the radiation emitted by the electron. The trajectory of the electron's motion is [equation (2.96), $e \to -e$]

$$\boldsymbol{r}(t') = \frac{c\beta \sin \theta}{\omega_H} [\boldsymbol{l} \cos \omega_H t' + \boldsymbol{l}_2 \sin \omega_H t'] + \boldsymbol{l}_3 t' c\beta \cos \theta, \tag{3.12}$$

while the velocity $\boldsymbol{\beta}'$ (in units of c) and the acceleration $\dot{\boldsymbol{\beta}}'$ are [cf. equations (2.97) and (2.90)]

$$\begin{aligned} \boldsymbol{\beta}' &= \beta \boldsymbol{n}, \\ \boldsymbol{n} &= \sin \theta \, [-\boldsymbol{l} \sin \omega_H t' + \boldsymbol{l}_2 \cos \omega_H t'] + \boldsymbol{l}_3 \cos \theta \end{aligned} \tag{3.13}$$

and

$$\dot{\boldsymbol{\beta}}' = \beta \omega_H \boldsymbol{l}_3 \times \boldsymbol{n}. \tag{3.14}$$

Here $\boldsymbol{l}$, $\boldsymbol{l}_2$, and $\boldsymbol{l}_3$ form a Cartesian system of coordinates oriented in such a way that the external magnetic field is parallel to the direction $\boldsymbol{l}_3$; θ is the angle between the direction of the electron velocity and that of the magnetic field. We assume that the observer is located within the $\boldsymbol{l}_2\boldsymbol{l}_3$ plane and that the direction toward the observer $\boldsymbol{k}$ is

$$\boldsymbol{k} = \boldsymbol{l}_2 \sin (\theta - \psi) + \boldsymbol{l}_3 \cos (\theta - \psi), \tag{3.15}$$

where ψ is the value of the angle η between the direction $\boldsymbol{n}$ of the electron's velocity and the direction $\boldsymbol{k}$ toward the observer, when $\boldsymbol{n}$ is within the $\boldsymbol{l}_2\boldsymbol{l}_3$ plane (see Figure 3.1).

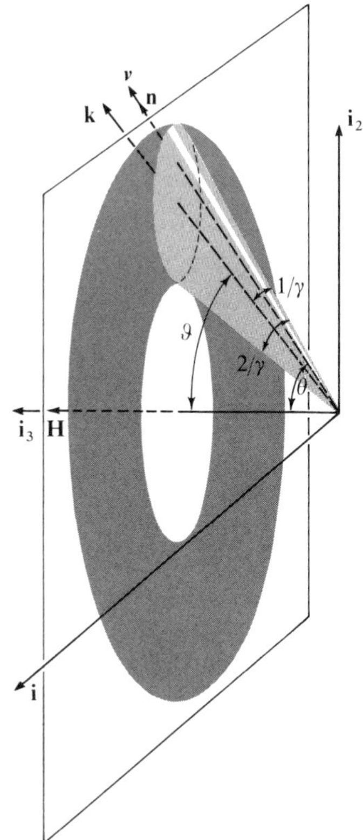

Fig. 3.1 Geometry of synchrotron radiation by a single electron.

The electric field $E(t)$ of the radiation emitted by the electron is a periodic function of time with the approximate period $2\pi \sin^2 \theta/\omega_H$. Indeed, an observer located along the direction $\boldsymbol{k}$ sees pulses of radiation when the direction of instantaneous velocity $\boldsymbol{n}$ coincides with $\boldsymbol{k}$. Those pulses will occur periodically at the time interval of T such that

$$T = \frac{2\pi}{\omega_H}(1 - \beta_{\parallel} \cos \vartheta) = \frac{2\pi}{\omega_H}(1 - \beta \cos \theta \cos \vartheta)$$

(see Figure 3.2). For a very relativistic electron radiating within a narrow angle ψ around the direction of velocity ($\vartheta \approx \theta$, $\beta \approx 1$), in the first approximation,

$$T \approx \frac{2\pi}{\omega_H}(1 - \beta \cos^2 \theta) \approx \frac{2\pi}{\omega_H} \sin^2 \theta.$$

We can therefore represent the electric vector $\boldsymbol{E}(t)$ of radiation as a Fourier series of monochromatic waves $\exp\,[-i\,(\omega_H/\sin^2 \theta)\,nt]$ of

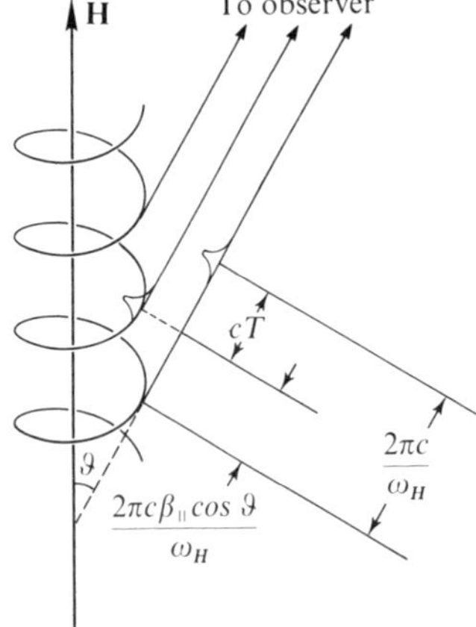

Fig. 3.2 Deriving the observed time between pulses of synchrotron emission by a single electron.

frequencies $n\ (\omega_H/\sin^2\theta)$:

$$\boldsymbol{E}(t) = \sum_{-\infty}^{+\infty} \boldsymbol{E}_n \exp\left(-i\,\frac{\omega_H}{\sin^2\theta}\,nt\right),$$

where the amplitudes $\boldsymbol{E}_n$ of these waves, given by

$$\boldsymbol{E}_n(\boldsymbol{R}) = \frac{\omega_H}{2\pi\sin^2\theta}\int_0^{2\pi\sin^2\theta/\omega_H} \boldsymbol{E}(t)\exp\left(i\,\frac{\omega_H}{\sin^2\theta}\,nt\right)dt, \tag{3.16}$$

have the property $\boldsymbol{E}_n^{\dagger} = -\boldsymbol{E}_{-n}$, since $\boldsymbol{E}(t)$ is real.§ The average energy (over the period) $\tilde{p}_{n\Omega} = (c/4\pi)\ \langle|\boldsymbol{E}(t)|^2\rangle\ R^2$, emitted by the particle into a unit solid angle $d\Omega = 1$ received in unit of time $dt = 1$ by the observer located at a distance R can be expressed in terms of the amplitudes $\boldsymbol{E}_n$ in the following way:

$$\frac{4\pi}{cR^2}\,\tilde{p}_{n\Omega} = \frac{4\pi}{cR^2}\left(\tilde{p}_{0\Omega} + \sum_{n=1}^{\infty}\tilde{p}_{n\Omega}\right) = \boldsymbol{E}_0^2 + 2\sum_{n=1}^{\infty}|\boldsymbol{E}_n|^2, \tag{3.17}$$

where $\tilde{p}_{n\Omega}$ is the power associated with one Fourier component (harmonic) of the electric field. For a moving charge the electric field $\boldsymbol{E}(t)$ at a large distance is given by equation (3.8). Therefore, to compute the power [equation (3.17)] of synchrotron radiation we will use equation (3.16) for the amplitudes $\boldsymbol{E}_n$ into which we will introduce $\boldsymbol{E}(t)$ from equation (3.8), with $\boldsymbol{\beta}'$ and $\dot{\boldsymbol{\beta}}'$ specified by equations (3.13) and (3.14). The expression for $\boldsymbol{E}_n$ obtained in this way can be simplified by choosing the origin of the reference system close to the electron and by noting that

§ The symbol † denotes the complex conjugate.

the observer is located at a distance that is very large compared with the electron's radius-vector. Then, since $r \ll R$ from $\boldsymbol{R}_0(t') = \boldsymbol{R} - \boldsymbol{r}(t')$, we have $R_0(t') = R - \boldsymbol{r}(t') \cdot \boldsymbol{R}_0'^* = R - \boldsymbol{r} \cdot \boldsymbol{k}$ where $\boldsymbol{R}^* \approx \boldsymbol{R}_0'^* = \boldsymbol{k}$. We have, therefore, from equation (3.16)

$$\boldsymbol{E}_n(\boldsymbol{R}) = \frac{\omega_H}{2\pi \sin^2\theta} \int_0^{2\pi \sin^2\theta/\omega_H} \boldsymbol{E}(t') \exp\left[in \frac{\omega_H}{\sin^2\theta}\left(t' + \frac{R_0(t')}{c}\right)\right] \frac{\partial t}{\partial t'}\, dt'$$

$$= \frac{\omega_H}{2\pi \sin^2\theta} \frac{e}{Rc} \exp\left(in \frac{\omega_H}{\sin^2\theta} \frac{R}{c}\right)$$

$$\int_0^{2\pi \sin^2\theta/\omega_H} \frac{\boldsymbol{k} \times [(\boldsymbol{k} - \boldsymbol{\beta}') \times \dot{\boldsymbol{\beta}}']}{(1 - \boldsymbol{\beta}' \cdot \boldsymbol{k})^2} \exp\left[in \frac{\omega_H}{\sin^2\theta}\left(t' - \frac{\boldsymbol{k} \cdot \boldsymbol{r}(t')}{c}\right)\right] dt' \quad (3.18)$$

with the aid of equations (3.8) and (3.4). To simplify equation (3.18) further we make use of the fact that the motion is ultrarelativistic and that therefore most of the synchrotron radiation is emitted within a small angle around the direction of electron velocity. Neglecting the fourth and higher order terms in $1/\gamma$, we have for small $1/\gamma$

$$\beta = 1 - \frac{1}{2}\left(\frac{1}{\gamma}\right)^2,$$

$$1 - \boldsymbol{\beta}' \cdot \boldsymbol{k} = \frac{1}{2\gamma^2}(1 + \gamma^2\eta^2). \quad (3.19)$$

Furthermore, neglecting second and higher order terms in $1/\gamma$, we can write

$$\dot{\boldsymbol{\beta}}' = \beta\omega_H\, \boldsymbol{l}_3 \times \boldsymbol{n} = -\omega_H \sin\theta\, \boldsymbol{l} - \omega_H \sin\theta \cdot \chi \boldsymbol{l}_2,$$

$$\boldsymbol{k} - \boldsymbol{n} = \chi \sin\theta \boldsymbol{l} - \psi \boldsymbol{m},$$

$$\eta^2 = \chi^2 \sin^2\theta + \psi^2, \quad (3.20)$$

where $\chi = \omega_H t'$ and $\boldsymbol{m} = \boldsymbol{l}_2 \cos\theta - \boldsymbol{l}_3 \sin\theta$. Using equations (3.12), (3.19), and (3.20), we can compute the following expressions:

$$\frac{\omega_H}{\sin^2\theta}\left(t' - \frac{\boldsymbol{k} \cdot \boldsymbol{r}}{c}\right) = \frac{1}{\sin^2\theta}\left[\frac{\chi}{2\gamma^2}(1 + \gamma^2\psi^2) + \frac{\chi^3}{6}\sin^2\theta\right],$$

$$\boldsymbol{k} \times [(\boldsymbol{k} - \boldsymbol{\beta}') \times \dot{\boldsymbol{\beta}}']$$

$$= (\boldsymbol{k} - \boldsymbol{n})\, \dot{\boldsymbol{\beta}}' \cdot (\boldsymbol{k} - \boldsymbol{n}) - \frac{1}{2\gamma^2}(1 + \gamma^2\psi^2 + \gamma^2\chi^2 \sin^2\theta)\, \dot{\boldsymbol{\beta}}'$$

$$= \frac{1}{2}\omega_H \sin\theta\left[\boldsymbol{l}\left(\frac{1}{\gamma^2} + \psi^2 - \chi^2 \sin^2\theta\right) + \boldsymbol{m}\, 2\chi\psi \sin\theta\right],$$

$$1 - \boldsymbol{\beta}' \cdot \boldsymbol{k} = \frac{1}{2}\left(\frac{1}{\gamma^2} + \psi^2 + \chi^2 \sin^2 \theta\right), \tag{3.21}$$

in which the terms of fourth and higher orders in $1/\gamma$ are neglected. With the aid of equation (3.21) the equation (3.18) for the amplitudes $\boldsymbol{E}_n$ can be approximated by

$$\boldsymbol{E}_n(R) = \frac{\omega_H}{\pi \sin^2\theta} \frac{e}{Rc} \exp\left(in \frac{\omega_H}{\sin^2\theta}\frac{R}{c}\right)$$
$$\int_{-\infty}^{+\infty} \exp\left\{in \frac{1}{\sin^2\theta}\left[\frac{\chi}{2\gamma^2}(1+\gamma^2\psi^2) + \frac{\chi^3}{6}\sin^2\theta\right]\right\}$$
$$\frac{\boldsymbol{l}\left(\frac{1}{\gamma^2} + \psi^2 - \chi^2\sin^2\theta\right) + \boldsymbol{m}\, 2\chi\psi\sin\theta}{\left(\frac{1}{\gamma^2} + \psi^2 + \chi^2\sin^2\theta\right)^2} \sin\vartheta\, d\chi$$
$$= \frac{e}{\pi Rc}\frac{\omega_H}{\sin^2\theta} \exp\left(in \frac{\omega_H}{\sin^2\theta}\frac{R}{c}\right)$$
$$\int_{-\infty}^{+\infty} \exp\left[is\left(w^2 u + \frac{1}{3}u^3\right)\right] \frac{\boldsymbol{l}(w^2 - u^2 + \boldsymbol{m}\, 2u\psi}{(w^2+u^2)^2}\, du, \tag{3.22}$$

where

$$w = \frac{1}{\gamma}\sqrt{1+\gamma^2\psi^2}, \quad s = \frac{n}{2\sin^3\theta}, \quad u = \chi\sin\vartheta.$$

The integration limits are extended to $(-\infty, +\infty)$ to facilitate the integration further; this procedure is permitted since the integrand is negligible for χ large compared with $1/\gamma$. By using the following relations (for their derivation see Ref. 13):

$$\int_{-\infty}^{+\infty} \exp\left[is\left(w^2u + \frac{1}{3}u^3\right)\right] \cdot \frac{w^2 - u^2}{(w^2+u^2)^2}\, du = \frac{2}{\sqrt{3}} sw^2 K_{2/3}\left(\frac{2}{3}sw^3\right),$$

$$\int_{-\infty}^{+\infty} \exp\left[is\left(w^2u + \frac{1}{3}u^3\right)\right] \cdot \frac{2u}{(w^2+u^2)^2}\, du = i\frac{2}{\sqrt{3}} sw K_{1/3}\left(\frac{2}{3}sw^3\right),$$

where $K_{1/3}$ and $K_{2/3}$ are Bessel functions of the second kind with imaginary arguments, $\boldsymbol{E}_n$ becomes

$$\boldsymbol{E}_n = n\frac{e}{\sqrt{3}\pi Rc}\frac{\omega_H}{\sin^5\theta} \exp\left(in\frac{\omega_H}{\sin^2\theta}\frac{R}{c}\right)$$
$$\left[\boldsymbol{l}\frac{1}{\gamma^2}(1+\gamma^2\psi^2)K_{2/3}(y) + i\boldsymbol{m}\frac{\psi}{\gamma}\sqrt{1+\gamma^2\psi^2}\, K_{1/3}(y)\right] \tag{3.23}$$

with

$$y = \frac{2}{3} s w^3 = \frac{n}{3\gamma^3 \sin^3\theta} (1 + \gamma^2 \psi^2)^{3/2}. \tag{3.24}$$

The average power $\tilde{p}_{n\Omega}\, d\Omega$ radiated in the nth harmonic into a solid angle $d\tilde{\Omega}$ can now be computed by substituting equation (3.23) into equation (3.17). We see that $\tilde{p}_{n\Omega}$ can be represented as a sum of the two components:

$$\tilde{p}_{n\Omega} = \frac{c}{2\pi} |\boldsymbol{E}_n|^2 R^2 = \tilde{p}_{n\Omega}{}^{(1)} + \tilde{p}_{n\Omega}{}^{(2)}, \tag{3.25}$$

one corresponding to E_n parallel to $\boldsymbol{l}$ and the other parallel to $\boldsymbol{m}$:

$$\tilde{p}_{n\Omega}{}^{(1)} = n^2 \frac{e^2 \omega_H^2}{6\pi^3 c \sin^{10}\theta} \frac{1}{\gamma^4} (1 + \gamma^2\psi^2)^2 K_{2/3}^2(y),$$

$$\tilde{p}_{n\Omega}{}^{(2)} = n^2 \frac{e^2 \omega_H^2}{6\pi^3 c \sin^{10}\theta} \frac{1}{\gamma^2} (1 + \gamma^2\psi^2)\psi^2 K_{1/3}^2(y).$$

For large γ most of the energy is radiated in the region of higher-order harmonics. In this region the spectrum can be considered practically continuous, and we can write

$$\tilde{p}_{\nu\Omega}{}^{(1)} = \tilde{p}_{n\Omega}{}^{(1)} \frac{dn}{d\nu} = \frac{3e^2}{4\pi^2 c} \frac{\omega_H}{\sin^2\theta} \gamma^2 (1 + \gamma^2\psi^2)^2 x^2 K_{2/3}^2(y),$$

$$\tilde{p}_{\nu\Omega}{}^{(2)} = \tilde{p}_{n\Omega}{}^{(2)} \frac{dn}{d\nu} = \frac{3e^2}{4\pi^2 c} \frac{\omega_H}{\sin^2\theta} \gamma^4\psi^2(1 + \gamma^2\psi^2) x^2 K_{1/3}^2(y), \tag{3.26}$$

where instead of the harmonic number n the frequency

$$\nu = n \frac{\omega_H}{2\pi \sin^2\theta}$$

is introduced, and

$$x = \frac{\nu}{\nu_C},$$

$$y = \frac{x}{2}(1 + \gamma^2\psi^2)^{3/2}, \tag{3.27}$$

where

$$\nu_C = \frac{3}{4\pi} \omega_H \sin\vartheta\, \gamma^3 = c_1 H \sin\vartheta\, E^2 \tag{3.28}$$

is called the critical frequency ($\theta \approx \vartheta$). The constant $c_1 = (3e)/(4\pi m^3 c^5)$

$= 6.27 \times 10^{18}$. Equation (3.23) indicates that the nth harmonic of the electric vector is tracing an ellipse with the ellipticity b

$$\tan b = \psi \cdot \frac{\gamma K_{1/3}(y)}{\sqrt{1+\gamma^2\psi^2} \cdot K_{2/3}(y)}; \tag{3.29}$$

the synchrotron radiation from a single electron is therefore elliptically polarized. The minor axis of the polarization ellipse is parallel to the direction $\boldsymbol{m}$, i.e. to the projection of the magnetic field onto the plane perpendicular to the wave propagation.

At a distance $\dot{R}(t')$ from the observer a particle moving with a velocity β will traverse a radial distance dR in a time $dt' = c\,dR/\beta_r$ where β_r, the projection onto R of the mean translational velocity of the particle, is equal to $\beta \cos\theta \cos\vartheta \approx \beta \cos^2\theta$. The radiation emitted by the particle in dt' will be received by the observer during the time

$$dt = (1-\beta_r)\; dt'$$

resulting from equation (3.2) (note that the radial velocity β_r is considered positive when directed toward the observer). Therefore the energy emitted by the particle in dt' and received by a unit surface at the observer in dt is

$$\frac{1}{R^2}\,\tilde{p}_{\nu\Omega}\; dt = \frac{1}{R^2}\,\tilde{p}_{\nu\Omega}(1-\beta_r)\; dt' = \frac{1}{R^2}\, p_{\nu\Omega}\; dt', \tag{3.30}$$

where

$$p_{\nu\Omega} \equiv \tilde{p}_{\nu\Omega}(1-\beta_r) \approx \tilde{p}_{\nu\Omega} \sin^2\theta \tag{3.31}$$

is the power emitted by the particle within a unit solid angle at a frequency ν. Integrating it over a full solid angle and over all frequencies we obtain the total power emitted by the particle, i.e., the rate of loss of particle energy due to synchrotron radiation,

$$p = \iint p_{\nu\Omega}\; d\nu d\Omega = -\frac{dE}{dt} = \frac{2e^4H^2\sin^2\vartheta}{3m^2c^3}\,\gamma^2 = c_2H^2\sin^2\vartheta\; E^2, \tag{3.32}$$

↑energy

where $c_2 = (2e^4)/(3m^4c^7)$. For electrons and positrons, $c_2 = 2.37 \times 10^{-3}$. For particles of mass M and charge Ze the synchrotron losses are $(M/Zm)^4$ smaller. Synchrotron radiation of protrons is therefore negligible in comparison with that of electrons or positrons of the same energy E.

3.4 Synchrotron Radiation from an Ensemble of Electrons

We will assume that at a time t in a volume $d\tau = R^2 dR\, d\Omega$ we have $N(E, \boldsymbol{m}, \boldsymbol{R}, t)\; dE\, d\tilde{\Omega}\, d\tau$ electrons with energies between E and $E + dE$ and velocities within $d\tilde{\Omega}$ around some direction $\boldsymbol{m}$ (Figure 3.3). Since only the particles which have velocity within a narrow angle $\Delta\Omega = 2\pi \sin\mu\, \Delta\psi \simeq 2\pi \sin\vartheta\, \Delta\psi$ radiate appreciably, we can assume that

$$N(E, \boldsymbol{m}, \boldsymbol{R}, t) = N(E, \boldsymbol{k}, \boldsymbol{r}, t)$$

if the distribution function of electrons does not change much within the very small angle $\sim \gamma^{-1}$. The number of particles entering the volume $d\tau$ in a unit of time is

$$c\beta_r\, N\left(E,\, \boldsymbol{k},\, \boldsymbol{r},\, t - \frac{R}{c}\right) dE\, d\tilde{\Omega}\, d\Omega$$

where t is the time of observation, $t' = t - R/c$ is the time of emission. The total observed flux (in a given polarization i) will then be

$$F_\nu^{(i)} = \iiiint p_{\nu\Omega}^{(i)}\, N\left(E,\, \boldsymbol{k},\, \boldsymbol{R},\, t - \frac{R}{c}\right) dR\, d\Omega\, dE\, d\tilde{\Omega}, \qquad (3.33)$$

because every particle is radiating the energy given by equation (3.30). For a stationary cloud of radiating particles

$$N\left(E,\, \boldsymbol{k},\, \boldsymbol{m},\, t - \frac{r}{c}\right) \equiv N(E, \boldsymbol{k}, \boldsymbol{R})$$

and

$$F_\nu^{(i)} = \iiiint p_{\nu\Omega}^{(i)}\, N(E, \boldsymbol{k}, R)\; dR\, d\Omega\, dE\, d\tilde{\Omega}. \qquad (3.34)$$

For a cloud moving as a whole with velocity $\boldsymbol{V}$ we have $N(E, \boldsymbol{k}, \boldsymbol{R}, t) = N'(E, \boldsymbol{k}, \boldsymbol{R} - \boldsymbol{V}t)$ and

$$F_\nu^{(i)} = F_{\nu S}^{(i)} \left(1 - \frac{V_r}{c}\right)^{-1}, \qquad (3.35)$$

where $F_{\nu S}^{(i)}$ is the flux [equation (3.34)] observed from a stationary cloud with distribution of electrons $N'(E, \boldsymbol{k}, \boldsymbol{R})$.

As shown by equation (3.29), the ellipticity of the polarization of radiation from a single electron is proportional to the first power of ψ. Therefore, if we have radiation from an ensemble of electrons, during integration over ψ, the contribution with negative ψ will cancel the

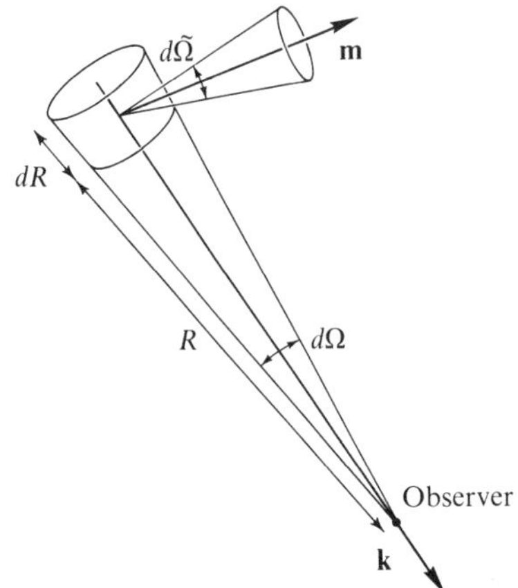

Fig. 3.3 Describing the synchrotron radiation from an ensemble of electrons.

contribution with positive ψ provided that the distribution function N of electrons does not vary sharply within the small angle $\sim \gamma^{-1}$. Under these assumptions the ellipticity of the polarization of synchrotron radiation from an ensemble of electrons is zero. We will retain the above assumptions and consider only the linear polarization of synchrotron radiation.

The emission coefficient $\mathcal{E}_{\nu}^{(i)}$ for synchrotron radiation coming from a stationary region with the uniform distribution of electrons in vacuum is

$$\mathcal{E}_{\nu}^{(i)} = \int_{4\pi}\int_{0}^{\infty} N(E, \boldsymbol{k})\, p_{\nu\Omega}^{(i)}\, d\Omega\, dE, \tag{3.36}$$

where $N(E, \boldsymbol{k})\, dE\, d\Omega$ is the number of electrons with velocity within $d\Omega$ around $\boldsymbol{k}$ and energy within dE around E and $p_{\nu\Omega}^{(i)}$ are given by equation (3.36). For an isotropic distribution of electron velocities

$$\mathcal{E}_{\nu}^{(i)} = \frac{1}{4\pi}\int_{0}^{\infty} N(E)\left(\int_{4\pi} p_{\nu\Omega}^{(i)}\, d\Omega\right) dE = \frac{1}{4\pi}\int_{0}^{\infty} N(E)\, p_{\nu}^{(i)}\, dE. \tag{3.37}$$

Because of the high anisotropy of synchrotron radiation, the integration of $p_{\nu\Omega}^{(i)}$ over $d\Omega$ can be limited to the integration over the shaded ring on Figure 3.1 which contains the directions in which a significant amount of synchrotron radiation is emitted. Then we can write $d\Omega \cong 2\pi \sin\vartheta\, d\psi$, and, since the extension of integration over $d\psi$ from $(-1/\gamma, 1/\gamma)$ to $(-\infty, +\infty)$ will not introduce an appreciable error because of the smallness of the integrand, we can write approximately

$$p_\nu^{(i)} = \int_{4\pi} p_{\nu\Omega}^{(i)}\, d\Omega \cong 2\pi \sin\vartheta \int_{-\infty}^{+\infty} p_{\nu\Omega}^{(i)}\, d\psi$$

$$= \begin{cases} \dfrac{3e^2}{2\pi c}\,\omega_H \sin\vartheta\, \gamma^2 x^2 \displaystyle\int_{-\infty}^{+\infty} (1+\gamma^2\psi^2)^2 \left[K_{2/3}\left(\frac{x}{2}\sqrt{(1+\gamma^2\psi^2)^3}\right)\right]^2 d\psi & \text{for } i=1, \\ \dfrac{3e^2}{2\pi c}\,\omega_H \sin\vartheta\, \gamma^2 x^2 \displaystyle\int_{-\infty}^{+\infty} \gamma^2\psi^2(1+\gamma^2\psi^2) \left[K_{1/3}\left(\frac{x}{2}\sqrt{(1+\gamma^2\psi^2)^3}\right)\right]^2 d\psi & \text{for } i=2. \end{cases}$$

The integrals are:†

$$\int_{-\infty}^{+\infty} (1+\gamma^2\psi^2)^2 \left[K_{2/3}\left(\frac{x}{2}\sqrt{(1+\gamma^2\psi^2)^3}\right)\right]^2 d\psi = \frac{\pi}{\sqrt{3}\gamma x}\left[\int_x^\infty K_{5/3}(z)\, dz + K_{2/3}(x)\right],$$

$$\int_{-\infty}^{+\infty} \gamma^2\psi^2(1+\gamma^2\psi^2) \left[K_{1/3}\left(\frac{x}{2}\sqrt{(1+\gamma^2\psi^2)^3}\right)\right]^2 d\psi = \frac{\pi}{\sqrt{3}\gamma x}\left[\int_x^\infty K_{5/3}(z)\, dz - K_{2/3}(x)\right].$$

Therefore,

$$p_\nu^{(i)} = \int_{4\pi} p_{\nu\Omega}^{(i)}\, d\Omega \cong \frac{\sqrt{3}e^3}{2mc^2} H \sin\vartheta\, [F(x) \pm G(x)], \tag{3.38}$$

where

$$F(x) = x\int_x^\infty K_{5/3}(z)\, dz$$

$$G(x) = x\, K_{2/3}(x)$$

and $K_{5/3}$ and $K_{2/3}$ are corresponding Bessel functions. The emission coefficient is then [x is a function of E, see equations (3.27) and (3.28)]

$$\varepsilon_\nu^{(i)} = \frac{1}{2} c_3 H \sin\vartheta \int_0^\infty N(E)\, [F(x) \pm G(x)]\, dE, \tag{3.39}$$

† The integrals are computed in Ref. 13.

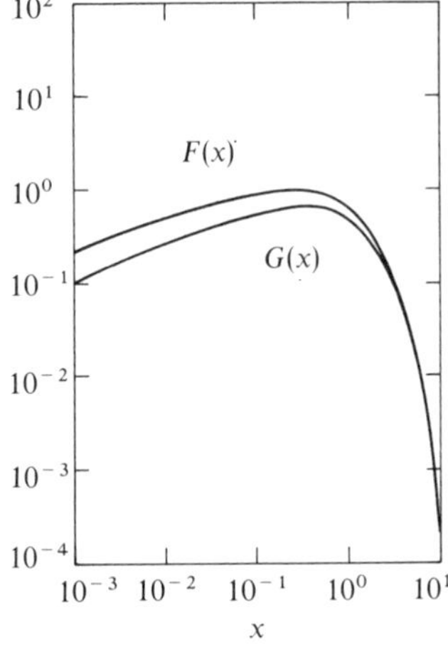

Fig. 3.4 The functions $F(x)$ and $G(x)$.

where

$$c_3 = \frac{\sqrt{3}}{4\pi} \frac{e^3}{mc^2} = 1.87 \times 10^{-23}.$$

The total emission coefficient, $\mathcal{E}_\nu = \mathcal{E}_\omega^{(1)} + \mathcal{E}_\nu^{(2)}$, is

$$\mathcal{E}_\nu = c_3 H \sin\vartheta \int_0^\infty N(E)\, F(x)\, dE. \tag{3.40}$$

The functions $F(x)$ and $G(x)$ are presented in Figure 3.4 and tabulated in Appendix 2 (Tables 1 and 5). $F(x)$ attains maximum at $x = 0.29$ while the maximum of $G(x)$ occurs at $x = 0.4$. The asymptotic behavior of these functions for small x is

$$F(x) \propto \frac{4\pi}{\sqrt{3}\,\Gamma(1/3)\,\sqrt[3]{2}} x^{1/3},$$

$$G(x) \propto \frac{2\pi}{\sqrt{3}\,\Gamma(1/3)\,\sqrt[3]{2}} x^{1/3},$$

and for large x

$$F(x) \propto \sqrt{\frac{\pi x}{2}}\, e^{-x},$$

$$G(x) \propto \sqrt{\frac{\pi x}{2}}\, e^{-x}.$$

To determine *the absorption coefficient* $\kappa_\nu^{(i)}$ of synchrotron radiation, let us consider the processes of absorption and stimulated emission of

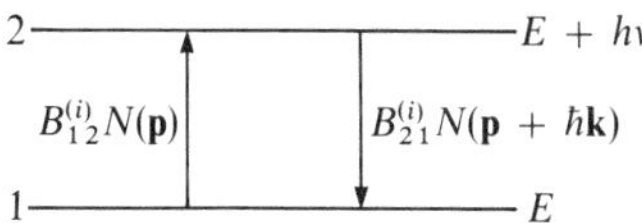

Fig. 3.5 Deriving the synchrotron absorption coefficient.

photons of energy $h\nu = \hbar kc$ during transitions between the two energy levels E and $E + h\nu$ in a system composed of a relativistic electron and a magnetic field as in Figure 3.5. The net change of the number density of photons in a unit of time in the momentum space is

$$[B_{21}{}^{(i)}\, N(\boldsymbol{p} + \hbar \boldsymbol{k}) - B_{12}{}^{(i)}\, N(\boldsymbol{p})]\; I_\nu{}^{(i)},$$

where $B_{21}{}^{(i)}$ and $B_{12}{}^{(i)}$ are Einstein coefficients for a given polarization (i), $N(\boldsymbol{p})$ is the distribution function of electrons in this space, and $I_\nu{}^{(i)}$ is the intensity of radiation of the same polarization. The coefficient of absorption $\kappa_\nu{}^{(i)}$ for a given polarization (i) is then

$$\kappa_\nu{}^{(i)} \equiv \frac{1}{I_\nu{}^{(i)}}\frac{dI_\nu{}^{(a,i)}}{ds} = \int [B_{12}{}^{(i)}\, N(\boldsymbol{p}) - B_{21}{}^{(i)}\, N(\boldsymbol{p} + \hbar\boldsymbol{k})]\; h\nu\; d\boldsymbol{p} \quad (3.41)$$

Using Einstein relations for one polarization,

$$B_{12}{}^{(i)} = B_{21}{}^{(i)} = A^{(i)}\,\frac{c^2}{h\nu^3},$$

we have

$$\kappa_\nu{}^{(i)} = \int [N(\boldsymbol{p}) - N(\boldsymbol{p} + \hbar\boldsymbol{k})]\,\frac{c^2}{h\nu^3}\,A^{(i)}\,h\nu\; d\boldsymbol{p}.$$

If θ and φ are azimuthal and polar angles in a spherical system of coordinates, we have

$$\kappa_\nu{}^{(i)} = \iint \left[N(p, \theta, \varphi) - N\left(p + \frac{h\nu}{c}, \theta, \varphi\right)\right] \frac{c^2}{\nu^2}\,A^{(i)}\,p^2\,dp\,d\Omega.$$

For an isotropic distribution of electrons, since $N(p) = \int N(p, \theta, \varphi)\; d\Omega$,

$$\kappa_\nu{}^{(i)} = \frac{1}{4\pi}\int \left[N(p) - N\left(p + \frac{h\nu}{c}\right)\right]\frac{c^2}{\nu^2}\left[\int A^{(i)}\,d\Omega\right] p^2\,dp.$$

If we consider that we have significant intensity only for transitions with $(h\nu/c) \ll p$, we can write

$$N\left(p + \frac{h\nu}{c}\right) - N(p) \cong \frac{h\nu}{c}\frac{dN}{dp},$$

and

$$\kappa_\nu^{(i)} = -\frac{hc}{4\pi\nu}\int p^2 \frac{dN}{dp}\left[\int A^{(i)}\,d\Omega\right] dp.$$

In terms of energy $(E = cp)$ we have for an isotropic distribution of electrons

$$N(E)\,dE = N(p)\,p^2\,dp,$$

and

$$\kappa_\nu^{(i)} = -\frac{hc^2}{4\pi\nu}\int E^2 \frac{d}{dE}\left(\frac{N(E)}{E^2}\right)\int A^{(i)}\,d\Omega\,dE;$$

but since

$$\int A^{(i)}\,d\Omega = \frac{1}{h\nu}\int p_{\nu\Omega}^{(i)}\,d\Omega = \frac{p_\nu^{(i)}}{h\nu}$$

is given by equation (3.38), we have finally

$$\kappa_\nu^{(i)} = -\frac{c^2}{8\pi\nu^2}\frac{\sqrt{3}e^3}{mc^2} H \sin\vartheta \int_0^\infty E^2 \frac{d}{dE}\left(\frac{N(E)}{E^2}\right)[F(x) \pm G(x)]\,dE.$$

The average absorption coefficient $\kappa_\nu = \tfrac{1}{2}(\kappa_\nu^{(1)} + \kappa_\nu^{(2)})$ is:

$$\kappa_\nu = -\frac{c^2}{2\nu^2} c_3 H \sin\vartheta \int_0^\infty E^2 \frac{d}{dE}\left(\frac{N(E)}{E^2}\right) F(x)\,dE. \qquad (3.42)$$

Let us remark here that a coherent synchrotron radiation leading to a maser-type effect in vacuum is not possible. We will prove it by pointing out that the absorption coefficient κ_ν is always positive, regardless of the shape of $N(E)$. Integrating equation (3.42) by parts we have

$$\kappa_\nu = -\frac{c^2}{2\nu^2} c_3 H \sin\vartheta\, N(E)\, F(x)\Big|_{E=0}^{E=\infty} + \frac{c^2}{2\nu^2} c_3 H \sin\vartheta$$

$$\int_0^\infty \frac{N(E)}{E^2}\frac{d}{dE}[E^2 F(x)]\,dE.$$

The first term in the above equations vanishes for regular electron distributions since $N(E) \to 0$ as $E \to \infty$; and since as $E \to 0$, $x \to \infty$, and $F(x) \propto (e^{-x} x^{1/2})$ gives $e^{-x} x^{1/2} N(E) \to 0$. We have then

$$\kappa_\nu = \frac{c^2}{2\nu^2} c_3 H \sin\vartheta \int_0^\infty \frac{N(E)}{E^2}\frac{d}{dE}[E^2 F(x)]\,dE.$$

The derivative in the integrand in the above expression is proportional to

$$E\left(2F + E\frac{dx}{dE}\frac{dF}{dx}\right) = 2\left(F - x\frac{dF}{dx}\right) = 2F\left(1 - \frac{d\log F}{d\log x}\right)$$

since $x = \text{const} \cdot E^{-2}$, and $E(dx/dE) = -2x$. The function $F(x) \propto x^{1/3}$ for small x and flattens as x increases (see Figure 3.4); therefore $(d \log F)/(d \log x) \leq 1/3$, and κ_ν is always positive.

We will write the form of the absorption and emission coefficients and discuss the spectrum for a few specific distribution functions of relativistic electrons. We begin with *monoenergetic electrons*, in which $N(E) = N_0 \delta(E - E_0)$. The total emission coefficient given by equation (3.40) becomes

$$\mathcal{E}_\nu = c_3 H \sin\vartheta \, N_0 F(x), \tag{3.43}$$

and, after integrating equation (3.42) by parts, the average absorption coefficient is equal to

$$\kappa_\nu = \frac{c^2}{2\nu^2} c_3 H \sin\vartheta \frac{N_0}{E_0^2} \left[\frac{d}{dE} (E^2 F(x)) \right]_{E=E_0}$$

since the first term after integration vanishes at both energy limits $(0, \infty)$. If we write

$$F(x) = \frac{\nu}{c_1 H \sin\vartheta} \frac{1}{E^2} \int_{\nu/\nu_C}^{\infty} K_{5/3}(z) \, dz$$

and introduce it into the above equation, we have

$$\kappa_\nu = -\frac{c^2}{2} \frac{1}{E_0^2} \frac{c_3}{c_1} \frac{N_0}{\nu} K_{5/3}\left(\frac{\nu}{\nu_C(E_0)}\right) \left[\frac{d}{dE}\left(\frac{\nu}{\nu_C}\right)\right]_{E=E_0}$$

$$= +c^2 \frac{c_3}{c_1^2} \frac{N_0}{H \sin\vartheta} \frac{1}{E_0^5} K(x) = c_4 \frac{(H \sin\vartheta)^{3/2} N_0}{\nu_C^{5/2}} K(x) \tag{3.44}$$

where $c_4 = c_1^{1/2} c_3 c^2 = 4.20 \times 10^7$, and $K(x) \equiv K_{5/3}(x)$ is represented in Figure 3.6 and tabulated in Appendix 2 (Table 1). If λ_m is the wavelength corresponding to $\nu_m = 0.29\nu_C(E_0)$, then

$$\kappa_\nu(\lambda_m) = 1.72 \times 10^{-23} \frac{\lambda_m^2}{E_0} N_0 H \sin\vartheta. \tag{3.45}$$

The source function, $S_\nu = \mathcal{E}_\nu/\kappa_\nu$, has the form,

$$S_\nu = \frac{c_1^2}{c^2} (H \sin\vartheta)^2 E_0^5 S(x) = \frac{\nu_C^{5/2}}{c^2 \sqrt{c_1 H \sin\vartheta}} S(x) = \frac{E_0}{\lambda_0^2} S(x), \tag{3.46}$$

where λ_0 is the wavelength corresponding to $\nu_0(E_0)$ [not to $0.29\,\nu_C(E_0)$], and $S(x) = F(x)/K(x)$ is represented in Figure 3.6 and tabulated in Appendix 2 (Table 1). If we assume the source function S_ν to be constant in the radiating region, and if we assume that no incident radiation is

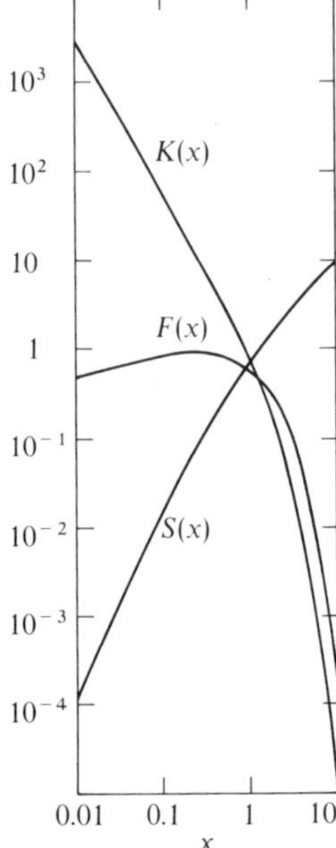

Fig. 3.6 The functions $F(x)$, $K(x)$, and $S(x)$.

present $[I_\nu(0) = 0]$, we can easily solve the transfer equation (s is the extent of the region)

$$I_\nu(s) = I_\nu(0)e^{-\tau_\nu(s,0)} + \int_0^s e^{-\tau_\nu(s,s')}\, \kappa_\nu\, S_\nu\, ds'.$$

Its solution is

$$I_\nu(\tau_\nu) = S_\nu \int_0^s e^{-\tau_\nu(s,s')}\, d\tau_\nu' = S_\nu(1 - e^{-\tau_\nu}), \tag{3.47}$$

since $\kappa_\nu\, ds = d\tau_\nu$. If the absorption coefficient is assumed to be constant in the radiating region,

$$\tau_\nu = \kappa_\nu s = c_4 \frac{(H \sin\vartheta)^{3/2}}{\nu_C^{5/2}} N_0 \cdot s K(x) = c_4 \frac{(H \sin\vartheta)^{3/2}}{\nu_C^{5/2}} N_T K(x)$$

where $N_T = N_0 s$ is the total number of electrons along the line of sight. We can write equation (3.47) in the form

$$I_\nu(\tau_\nu) = \frac{\nu_C^{5/2}}{c^2\sqrt{c_1\, H \sin\vartheta}} S(x)\,[1 - e^{-\tau(x)}] = \frac{\nu_C^{5/2}\, S(0.29)}{c^2\sqrt{c_1\, H \sin\vartheta}} J(\tau_m, x), \tag{3.48}$$

where

$$J(\tau_m, x) = S(x)\left[1 - e^{-\tau_m}\frac{K(x)}{K(0.29)}\right]$$

and

$$\tau_m = \tau_\nu(0.29)$$

The function $J(\tau_m, x)$ is represented in Figure 3.7 and tabulated in Appendix 2 (Table 2).

For a *power-law distribution of electrons*, $N(E) = N_0 E^{-\gamma}$,† the emission coefficient $\mathcal{E}_\nu$ becomes

$$\mathcal{E}_\nu^{(i)} = \frac{1}{2} c_3 H \sin\vartheta\, N_0 \int_0^\infty E^{-\gamma}[F(x) \pm G(x)]\, dE$$

$$= \frac{1}{4} c_3 N_0 H \sin\vartheta \left(c_1 \frac{H \sin\vartheta}{\nu}\right)^{(\gamma-1)/2} \int_0^\infty x^{(\gamma-1)/2}$$

$$\left[\int_0^\infty K_{5/3}(z)\, dz \pm K_{2/3}(x)\right] dx.$$

With the help of the following relations between Bessel functions‡ valid for $\gamma > 1/3$,

$$\int_0^\infty x^{(\gamma-1)/2} \int_x^\infty K_{5/3}(z)\, dz\, dx = \frac{\gamma + 7/3}{\gamma + 1} 2^{(\gamma-3)/2} \Gamma\left(\frac{3\gamma - 1}{12}\right) \Gamma\left(\frac{3\gamma + 7}{12}\right),$$

$$\int_0^\infty x^{(\gamma-1)/2} K_{2/3}(x)\, dx = 2^{(\gamma-3)/2} \Gamma\left(\frac{3\gamma - 1}{12}\right) \Gamma\left(\frac{3\gamma + 7}{12}\right),$$

We can write the emission coefficients in the final form

$$\mathcal{E}_\nu^{(i)} = \frac{1}{2} c_5(\gamma) N_0 (H \sin\vartheta)^{(\gamma+1)/2} \left(\frac{\nu}{2c_1}\right)^{(1-\gamma)/2} \left[1 \pm \frac{\gamma + 1}{\gamma + 7/3}\right] \quad (3.49)$$

where

$$c_5(\gamma) = \frac{1}{4} c_3 \Gamma\left(\frac{3\gamma - 1}{12}\right) \Gamma\left(\frac{3\gamma + 7}{12}\right) \cdot \left(\frac{\gamma + 7/3}{\gamma + 1}\right)$$

is tabulated in Appendix 2 (Table 7). The total emission coefficient is

$$\mathcal{E}_\nu = c_5(\gamma) N_0 (H \sin\vartheta)^{(\gamma+1)/2} \left(\frac{\nu}{2c_1}\right)^{(1-\gamma)/2}. \quad (3.50)$$

---

† Throughout the remainder of this chapter, γ will be used to designate the exponent in the electron energy spectrum, not the ratio E/mc^2.

‡ The relations are derived in Ref. 13.

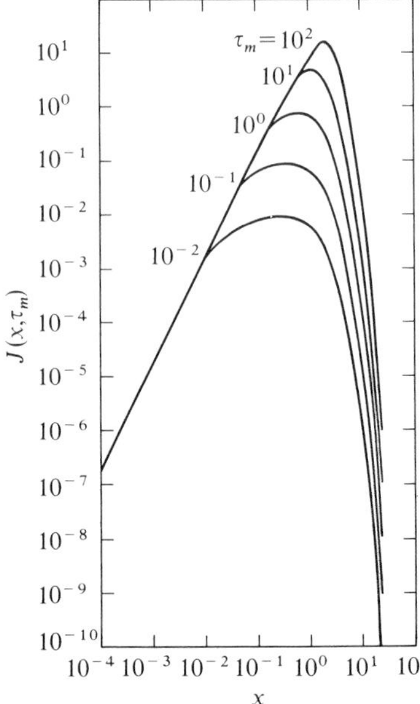

Fig. 3.7 The function $J(x, \tau_m)$.

The absorption coefficient $\kappa_\nu^{(i)}$ is equal to

$$\kappa_\nu^{(i)} = -\frac{c^2 N_0}{2\nu^2} c_3 \; H \sin\vartheta \int_0^\infty E^2 \frac{d}{dE} (E^{-\gamma-2}) \; [F(x) \pm G(x)] \; dE$$

$$= \frac{c^2}{4\nu^2} N_0 \, c_3 \, (H \sin\vartheta)^{(\gamma+2)/2} \; (\gamma+2) \left(\frac{c_1}{\nu}\right)^{\gamma/2}$$

$$\int_0^\infty x^{\gamma/2} \left[\int_x^\infty K_{5/3}(z) \; dz \pm K_{2/3} \right] dx.$$

Using the first relation preceding equation (3.49), but with $\gamma - 1 \to \gamma$, we obtain

$$\kappa_\nu^{(i)} = c_6(\gamma) \; N_0 (H \sin\vartheta)^{(\gamma+2)/2} \left(\frac{\nu}{2c_1}\right)^{-(\gamma+4)/2} \left(1 \pm \frac{\gamma+2}{\gamma + {}^{10}\!/_3}\right), \quad (3.51)$$

where

$$c_6(\gamma) = \frac{1}{32}\left(\frac{c}{c_1}\right)^2 c_3 \left(\gamma + \frac{10}{3}\right) \Gamma\left(\frac{3\gamma+2}{12}\right) \Gamma\left(\frac{3\gamma+10}{12}\right).$$

The average absorption coefficient $\kappa_\nu = {}^1\!/_2(\kappa_\nu^{(1)} + \kappa_\nu^{(2)})$ is therefore

$$\kappa_\nu = c_6(\gamma) \; N_0 (H \sin\vartheta)^{(\gamma+2)/2} \left(\frac{\nu}{2c_1}\right)^{-(\gamma+4)/2} \quad (3.52)$$

The function c_6 is tabulated in Appendix 2 (Table 7). The solution given

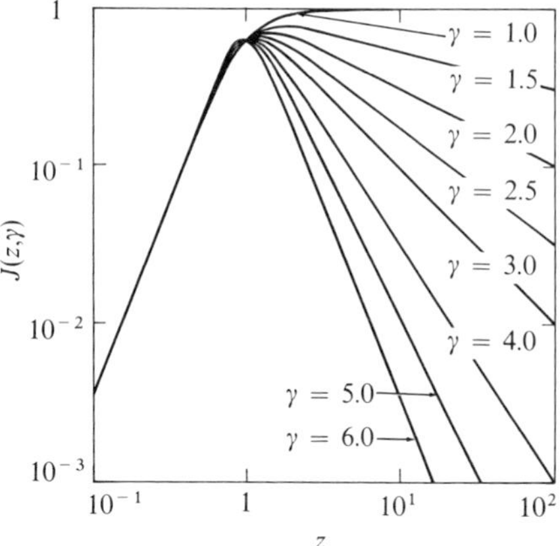

Fig. 3.8 The function $J(z, \gamma)$.

by equation (3.47) of the transfer equation for a power-law distribution of electrons can be written in the form:

$$I_\nu = S(\nu_1) \cdot J\left(\frac{\nu}{\nu_1}, \gamma\right), \tag{3.53}$$

where ν_1, defined by the condition $\tau(\nu_1) = 1$, is given by (s is the extent of the radiating region)

$$\nu_1 = 2c_1(sc_6)^{2/(\gamma+4)} N_0^{2/(\gamma+4)} (H \sin\vartheta)^{(\gamma+2)/(\gamma+4)},$$

$$S(\nu_1) = \frac{c_5}{c_6} (H \sin\vartheta)^{-1/2} \left(\frac{\nu_1}{2c_1}\right)^{5/2},$$

and the function $J(z, \gamma)$, defined as

$$J(z, \gamma) = z^{5/2} \left[1 - \exp\left(-z^{-(\gamma+4)/2}\right)\right],$$

is represented in Figure 3.8 and tabulated in Appendix 2 (Table 3). We see that the synchrotron spectrum from a power-law distribution of electrons has a power-law form with the index α at high frequencies

$$I_\nu \cong S_\nu \tau_\nu \propto \nu^{-(\gamma-1)/2} = \nu^{-\alpha},$$

where

$$\alpha \equiv \frac{\gamma - 1}{2}.$$

At low frequencies,

$$I_\nu \cong S_\nu \propto \nu^{5/2};$$

the slope of the spectrum does not depend on γ. For $\gamma > 1$ a maximum in the spectrum exists; it occurs at the frequency ν_m, which can be obtained by differentiating equation (3.52) with respect to frequency and by equating the result to zero. This procedure gives for ν_m the following equation

$$e^{\tau_m} = 1 + \frac{\gamma + 4}{5} \tau_m ,$$

where $\tau_m = \tau(\nu_m)$. The solution of this equation for several values of γ is

γ	2	3	4	5
τ_m	0.35	0.65	0.88	1.08.

We see that ν_1 and ν_m do not coincide. Their ratio is

$$\frac{\nu_1}{\nu_m} = \tau_m^{2/(\gamma+4)}.$$

For a *relativistic Maxwellian distribution of electrons*, $N(E) = N_0 E^2 \exp(-E/kT)$ (k is the Boltzmann constant, T is the electron temperature and N_0 is a constant), the emission and absorption coefficients, $\mathcal{E}_\nu$ and κ_ν, of synchrotron radiation are

$$\mathcal{E}_\nu = \frac{c_3}{c_1} N_0 k T \nu I(x_M) = 4.11 \times 10^{-58} N_0 T \nu I(x_M), \tag{3.54}$$

$$\kappa_\nu = \frac{c^2}{2} \frac{c_3}{c_1} N_0 \frac{1}{\nu} I(x_M) = 1.34 \times 10^{-21} \frac{N_0}{\nu} I(x_M), \tag{3.55}$$

and the source function is

$$S_\nu = \frac{2kT\nu^2}{c^2} = 3.07 \times 10^{-37} T\nu^2. \tag{3.56}$$

In deriving the above formula we made the substitutions $z = E/kT$ and $x_M = \nu/\nu_M$ where $\nu_M = c_1 H \sin\vartheta (kT)^2$. In this notation the function $I(x_M)$ has the form,

$$I(x_M) = \frac{1}{x_M} \int_0^\infty z^2 \exp(-z) F\left(\frac{x_M}{z^2}\right) dz.$$

The function $I(x_M)$ is illustrated in Figure 3.9 and tabulated in Appendix 2 (Table 4). For small values of $x_M (\lesssim 10^{-3})$ the following asymptotic formula for $I(x_M)$ can be used:

$$I(x_M) \cong \frac{1}{x_M} \frac{16\pi}{9\sqrt{3}} \left(\frac{x_M}{2}\right)^{1/3} \cong 2.56\, x_M^{-2/3}.$$

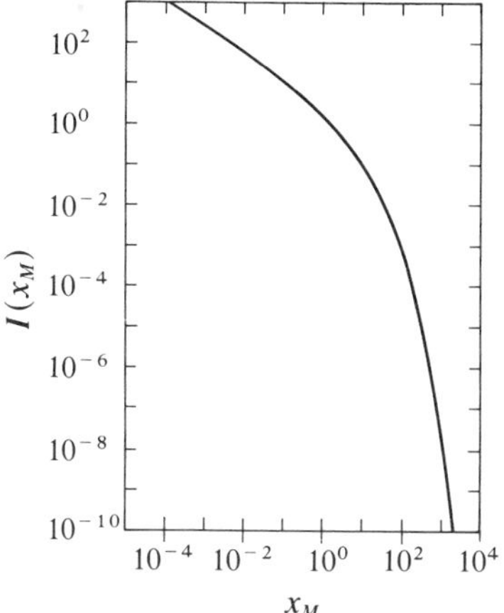

Fig. 3.9 The function $I(x_M)$.

3.5 The Polarization of Synchrotron Radiation

In the preceding section we derived expressions for the emission and absorption coefficients of synchrotron radiation for different polarizations. We have also shown that elliptical polarization can be neglected for very relativistic electrons and relatively smooth electron distributions. We will now discuss the transfer of polarized synchrotron radiation through an extended region taking into account possible Faraday rotation of the plane of polarization of synchrotron radiation traversing this region (see Section 2.3). It will be convenient to use a set of three parameters $I^{(x)}$, $I^{(y)}$, $I^{(xy)}$ related to the Stokes parameters I, Q, U (see Appendix 1) in the following way:†

$$\begin{aligned} I &= I^{(x)} + I^{(y)} \\ Q &= I^{(x)} - I^{(y)}, \\ U &\equiv U^{(xy)} = (I^{(x)} - I^{(y)}) \tan 2\chi^{(xy)} \end{aligned} \tag{3.57}$$

(we assume the Stokes parameter $V = 0$ since we are neglecting elliptical polarization). It is useful to introduce two reference systems to describe the vibrations of the electric vector of the wave: the "observer's" system (a, b), and the "magnetic field" system $(1, 2)$ in which the projection of the magnetic field at a given point within the source onto the plane perpendicular to the direction of wave propagation is parallel to the direction 2. The magnetic field system may be different at different points

† The subscript ν will be omitted from the notation in this section.

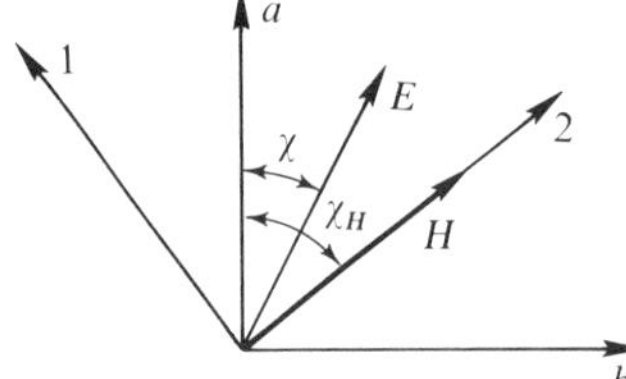

Fig. 3.10 The relationship between the reference systems (a, b) and (x, y).

depending on the distribution of the magnetic field within the source. The relationship between these two systems of reference is illustrated in Figure 3.10; this figure defines the angles χ and χ_H.

The change of parameters $I^{(a)}$, $I^{(b)}$, $U^{(ab)}$ characterizing the radiation passing through a volume element of length ds can be represented as a sum of changes due to absorption ($dI^{(a,a)}$, $dI^{(a,b)}$, $dU^{(a,ab)}$), emission ($dI^{(e,a)}$, $dI^{(e,b)}$, $dU^{(e,ab)}$), and Faraday rotation ($dI^{(f,a)}$, $dI^{(f,b)}$, $dU^{(f,ab)}$):

$$dI^{(a)} = dI^{(a,a)} + dI^{(e,a)} + dI^{(f,a)},$$

$$dI^{(b)} = dI^{(a,b)} + dI^{(e,b)} + dI^{(f,b)},$$

$$dU^{(ab)} = dU^{(a,ab)} + dU^{(e,ab)} + dU^{(f,ab)}. \tag{3.58}$$

The changes of parameters due to absorption can be expressed in the magnetic field system in terms of the absorption coefficients, $\kappa^{(1)}$ and $\kappa^{(2)}$, for the two orthogonal polarizations:

$$dI^{(a,1)} = -\kappa^{(1)} I^{(1)} ds,$$

$$dI^{(a,2)} = -\kappa^{(2)} I^{(2)} ds,$$

$$dU^{(a,12)} = -\kappa\, U^{(12)} ds, \tag{3.59}$$

where $\kappa = 1/2(\kappa^{(1)} + \kappa^{(2)})$ is the average absorption coefficient. The latter equation follows from the fact that the unpolarized part of synchrotron radiation passing through the volume element of length ds may acquire a certain polarization (due to polarized absorption) which will be either in the direction 1 or 2 depending on whether or not $\kappa^{(1)} > \kappa^{(2)}$. In either case the parameter $U^{(12)}$ of the originally unpolarized part of the radiation will remain zero, and the change in the U parameter of the total radiation is solely due to the change of the U parameter of the completely polarized part of radiation. Since for that radiation $(U^{(12)})^2 = 4I^{(1)}I^{(2)}$, after differentiating and using the first two equations (3.59) we obtain the third equation (3.59).

The change of the parameters $I^{(1)}$, $I^{(2)}$, $U^{(12)}$ due to emission can be expressed in terms of the emission coefficients, $\varepsilon^{(1)}$ and $\varepsilon^{(2)}$, in the following way:

$$dI^{(e,1)} = \mathcal{E}^{(1)}\, ds,$$
$$dI^{(e,2)} = \mathcal{E}^{(2)}\, ds,$$
$$dU^{(e,12)} = 0, \tag{3.60}$$

in which the last equation results from the fact that the plane of polarization of the locally emitted synchrotron radiation is parallel to the direction 1.

The change of the parameters due to Faraday rotation can be easily expressed directly in the (a, b) system:

$$\left\| \begin{matrix} I^{(a)} + dI^{(f,a)} \\ I^{(b)} + dI^{(f,b)} \\ U^{(ab)} + dU^{(f,ab)} \end{matrix} \right\| = L(d\chi_F) \left\| \begin{matrix} I^{(a)} \\ I^{(b)} \\ U^{(ab)} \end{matrix} \right\| , \tag{3.61}$$

where $d\chi_F$ is the Faraday rotation measure per unit ds, and

$$L(\alpha) = \left\| \begin{matrix} \cos^2\alpha & \sin^2\alpha & \frac{1}{2}\sin 2\alpha \\ \sin^2\alpha & \cos^2\alpha & -\frac{1}{2}\sin 2\alpha \\ -\sin 2\alpha & \sin 2\alpha & \cos 2\alpha \end{matrix} \right\| \tag{3.62}$$

is the rotation matrix for the Stokes parameters.† Equation (3.61) yields

$$I^{(a)} + dI^{(f,a)} = I^{(a)} \cos^2 d\chi_F + I^{(b)} \sin^2 d\chi_F + \frac{1}{2} U^{(ab)} \sin 2d\chi_F\,,$$
$$I^{(b)} + dI^{(f,b)} = I^{(a)} \sin^2 d\chi_F + I^{(b)} \cos^2 d\chi_F - \frac{1}{2} U^{(ab)} \sin 2d\chi_F\,,$$
$$U^{(b)} + dU^{(f,ab)} = -I^{(a)} \sin 2d\chi_F + I^{(b)} \sin 2d\chi_F + U^{(ab)} \cos 2d\chi_F\,,$$

which with accuracy to first-order terms becomes

$$dI^{(f,a)} = U^{(ab)}\, d\chi_F\,,$$
$$dI^{(f,b)} = -U^{(ab)}\, d\chi_F\,,$$
$$dU^{(f,ab)} = -2I^{(a)}\, d\chi_F + 2I^{(b)}\, d\chi_F\,. \tag{3.63}$$

Before inserting equations (3.59) and (3.60) into the transfer equations (3.58), we have to transform the parameters $I_1^{(1)}$, $I_2^{(2)}$, $U_{12}^{(12)}$ and their increments into the (a, b) system by performing a rotation through the angle $90° - \chi_H$ (cf. Figure 3.10):

† This matrix is discussed, for example, in Ref. A1.1.

$$\begin{Vmatrix} dI^{(a)} \\ dI^{(b)} \\ dU^{(ab)} \end{Vmatrix} = L(90° - \chi_H) \begin{Vmatrix} dI^{(1)} \\ dI^{(2)} \\ dU^{(12)} \end{Vmatrix}$$

$$= \begin{Vmatrix} \sin^2 \chi_H & \cos^2 \chi_H & \frac{1}{2} \sin 2\chi_H \\ \cos^2 \chi_H & \sin^2 \chi_H & -\frac{1}{2} \sin 2\chi_H \\ -\sin 2\chi_H & \sin 2\chi_H & -\cos 2\chi_H \end{Vmatrix} \begin{Vmatrix} dI^{(1)} \\ dI^{(2)} \\ dU^{(12)} \end{Vmatrix} \tag{3.64}$$

$$\begin{Vmatrix} I^{(1)} \\ I^{(2)} \\ U^{(12)} \end{Vmatrix} = L(\chi_H - 90°) \begin{Vmatrix} I^{(a)} \\ I^{(b)} \\ U^{(ab)} \end{Vmatrix} . \tag{3.65}$$

Inserting equations (3.64) and (3.65) into equation (3.59), inserting equation (3.64) into equation (3.60), and then inserting the resulting equations for the changes of the parameters $I_a{}^{(a)}$, $I_b{}^{(b)}$ and $U_{ab}{}^{(ab)}$ together with equation (3.63) for Faraday rotation into the transfer equations (3.58), we obtain, after some algebra, the following expressions:

$$\begin{aligned} \frac{dI^{(a)}}{ds} &= I^{(a)} \left[-\kappa^{(1)} \sin^4 \chi_H - \kappa^{(2)} \cos^4 \chi_H - \frac{1}{2} \kappa \sin^2 2\chi_H \right] \\ &\quad + U^{(ab)} \left[\frac{1}{4} (\kappa^{(1)} - \kappa^{(2)}) \sin 2\chi_H + \frac{d\chi_F}{ds} \right] \\ &\quad + \varepsilon^{(1)} \sin^2 \chi_H + \varepsilon^{(2)} \cos^2 \chi_H , \\ \frac{dI^{(b)}}{ds} &= I^{(b)} \left[-\kappa^{(1)} \cos^4 \chi_H - \kappa^{(2)} \sin^4 \chi_H - \frac{1}{2} \kappa \sin^2 2\chi_H \right] \\ &\quad + U^{(ab)} \left[\frac{1}{4} (\kappa^{(1)} - \kappa^{(2)}) \sin 2\chi_H - \frac{d\chi_F}{ds} \right] \\ &\quad + \varepsilon^{(1)} \cos^2 \chi_H + \varepsilon^{(2)} \sin^2 \chi_H , \\ \frac{dU^{(ab)}}{ds} &= I^{(a)} \left[\frac{1}{2} (\kappa^{(1)} - \kappa^{(2)}) \sin 2\chi_H - 2 \frac{d\chi_F}{ds} \right] \\ &\quad + I^{(b)} \left[\frac{1}{2} (\kappa^{(1)} - \kappa^{(2)}) \sin 2\chi_H + 2 \frac{d\chi_F}{ds} \right] \\ &\quad - \kappa U^{(ab)} - (\varepsilon^{(1)} - \varepsilon^{(2)}) \sin 2\chi_H . \end{aligned} \tag{3.66}$$

The above transfer equations in their final form express the fact that the changes of the Stokes parameters $dI^{(a)}$, $dI^{(b)}$, $dU^{(ab)}$ during the passage of the radiation through ds are due to absorption over ds, emission within ds, and Faraday rotation.

For a homogeneous source with a uniform magnetic field, the transfer equations (3.66) are rather simple if the reference system is rotated such that $\chi_H = 0$:

$$\frac{dI^{(a)}}{ds} = -\kappa^{(2)} I^{(a)} + \tilde{\beta} U^{(ab)} + \mathcal{E}^{(2)},$$

$$\frac{dI^{(b)}}{ds} = -\kappa^{(1)} I^{(b)} - \tilde{\beta} U^{(ab)} + \mathcal{E}^{(1)},$$

$$\frac{dU^{(ab)}}{ds} = -\kappa U^{(ab)} - 2\tilde{\beta} I^{(a)} + 2\tilde{\beta} I^{(b)}, \tag{3.67}$$

where $\tilde{\beta} = d\chi_F/ds$. With the notation:

$$\eta = \tilde{\beta} s, \qquad S_Q = \frac{e\Delta\delta - \delta\Delta e}{\omega^2 + \delta^2}$$

$$\delta = \kappa/\tilde{\beta},$$

$$\Delta\delta = (\kappa^{(1)} - \kappa^{(2)})/2\tilde{\beta}, \qquad S_G = \frac{\omega^2 \Delta e + e\delta\Delta\delta}{\omega(\omega^2 + \delta^2)}$$

$$\omega = \sqrt{4 - \Delta\delta^2},$$

$$e = (\mathcal{E}^{(1)} + \mathcal{E}^{(2)})/\tilde{\beta}, \qquad F = \frac{2}{\omega} I + \frac{\Delta\delta}{\omega} U,$$

$$\Delta e = (\mathcal{E}^{(1)} - \mathcal{E}^{(2)})/\tilde{\beta}, \qquad Q = Q,$$

$$S_F = \frac{2e}{\omega\delta},^{\dagger} \qquad G = \frac{\Delta\delta}{\omega} I + \frac{2}{\omega} U,$$

the system of equations (3.67) can be written in the form:

$$\frac{dF}{d\eta} = -\delta F + \delta S_F,$$

$$\frac{dQ}{d\eta} = -\delta Q + \omega G - \Delta e,$$

$$\frac{dG}{d\eta} = -\delta G - \omega Q + \frac{\Delta\delta}{\omega} e, \tag{3.69}$$

with the solution

$$F = (F_0 - S_F)\, e^{-\delta\eta} + S_F,$$

$$Q = [(Q_0 - S_Q) \cos \omega\eta + (G_0 - S_G) \sin \omega\eta]\, e^{-\delta\eta} + S_Q,$$

$$G = [(G_0 - S_G) \cos \omega\eta - (Q_0 - S_Q) \sin \omega\eta]\, e^{-\delta\eta} + S_G. \tag{3.70}$$

† S_F can be interpreted as the source function for the variable F. For unpolarized absorption ($\kappa^{(1)} = \kappa^{(2)} = \kappa$), $F = I$, $G = U$.

Let us briefly discuss the degree of polarization of synchrotron radiation determined from equation (3.70). If the absorption takes place between the source and the observer ($e^{(1)} = e^{(2)} = 0$ within this region), and Q_0, F_0, and G_0 are the parameters describing the incident radiation, then in the case of synchrotron (polarized) absorption ($\kappa^{(1)} \neq \kappa^{(2)}$),

$$\Pi^2 = \frac{[\omega Q_0 \cos\omega\eta + \omega G_0 \sin\omega\eta]^2 + [2G_0 \cos\omega\eta - 2Q_0 \sin\omega\eta - \Delta\delta F_0]^2}{[-\Delta\delta G_0 \cos\omega\eta + \Delta\delta Q_0 \sin\omega\eta + 2F_0]^2}. \tag{3.71}$$

In the case of thermal (unpolarized) absorption ($\kappa^{(1)} = \kappa^{(2)} = \kappa$), the degree of polarization is unchanged:

$$\Pi^2 = \frac{Q^2 + G^2}{F^2} = \frac{Q^2 + U^2}{I^2} = \frac{Q_0^2 + U_0^2}{I_0^2} = \Pi_0^2. \tag{3.72}$$

Let us consider the absorption taking place within the source (self-absorption). The degree of polarization is then ($Q_0 = F_0 = G_0 = 0$)

$$\begin{aligned}\Pi^2 = \{&[(-S_Q \cos\omega\eta - S_G \sin\omega\eta)\, e^{-\delta\eta} + S_Q]^2 \\ &+ \left[\left(-\frac{2}{\omega} S_G \cos\omega\eta + \frac{2}{\omega} S_Q \sin\omega\eta + \frac{\Delta\delta}{\omega} S_F\right) e^{-\delta\eta} - \frac{2}{\delta} S_Q\right]^2\Bigg\} \\ &\times \left[\left(\frac{\Delta\delta}{\omega} S_G \cos\omega\eta - \frac{\Delta\delta}{\omega} S_Q \sin\omega\eta - \frac{2}{\omega} S_F\right) e^{-\delta\eta} + \frac{\omega}{2} S_F + \frac{\Delta\delta}{\delta} S_Q\right]^{-2}\end{aligned} \tag{3.73}$$

If the source is optically thick ($\delta\eta = \kappa s \gg 1$), then

$$\Pi = \left| \frac{\sqrt{4\beta^2 + \kappa^2}}{\dfrac{\kappa^{(1)} - \kappa^{(2)}}{2} + \dfrac{\varepsilon\left[4\beta^2 - \frac{1}{4}(\kappa^{(1)} - \kappa^{(2)})^2 + \kappa^2\right]}{\kappa^{(1)}\varepsilon^{(2)} - \kappa^{(2)}\varepsilon^{(1)}}} \right|, \tag{3.74}$$

which reduces

$$\Pi = \left| \frac{\varepsilon^{(2)}\kappa^{(1)} - \varepsilon^{(1)}\kappa^{(2)}}{\varepsilon^{(2)}\kappa^{(1)} + \varepsilon^{(1)}\kappa^{(2)}} \right|, \tag{3.75}$$

if the Faraday rotation is small over a distance of one photon mean free path ($\tilde{\beta} \ll \kappa$). If $\tilde{\beta} \gg \kappa$, the polarization is very small:

$$\Pi = \left| \frac{\kappa^{(1)}\varepsilon^{(2)} - \kappa^{(2)}\varepsilon^{(1)}}{2\tilde{\beta}(\varepsilon^{(1)} + \varepsilon^{(2)})} \right|. \tag{3.76}$$

If the source is optically thin, equation (3.73) yields

$$\Pi = \left| \frac{\mathcal{E}^{(1)} - \mathcal{E}^{(2)}}{\mathcal{E}^{(1)} + \mathcal{E}^{(2)}} \right| \cdot \left| \frac{\sin \eta}{\eta} \right|. \tag{3.77}$$

We see that the regions of the source over which the polarization plane experiences full Faraday rotation contribute to the unpolarized portion of the radiation only, bringing the polarization degree to zero every time η reaches a multiple of π. When the absorption is unpolarized (thermal), equation (3.73) reduces to

$$\Pi = \left| \frac{\mathcal{E}^{(1)} - \mathcal{E}^{(2)}}{\mathcal{E}^{(1)} + \mathcal{E}^{(2)}} \right| \sqrt{\frac{\delta^2}{\delta^2 + 4}} \sqrt{1 + \frac{4 \sin^2 \eta \, e^{-\kappa s}}{(1 - e^{-\kappa s})^2}}. \tag{3.78}$$

If there is no Faraday rotation ($\tilde{\beta} = 0$), equation (3.73) simplifies to the form

$$\Pi = \left| \frac{\dfrac{\mathcal{E}^{(2)}\kappa^{(1)}}{\mathcal{E}^{(1)}\kappa^{(2)}} \left(\dfrac{1 - e^{\kappa^{(2)} s}}{1 - e^{\kappa^{(1)} s}} - 1 \right)}{\dfrac{\mathcal{E}^{(2)}\kappa^{(1)}}{\mathcal{E}^{(1)}\kappa^{(2)}} \left(\dfrac{1 - e^{\kappa^{(2)} s}}{1 - e^{\kappa^{(1)} s}} + 1 \right)} \right|. \tag{3.79}$$

Equations (3.77), (3.78), and (3.74) are illustrated on Figures 3.11, 3.12, and 3.13, respectively.

If we have a monoenergetic (with energy E_0) distribution of electrons,

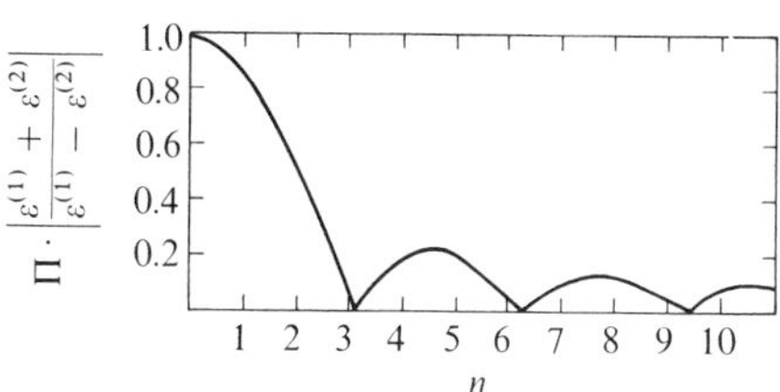

Fig. 3.11 The degree of polarization Π [equation (3.77)] for an optically thin medium with Faraday rotation.

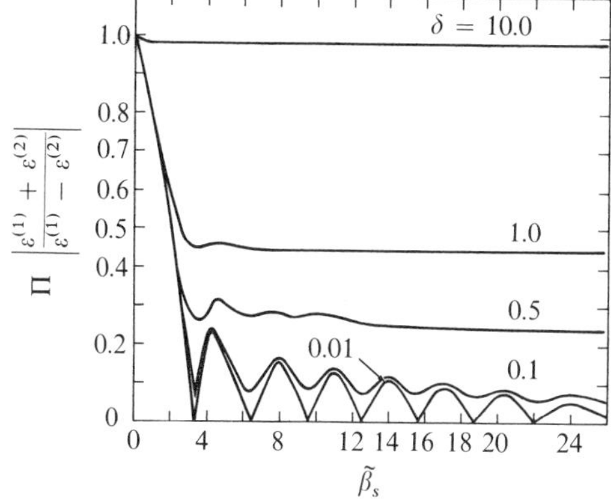

Fig. 3.12 The degree of polarization Π [equation (3.78)] for a medium with unpolarized absorption.

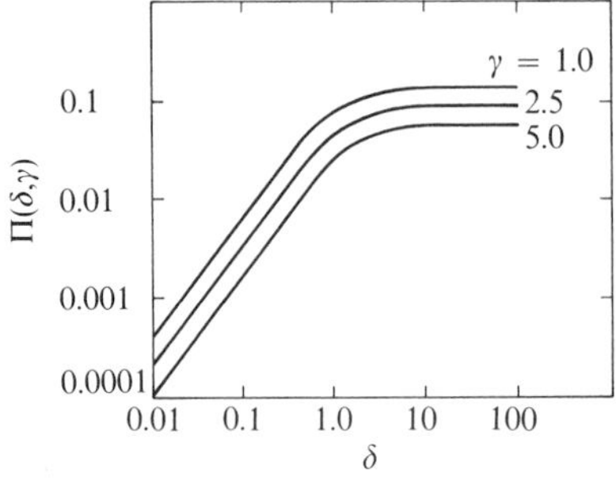

Fig. 3.13 The degree of polarization Π [equation (3.74)] for an optically thick medium with polarized (synchrotron) absorption.

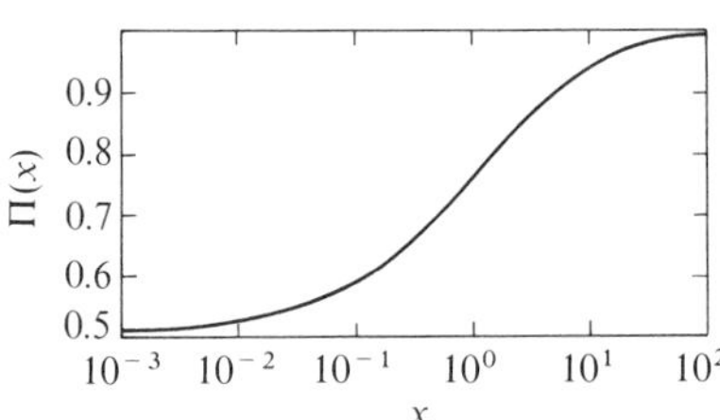

Fig. 3.14 The degree of polarization Π [equation (3.80)] for monoenergetic electrons.

the emission and absorption coefficients are given by equations (3.43) and (3.44). In this case the optically thin homogeneous source (without Faraday rotation) is characterized by the degree of polarization,

$$\Pi = \left| \frac{\varepsilon^{(1)} - \varepsilon^{(2)}}{\varepsilon^{(1)} + \varepsilon^{(2)}} \right| = \frac{G(x)}{F(x)}, \tag{3.80}$$

where $x = \nu/\nu_C$ and ν_C is the critical frequency corresponding to the energy E_0. The degree of polarization therefore depends on frequency, varying from 0.5 to 1.0 for high frequencies (Figure 3.14). It should, however, be kept in mind that most of the radiation will be emitted around the critical frequency ν_C and will have a degree of polarization around 0.7. For an optically thick source the degree of polarization is zero.

For a power-law distribution of electrons [see equations (3.50) and (3.51) for emission and absorption coefficients], the degree of polarization of an optically thin homogeneous source without Faraday rotation is

$$\Pi = \left| \frac{\varepsilon^{(1)} - \varepsilon^{(2)}}{\varepsilon^{(1)} + \varepsilon^{(2)}} \right| = \frac{\gamma + 1}{\gamma + 7/3} \tag{3.81}$$

and is independent of frequency. Here are a few values of Π for various γ:

γ	2	3	4	5	6
Π	0.69	0.75	0.79	0.82	0.84.

This result, as well as all of the preceding discussion, holds for a uniform magnetic field. Any disordering of the magnetic lines of force will, of course, lower the degree of polarization. In the similar case of an optically thick source the degree of polarization is also independent of frequency, but it is smaller than in the optically thin source:

$$\Pi = \left| \frac{\mathcal{E}^{(2)}\kappa^{(1)} - \mathcal{E}^{(1)}\kappa^{(2)}}{\mathcal{E}^{(2)}\kappa^{(1)} + \mathcal{E}^{(1)}\kappa^{(2)}} \right| = \frac{3}{6\gamma + 13}; \tag{3.82}$$

or for

γ	2	3	4	5	6
Π	0.12	0.10	0.08	0.07	0.06.

In general, looking at a homogeneous source of synchrotron radiation with an isotropic power-law distribution of electrons, we will observe the degree of polarization given by equation (3.81) at high frequencies. At lower frequencies polarization will be reduced by Faraday depolarization according to equation (3.77) (see Figure 3.11). Then at still lower frequencies the source will become optically thick and the polarization negligible. However, because of a different frequency dependence of the absorption and Faraday rotation at very low frequencies, where rotation over a mean photon free path becomes small, we will observe an increase of polarization, which will reach the degree given by equation (3.82).

Bibliographical Notes to Chapter 3

3.1-3.4. The classical theory of radiation of an electron gyrating in a uniform magnetic field was given by G. A. Schott.

1. G. A. Schott, "Über die Strahlung von Elektronengruppen," *Ann. Physik,* 4 Folge, **24**, 635–660 (1907).
2. G. A. Schott, *Electromagnetic Radiation*, Cambridge University Press, 1912.

The losses of energy by electrons in accelerators are discussed by J. Schwinger in Reference 10, as well as in the two papers noted here, in the second of which it is pointed out that the maximum of radiation of a gyrating electron will be emitted around ω_C.

3. D. D. Ivanenko and I. Ya. Pomeranchuk "On the Maximal Energy Attainable in a Betatron," *Dokl. Akad. Nauk SSSR* **44**, 315–316 (1944).

4. L. Artsimovich and I. Ya. Pomeranchuk, "The Radiation of Fast Electrons in the Magnetic Field," *J. Phys. USSR* **9**, 267–276 (1945); *Zh. Eksp. Teor. Fiz.* **16**, 379–390 (1946).

Synchrotron radiation was detected indirectly by Blewett.

5. J. P. Blewett, "Radiation Losses in the Induction Electron Accelerator," *Phys. Rev.* **69**, 87–95 (1946).

The radiation was later observed by, among others, the authors of the following articles.

6. F. Elder, A. Gurewitsch, R. V. Langmuir, and H. C. Pollock, "Radiation from Electrons in a Synchrotron," *Phys. Rev.* **71**, 829–830 (1947).
7. F. Elder, R. V. Langmuir, and H. C. Pollock, "Radiation from Electrons Accelerated in a Synchrotron," *Phys. Rev.* **74**, 52–56 (1948).

The theory of synchrotron radiation was developed in three important papers:

8. D. D. Ivanenko and A. A. Sokolov, "On the Theory of the 'Shining' Electron," *Dokl. Akad. Nauk SSSR* **59**, 1551–1554 (1948).
9. V. V. Vladimirsky, "The Influence of Earth's Magnetic Field on Large Auger Showers," *Zh. Eksp. Teor. Fiz.* **18**, 392–401 (1948).
10. J. Schwinger, "On the Classical Radiation of Accelerated Electrons," *Phys. Rev.* **75**, 1912–1925 (1949).

Investigation of the polarization of synchrotron radiation was reported in the first three papers listed below, and experimental confirmation was reported in the last two.

11. A. A. Sokolov and I. M. Ternov, "On Polarization Effects in the Radiation of an Accelerated Electron," *Zh. Eksp. Teor. Fiz.* **31**, 473–478 (1956).
12. J. H. Oort and T. Walraven, "Polarization and Composition of the Crab Nebula," *Bull. Astron. Inst. Netherlands* **12**, 285–308 (1956).
13. K. C. Westfold, "The Polarization of Synchrotron Radiation," *Astrophys. J.* **130**, 241–258 (1959).
14. F. A. Korolev, V. S. Markov, E. M. Akimov, and O. F. Kulikov, "Experimental Investigation of the Angular Distribution and Polarization of the Optical Radiation of Electrons in a Synchrotron," *Dokl. Akad. Nauk SSSR* **110**, 542–544 (1956).
15. P. Joos, "Measurement of the Polarization of Synchrotron Radiation," *Phys. Rev. Letters* **4**, 558–559 (1960).

For an anisotropic distribution of low energy electrons some elliptical polarization of synchrotron radiation may be present. For a discussion of this problem see the following.

16. M. P. C. Legg and K. C. Westfold, "Elliptic Polarization of Synchrotron Radiation," *Proc. Astron. Soc. Australia* **1**, 27–28 (1967); *Astrophys. J.* **154**, 499–514 (1968).

Reviews of the classical theory of synchrotron radiation are given in the first two of the following papers; and of the quantum theory in the next three.

17. V. L. Ginzburg and S. I. Syrovatsky, "Cosmic Magnetobremsstrahlung (Synchrotron Radiation)," *Ann. Rev. Astron. Astrophys.* **3**, 297–350 (1965).
18. A. A. Sokolov, I. M. Ternov, and V. G. Bagrov, "Classical Theory of Synchrotron Radiation," *in* A. A. Sokolov and I. M. Ternov, eds., *Synchrotron Radiation*, Chap. I, Izdatelstvo Nauka, Moscow, 1966.
19. A. A. Sokolov, I. M. Ternov, V. G. Bagrov, and R. A. Rzaev, "Quantum Theory of the Radiation from Relativistic Electrons Moving in a Homogeneous and Uniform Magnetic Field," *in* A. A. Sokolov and I. M. Ternov, eds., *Synchrotron Radiation*, Chap. II, Izdatelstvo Nauka, Moscow, 1966.
20. T. Erber, "High-Energy Electromagnetic Conversion Processes in Intense Magnetic Fields," *Rev. Mod. Phys.* **38**, 626–659 (1966).
21. J. J. Klein, "Motion of Charged Particles in a Uniform Magnetic Field," *Rev. Mod. Phys.* **40**, 523–530 (1968).

It was noted by several people—notably, V. A. Razin, E. G. Mychelkin, G. B. Field, J. D. Scargle, and the authors of the next three papers—that in previous papers on synchrotron radiation the fundamental harmonic of the radiation is taken equal to ω_H, while in the general case of an electron moving at a pitch angle ϑ it should be equal to $\omega_H/\sin^2\vartheta$. For the discussion of the consequences of this error see Refs. 22, 25, and 26.

22. V. L. Ginzburg, V. N. Sazonov, and S. I. Syrovatsky, "On the Magnetobremsstrahlung (Synchrotron Radiation) and its Reabsorption," *Usp. Fiz. Nauk* **94**, 63–90 (1968).
23. R. I. Epstein and P. A. Feldman, "Synchrotron Radiation from Electrons in Helical Orbits," *Astrophys. J.* **150**, L 109–110 (1967).
24. T. Takakura and Y. Uchida, "On the Misunderstanding about the Synchrotron Emissivity for the Cosmic and Planetary Radio Waves," *Astrophys. Letters* **1**, 147–149 (1968).
25. P. A. G. Scheuer, "Synchrotron Radiation Formulae," *Astrophys. J.* **151**, L 139–142 (1968).
26. T. Takakura and Y. Uchida, "Clarification Note on Synchrotron Emissivity," *Astrophys. Letters* **2**, 87 (1968).

Synchrotron absorption was discussed by Wild, Smerd, and Weiss (Ref. 9, Chapter 2), Ginzburg and Syrovatsky (Ref. 17), and Le Roux (Ref. 27). For more astrophysical applications see Refs. 28–31.

27. R. Le Roux, "Etude théorique du rayonnement synchrotron des radio-sources," *Ann. Astrophys.* **24**, 71–85 (1961).
28. P. J. S. Williams, "Absorption in Radio Sources of High Brightness Temperature," *Nature* **200**, 56–57 (1963).
29. V. I. Slish, "Angular Size of Radio Sources," *Nature* **199**, 682 (1963).
30. S. Ya. Braude, "On the Reabsorption of Synchrotron Radiation in Discrete Sources," *Astron. Zh.* **42**, 1150–1153 (1965).
31. V. L. Bratman, "Reabsorption of Synchrotron Radiation," *Zh. Eksp. Teor. Fiz.* **55**, 1415–1422 (1968).

The treatment in Section 3.3 and 3.4 loosely follows Refs. 13 and 17, taking into account, however, the correction discussed in Ref. 22. Fig. 3.2 follows Fig. 2 of Ref. 22.

3.5. The polarization of synchrotron emission is investigated in Refs. 11–13 and 16, and in the following paper.

32. A. A. Korchak and S. I. Syrovatsky, "Polarization of Radiation and the Structure of Magnetic Fields in Cosmic Sources of Synchrotron Radiation, *Astron. Zh.* **38**, 885–897 (1961).

The depolarization by Faraday rotation is discussed in the next three papers.

33. M. H. Cohen, "Radio Astronomy Polarization Measurements," *Proc. IRE* **46**, 172–183 (1958).
34. L. Woltjer, "The Polarization of Radio Sources," *Astrophys. J.* **136**, 1152–1154 (1962).
35. B. J. Burn, "On the Depolarization of Discrete Radio Sources by Faraday Dispersion," *Monthly Notices Roy. Astron. Soc.* **133**, 67–83 (1966).

See also the next six papers (Refs. 39 and 40 are summaries of Ref. 38).

36. D. B. Chang and L. Davis, Jr., "Synchrotron Radiation as the Source of Jupiter's Polarized Decimeter Radiation," *Astrophys. J.* **136**, 567–581 (1962).
37. K. S. Thorne, "The Theory of Synchrotron Radiation from Stars with Dipole Magnetic Fields," *Astrophys. J. Supplement* **8**, 1–29 (1963).
38. A. A. Korchak, "Synchrotron Radiation of Charged Particles in a Dipole Magnetic Field. I," *Astron. Zh.* **40**, 994–1006 (1963).
39. A. A. Korchak, "On the Possibility of Detection and Investigation of Radiation Belts at Large Distances by Radioastronomical Methods," *Dokl. Akad. Nauk SSSR* **150**, 499–502 (1963).
40. A. A. Korchak, "On the Polarization of Synchrotron Radiation in a Dipole Magnetic Field," *Geomag. Aeron.* **3**, 394–396 (1962).

41. N. R. Ortwein, D. B. Chang, and L. Davis, Jr., "Synchrotron Radiation from a Dipole Field," *Astrophys. J. Supplement* **12**, 323–389 (1966).

The problem of transfer of radiation with polarized absorption was considered in the next paper.

42. W. Unno, "Line Formation of a Normal Zeeman Triplet," *Publ. Astron. Soc. Japan* **8**, 108–125 (1956).

The transfer of synchrotron radiation in the general case of arbitrary optical thickness was investigated independently in Ref. 25 and, with the Faraday rotation effect present, in the following:

43. A. G. Pacholczyk and T. L. Swihart, "Polarization of Radio Sources. I. Homogeneous Source of Arbitrary Optical Thickness," *Astrophys. J.* **150**, 647–650 (1967).

The text of Section 3.5 closely follows Ref. 43. Figs. 3.12 and 3.13 are taken from Ref. 43.

4

Synchrotron Radiation in a Plasma

4.1 Synchrotron Emission in an Isotropic Rarefied Plasma

If a plasma medium is isotropic,

$$\frac{\omega_G}{\omega} \ll 1 \tag{4.1}$$

and sufficiently rarefied,

$$1 - n \ll 1, \tag{4.2}$$

the plasma refractive index can be written as

$$n^2 \simeq 1 - \frac{\omega_0^{\,2}}{\omega^2} \tag{4.3}$$

(cf. Section 2.3). Synchrotron radiation in such a plasma can be described by using the formulae of the preceding chapter. In these formulae, however, the limiting angle around the instantaneous electron velocity, within which a significant radiation is emitted by the electron, is equal to $\sqrt{(1/\gamma^2 + \omega_0^{\,2}/\omega^2)}$ rather than $1/\gamma$, its value in vacuum. This is because the radiation in a medium can be described by replacing the velocity of radiation c in the formulae valid in vacuum with the phase velocity c/n in the medium. Substituting $\sqrt{(1/\gamma^2 + \omega_0^{\,2}/\omega^2)}$ for $1/\gamma$ in equations (3.38) and (3.28) wherever its presence derives from the limiting angle, we have the following expression for $p_\nu = p_\nu^{(1)} + p_\nu^{(2)}$ for synchrotron radiation in a plasma:

$$\hat{p}_\nu = \frac{\sqrt{3}\, e^3}{mc^2} H \sin\vartheta \left(1 + \frac{\omega_0^2}{\omega^2}\gamma^2\right)^{-1/2} F(\hat{x}), \tag{4.4}$$

where

$$\hat{x} = \frac{\nu}{\hat{\nu}_C} = \frac{\omega}{\hat{\omega}_C} \tag{4.5}$$

and

$$\hat{\nu}_C = \nu_C \left(1 + \frac{\omega_0^2}{\omega^2}\gamma^2\right)^{-3/2} \tag{4.6}$$

with ν_C given by equation (3.28). With

$$f = \left(1 + \frac{\omega_0^2}{\omega^2}\gamma^2\right)^{-1/2} = \left[1 + \left(\frac{\zeta}{x}\right)^2\right]^{-1/2}, \tag{4.7}$$

where

$$\zeta = \frac{\gamma\omega_0}{\omega_C} = \frac{\gamma\nu_0}{\nu_C}, \tag{4.8}$$

the above equations can be written in the form

$$\hat{p}_\nu = \frac{\sqrt{3}\, e^3}{mc^2} H \sin\vartheta\, fF\left(\frac{x}{f^3}\right) = \frac{\sqrt{3}\, e^3}{mc^2} H \sin\vartheta\, \hat{F}(x, \zeta), \tag{4.9}$$

where

$$\hat{F}(x, \zeta) = fF\left(\frac{x}{f^3}\right),$$

since

$$\hat{\nu}_C = \nu_C f^3.$$

The function $\hat{F}(x, \zeta)$ is represented in Figure 4.1. For $\zeta \to 0$, $\hat{F} \to F$.

From the form of equation (4.4) as well as from Figure 4.1 we see that an appreciable influence of the medium on synchrotron emission takes place when $(\zeta/x)^2$ is of the order of unity or larger, i.e., when

$$\frac{\nu_0^2}{\nu^2}\gamma^2 = \frac{2\nu_0^2\nu_C}{3\nu^2\nu_G \sin\vartheta} \cong \frac{2\nu_0^2}{3\nu\nu_G \sin\vartheta} \gtrsim 1,$$

or, for frequencies of the order of ν_S or lower,

$$\nu \lesssim \nu_S = \frac{2\nu_0^2}{3\nu_G \sin\vartheta} \cong 20\,\frac{N_e}{H}. \tag{4.10}$$

For frequencies lower than ν_S the intensity of synchrotron radiation is lower than in the absence of plasma.

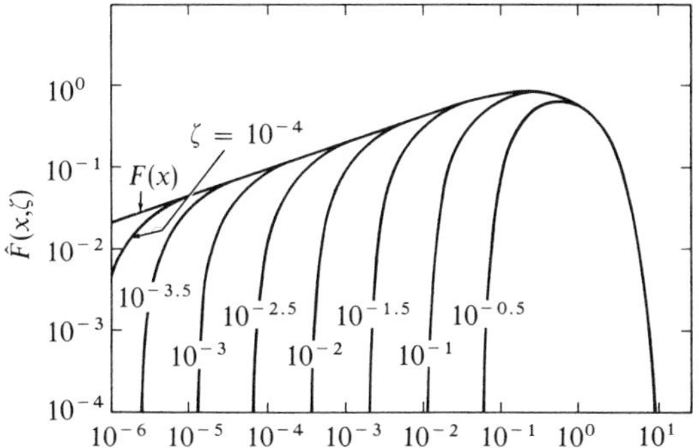

Fig. 4.1 The function $\hat{F}(x, \zeta)$ characterizing the spectral distribution of the power emitted by a single electron in a plasma plotted against $x = \nu/\nu_0$ for different values of the parameter $\zeta = \gamma\nu_0/\nu_C$.

The emission coefficient of synchrotron radiation in plasma is, under the same assumptions as equation (3.37),

$$\hat{\mathcal{E}}_\nu = \frac{1}{4\pi}\int_0^\infty N(E)\,\hat{p}_\nu\,dE = c_3\,H\,\sin\vartheta\int_0^\infty N(E)\,fF\left(\frac{x}{f^3}\right)dE$$

$$= c_3\,H\,\sin\vartheta\int_0^\infty N(E)\,\hat{F}(x,\zeta)\,dE. \tag{4.11}$$

For monoenergetic electrons, $N = N_0\,\delta(E - E_0)$, (4.12)

$$\hat{\mathcal{E}}_\nu = c_3\,H\,\sin\vartheta\,N_0\,\hat{F}(x,\zeta_0)$$

where ζ_0 is the value of ζ corresponding to $E = E_0$. For a power-law distribution of electrons, $N = N_0\,E^{-\gamma}$,

$$\hat{\mathcal{E}}_\nu = \frac{\sqrt{3}}{6}\,e^2\,mc\left(\frac{3\nu_G\sin\vartheta}{2mc^2}\right)^\gamma \nu_0^{-\gamma+1}\,N_0\,P(\alpha,\gamma), \tag{4.13}$$

where

$$P(\alpha,\gamma) = \alpha^{(\gamma-1)/2}\int_0^\infty fF\left(\frac{x}{f^3}\right)x^{(\gamma-3)/2}\,dx,$$

$$f = \left(1 + \frac{\alpha}{x}\right)^{-1/2},$$

$$\alpha = \frac{\nu_S}{\nu} = \frac{2}{3}\,\frac{\nu_0^2}{\nu\nu_G\sin\vartheta}.$$

The function $P(\alpha, \gamma)$ is shown in Figure 4.2. The influence of a plasma on synchrotron radiation is seen to be important for α close to or larger than unity, this condition being equivalent to equation (4.10). From Figure 4.2 one can see that the plasma affects the emission at lower fre-

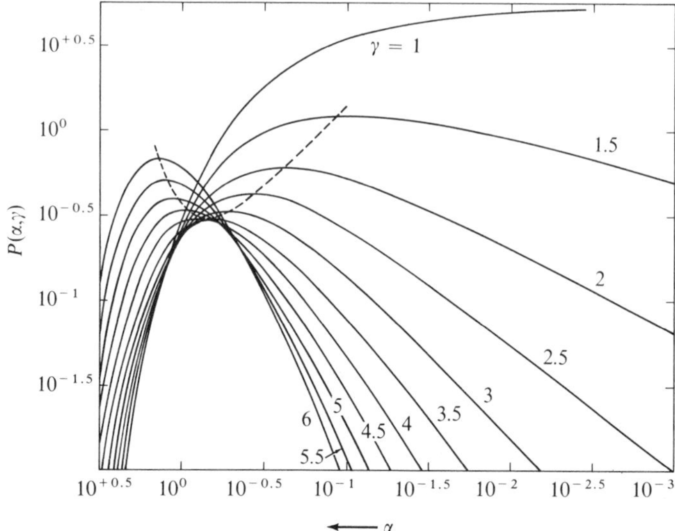

Fig. 4.2 The function $P(\alpha, \gamma)$ representing the optically thin synchrotron spectrum of a power-law distribution of electrons in a plasma plotted versus the parameter $\alpha = \nu_S/\nu$ for different values of the distribution index γ.

quencies, causing the spectral distribution of emission to curve down at lower frequencies and to achieve a maximum at $\alpha \sim 1$. The position of the maximum in the spectral distribution of synchrotron emission is a function of γ, the electron energy distribution index, and the locus of these maxima is represented by a broken curve in Figure 4.2. In summary, a plasma "suppresses" radiation at lower frequencies, contributing to a decrease of the amount of energy emitted.

Let us compute the total power of synchrotron radiation emitted in a plasma by an electron. Integrating equation (4.9) over all frequencies, we obtain

$$\hat{p} = \int_0^\infty \hat{p}_\nu \, d\nu = -\frac{d\hat{E}}{dt} = p\frac{9\sqrt{3}}{8\pi}\int_0^\infty \hat{F}(x, \zeta)\, dx, \qquad (4.14)$$

where p is the total power emitted in vacuum and is given by equation (3.32). The ratio of the total power emitted in a plasma to that emitted in a vacuum, i.e., the value of the integral $(9\sqrt{3})/(8\pi)\int_0^\infty \hat{F}(x, \zeta)\, dx$, is plotted in Figure 4.3 as a function of ζ. We see that the total power of synchrotron radiation emitted in plasma decreases rapidly with increasing ζ.

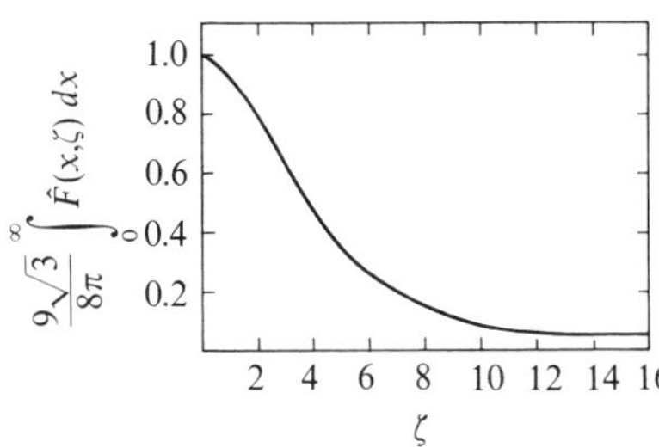

Fig. 4.3 The value of the integral $(9\sqrt{3}/8\pi)\int_0^\infty \hat{F}(x,\zeta)\,dx$ giving the ratio of the total power emitted by an electron in a plasma to the power emitted in vacuum as a function of the parameter $\zeta = \gamma\nu_0/\nu_C$

4.2 The Absorption of Synchrotron Radiation in a Plasma

Under the assumptions of an isotropic and rarefied plasma, specified in the preceding section, the absorption coefficient for the synchrotron radiation can be obtained in a way similar to that described in Chapter 3 and expressed by equation (3.42):

$$\hat{\kappa}_\nu = -\frac{\sqrt{3}\,e^3}{8\pi\nu^2 m} H \sin\vartheta \int_0^\infty E^2 \frac{d}{dE}\left(\frac{N(E)}{E^2}\right) \hat{F}(x,\zeta)\,dE$$

$$= \frac{\sqrt{3}\,ce^2}{4}\frac{\nu_G}{\nu^2}\sin\vartheta \int_0^\infty \frac{N(E)}{E^2}\frac{d}{dE}\,[E^2\,\hat{F}(x,\zeta)]\,dE, \qquad (4.15)$$

after integrating the first expression by parts. For large frequencies, such that $\zeta/x \ll 1$, the expression from equation (4.15) for the absorption coefficient is identical with equation (3.42) in the absence of plasma. In the absence of plasma the absorption coefficient is always positive. In the region of low frequencies, where $\zeta/x \gg 1$, equation (4.15) can be approximated by

$$\hat{\kappa}_\nu = \frac{\sqrt{3}}{4} e^2 mc^3 \frac{\nu_G \sin\vartheta}{\nu_0\,\nu} \int_{E^2 \gg \hat{E}^2}^\infty \frac{N(E)}{E^2} \hat{K}(\hat{x})\,dE, \qquad (4.16)$$

where

$$\hat{K}(\hat{x}) = 2F(\hat{x}) - \hat{x}^2 K_{5/3}(\hat{x}),$$

$$\hat{x} = \frac{x}{f^3} \cong \frac{\zeta^3}{x^2} = \frac{\alpha\zeta}{x},$$

and $\hat{E}$ is the value of energy determined from the condition $\zeta/x = 1$, or, $\hat{E} = (\nu/\nu_0)mc^2$. The function $\hat{K}(\hat{x})$ is represented in Figure 4.4. We can see that in the region from $\hat{x}^*$ to ∞ the function $\hat{K}(\hat{x})$ is negative ($\hat{x}^* \cong 1.35$). The following asymptotic expressions are valid for small

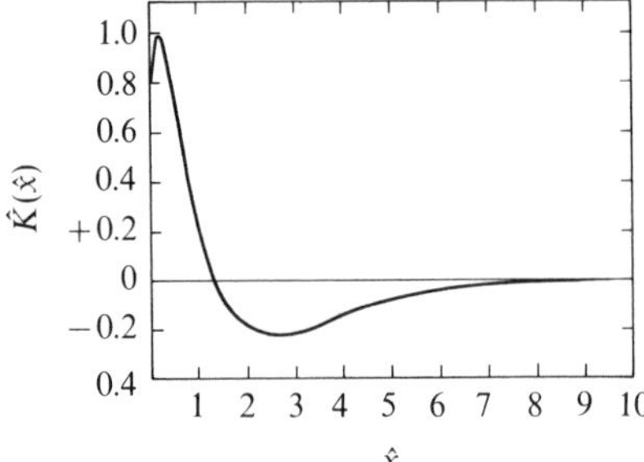

Fig. 4.4 The function $\hat{K}(\hat{x})$.

and large values of the argument, respectively,

$$\hat{K}(\hat{x}) \approx \frac{16\pi}{3\sqrt{3}\,\Gamma(1/3)}\left(\frac{\hat{x}}{2}\right)^{1/3}$$

and

$$\hat{K}(\hat{x}) \approx -\sqrt{\frac{\pi}{2}}\,\hat{x}^{3/2}\,e^{-\hat{x}}.$$

The properties of $\hat{K}(\hat{x})$ indicate that under certain circumstances the absorption coefficient given by equation (4.16) can assume a negative value (cf. Figure 4.4). Consequently, if the distribution of electrons is such that the main contribution to the absorption coefficient is made by electrons with energies E corresponding to

$$\hat{x} \approx \frac{2}{3}\frac{\nu_0^3}{\nu_G \sin\vartheta\,\nu^2}\gamma > \hat{x}^* \cong 1.35,$$

that is,

$$E > mc^2\,\frac{2\nu_G \sin\vartheta\,\nu^2}{\nu_0^3}, \tag{4.17}$$

then the total absorption coefficient [equation (4.15)] will be negative.

Let us examine the frequency dependence of the absorption coefficient in the case of a *monoenergetic electron distribution*, $N(E) = N_0\delta(E-E_0)$. At high frequencies, $E_0^2 \ll \hat{E}^2 = (\nu^2/\nu_0^2)(mc^2)^2$, the influence of the plasma is negligible, and the absorption coefficient has the form given by equation (3.44). At low frequencies, $E_0^2 \gg \hat{E}^2 = (\nu^2/\nu_0^2)(mc^2)^2$, the absorption coefficient [see equation (4.16)] has the form

$$\hat{\kappa}_\nu = \frac{\sqrt{3}}{4}\,e^2\,mc^3\,\frac{\nu_G \sin\vartheta}{\nu\,\nu_0}\,E_0^{-2}\,N_0\,\hat{K}(\hat{x}_0) \propto \sqrt{\hat{x}_0}\hat{K}(\hat{x}_0) \tag{4.18}$$

where $\hat{x}_0 = \hat{x}(E_0)$. The function $\sqrt{\hat{x}}\,\hat{K}(\hat{x})$ plotted against $\hat{x}^{-1/2} \propto \nu$ in Figure 4.5 illustrates the frequency dependence of the absorption coeffi-

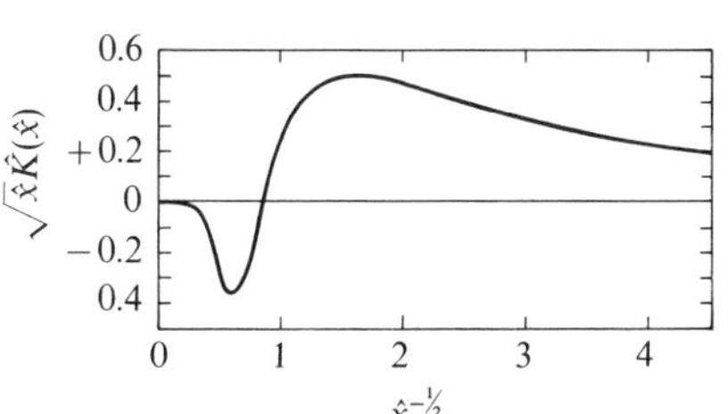

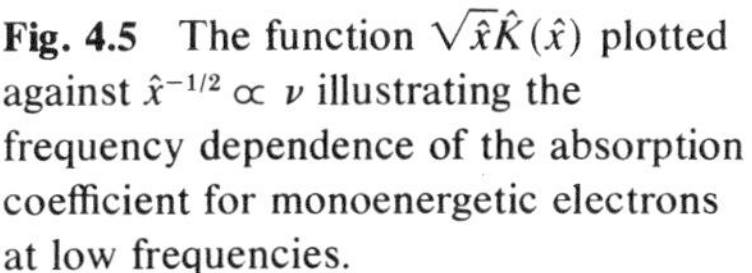

Fig. 4.5 The function $\sqrt{\hat{x}}\hat{K}(\hat{x})$ plotted against $\hat{x}^{-1/2} \propto \nu$ illustrating the frequency dependence of the absorption coefficient for monoenergetic electrons at low frequencies.

cient at low frequencies. If the frequency corresponding to $\hat{x} = \hat{x}^* = 1.35$ is comparable to or larger than the frequency corresponding to the condition $\zeta/x = 1$, that is, if

$$\frac{\nu_0}{2\nu_G \sin\vartheta} \gtrsim \frac{E_0}{mc^2},$$

then the absorption coefficient is negative in the entire frequency region in which the plasma effect is significant, that is, for $\nu^2 \ll \nu_0 E_0/mc^2$; however, for $\nu_0/(2\nu_G \sin\vartheta) \gg E/mc^2$ the absolute value of the coefficient is very small. If

$$\frac{\nu_0}{2\nu_G \sin\vartheta} \ll \frac{E_0}{mc^2},$$

there is a region of frequencies in which the absolute value of the negative absorption coefficient reaches its maximum at

$$\nu_{\max}{}^2 \simeq 0.24 \frac{\nu_0{}^3}{\nu_G \sin\vartheta} \frac{E_0}{mc^2} \tag{4.19}$$

(corresponding to $\hat{x}_{\max} \simeq 2.8$). The region of appreciable absolute value of the negative absorption coefficient is relatively narrow; it is of the order of $\pm 0.3\nu_{\max}$ (cf. Figures 4.4 and 4.5).

Bibliographical Notes to Chapter 4

4.1. The theory of synchrotron radiation in plasma was given by Eidman in two papers; the second paper is a brief correction of some points in the first one.

1. V. Ya. Eidman, "The Radiation from an Electron Moving in a Magnetoactive Plasma," *Zh. Eksp. Teor. Fiz.* **34**, 131–138 (1958).
2. V. Ya. Eidman, "Correction to the Paper on Radiation of an Electron in Magnetoactive Plasma," *Zh. Eksp. Teor. Fiz.* **36**, 1335–1336 (1959).

For further development of the theory of synchrotron radiation and of its applications to astrophysics, see the following papers.

3. V. A. Razin, "On the Theory of Radio Spectra of Discrete Sources at Frequencies Below 30 Mc," *Izvestiya Vys. Ucheb. Zaved. Radiofiz.* **3**, 584–594 (1960).
4. V. A. Razin, "On the Spectrum of Cosmic Non-thermal Radiation," *Izvestiya Vys. Ucheb. Zaved. Radiofiz.* **3**, 921–936 (1960).
5. V. Ya. Eidman, "Radiation of Plasma Waves by a Charge Moving in a Magnetoactive Plasma," *Zh Eksp. Teor. Fiz.* **41**, 1971–1977 (1961).
6. V. V. Zheleznyakov and V. Yu. Trakhtengerts, "Influence of the Medium on Generation of Type IV Solar Radio Emission," *Astron. Zh.* **42**, 1005–1010 (1965).
7. S. A. Kaplan and V. Yu. Trakhtengerts, "On the Theory of Synchrotron Radiation in Magnetoactive Plasma," *Izvestiya Vys. Ucheb. Zaved. Radiofiz.* **10**, 14–18 (1967).

Fig. 4.3 follows Fig. 1 of Ref. 6.

4.2. In the following paper, Twiss stated that the absorption coefficient of synchrotron radiation can become negative.

8. R. Q. Twiss, "Radiation Transfer and the Possibility of Negative Absorption in Radio Astronomy," *Australian J. Phys.* **11**, 564–579 (1958).

Twiss' statement, although correct, was shown by Wild, Smerd and Weiss (Ref. 9 of Chapter 2) to be based on erroneous reasoning. The same authors proved that negative absorption of synchrotron radiation in vacuum is not possible. In a plasma, however, if the refractive index differs from unity, negative absorption of synchrotron radiation is possible. This was shown independently by both Zheleznyakov and McCray. See also the paper by Kaplan.

9. V. V. Zheleznyakov, "Negative Reabsorption of Synchrotron Radiation," *Zh. Eksp. Teor. Fiz.* **51**, 381–386 (1967). (Paper submitted for publication February 26, 1966.)
10. R. McCray, "Possibility of Maser Action in Cosmic Radio Sources," *Science* **154**, 1320–1323 (1966). (Paper submitted for publication October 10, 1966.)
11. S. A. Kaplan, "On the Theory of Coherent Synchrotron Radiation of Cosmic Sources," *Astrofiz.* **2**, 409–418 (1966).

For applications to radio radiation from astronomical sources, see

12. V. V. Zheleznyakov, "On the Coherent Synchrotron Mechanism of Radio Emission from Certain Extraterrestrial Sources," *Astron. Zh.* **44**, 42–54 (1967).

The presentation in Section 4.2 follows that in Ref. 9. Figs. 4.4 and 4.5 are taken from Ref. 9.

5

Redistribution of Energy in the Spectrum by Electron Scattering

5.1 Introduction

In a compact and bright source of synchrotron radiation the collisions of fast electrons with radio photons may lead, under certain conditions, to a redistribution of the radiation spectrum. As a result of these collisions the radio photons will acquire some energy, and the electrons in turn will lose an equivalent amount of energy. The frequency of a photon after its collision with an electron will be greater than its initial frequency by a factor of the order of γ^2, where γ is the electron energy in units of mc^2. This process, called inverse Compton scattering, can be a substantial drain of energy from the relativistic electrons and an important source of high energy photons.

We will examine first the scattering of photons off electrons in the electron rest frame, i.e., the classical Compton scattering. Since, however, we are interested in the results expressed in the reference frame in which electrons have relativistic energies ("cosmic" or "laboratory" frame), we will transform the Compton scattering formulae into the laboratory frame. The scattering process considered in the laboratory frame is referred to as inverse Compton scattering because the energy is transferred from electrons to photons, while in the electron rest system (classical Compton case) the energy transfer takes place in the opposite direction.

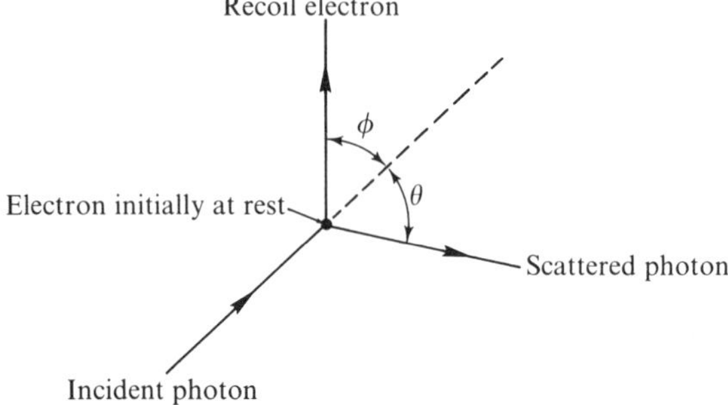

Fig. 5.1 The geometry of Compton scattering in the electron rest system. All three trajectories are coplanar in order to conserve momentum.

5.2 Compton Scattering in the Electron Rest Frame

The geometry of the scattering process is rather simple in the electron rest frame; it is represented in Figure 5.1. Conservation of momentum requires the trajectories of incident and scattered photons and that of the recoil electron to be coplanar. Since all the quantities in this section refer to the rest frame, we will omit the superscript R. Given the initial values of energy and momentum: E_i, W_i, P_i, and scattering angle θ (or γ_i, ϵ_i, Y_i, and θ), we will find the values of energy and momentum after scattering: E_f, W_f, P_f, and ϕ (or γ_f, ϵ_f, Y_f, and ϕ). To do it we need four equations: the two equations of conservation of momentum (since it is a plane problem), equations (5.1) and (5.2); the equation of conservation of energy, equation (5.3); and the relativistic relation between the energy and momentum of a particle (the electron) applied here to final values of the electron energy and momentum, equation (5.4). In these equations $P_i = 0$ by definition of the reference system, and hence $E_i = mc^2$. The equations are

$$W_i = W_f \cos\theta + P_f c \cos\phi, \quad (\parallel \text{ to initial photon trajectory}) \tag{5.1'}$$

$$O = W_f \sin\theta - P_f c \sin\phi, \quad (\perp \text{ to initial photon trajectory}) \tag{5.2'}$$

$$W_i + mc^2 = W_f + E_f, \tag{5.3'}$$

$$E_f^2 - P_f^2 c^2 = m^2 c^4. \tag{5.4'}$$

In dimensionless notation, which we will use from now on, $Y_i = 0$, $\gamma_i = 1$, and

$$\epsilon_i = \epsilon_f \cos\theta + Y_f \cos\phi, \tag{5.1}$$

$$O = \epsilon_f \sin\theta - Y_f \sin\phi, \tag{5.2}$$

$$\epsilon_i + 1 = \epsilon_f + \gamma_f, \tag{5.3}$$

$$\gamma_f^2 = 1 + Y_f^2. \tag{5.4}$$

The solutions for final values are (where $\lambda = \cos\theta$)†:

$$\epsilon_f = \frac{\epsilon_i}{1 + \epsilon_i(1-\lambda)}, \tag{5.7}$$

$$\gamma_f = 1 + \frac{\epsilon_i^2(1-\lambda)}{1 + \epsilon_i(1-\lambda)}, \tag{5.8}$$

$$Y_f = \frac{\epsilon_i}{1 + \epsilon_i(1-\lambda)} \sqrt{\epsilon_i(\epsilon_i + 2)(1-\lambda)^2 + 2(1-\lambda)}, \tag{5.9}$$

$$\cos\phi = (1 + \epsilon_i)\sqrt{\frac{1-\lambda}{2 + \epsilon_i(\epsilon_i + 2)(1-\lambda)}}. \tag{5.10}$$

It follows from equation (5.7) that for low-energy photons ($\epsilon_i \ll 1$) there is no change of frequency in scattering ($\epsilon_f \approx \epsilon_i$). For high-energy photons the change of frequency increases with the scattering angle θ. When the photons are extremely energetic ($\epsilon_i \gg 1$) we can distinguish two ranges of the scattering angle: the region of small angles θ [$\epsilon_i(1-\lambda) \ll 1$], in which there is no change of frequency after scattering ($\epsilon_f \approx \epsilon_i$); and the region of large angles θ [$\epsilon_i(1-\lambda) \gg 1$] increasing with ϵ_i, in which the scattered frequency is always of the order of $mc^2/h = \nu_C$ (Compton frequency) no matter what the initial frequency is [$\epsilon_f = (1-\lambda)^{-1} \approx 1$]. Equation (5.7) can be written in terms of the wavelength Λ of the photons:

$$\Lambda_f - \Lambda_i = \Lambda_C(1-\lambda), \tag{5.11}$$

where $\Lambda_C = (c/\nu_C) = (h/mc)$ is called the Compton wavelength and is equal to 0.02426 Å. This equation shows that the change of wavelength of a photon in Compton scattering is independent of the initial wavelength and depends solely upon the scattering angle θ. It follows from equation (5.8) that the final recoil electron energy γ_f ranges from one to its maximum value $(\gamma_f)_{\max} = 1 + (2\epsilon_i^2)/(1 + 2\epsilon_i)$ for $\theta = \pi$ (backward scattering). For low-energy photons $(\gamma_f)_{\max} \approx 1$, and for extremely energetic photons $(\gamma_f)_{\max} \approx \epsilon_i$.

† The reader may rearrange equations (5.1) and (5.2) and then square and add, thus eliminating ϕ from the result, which we will call equation (5.5). The quantity γ_f can be eliminated between equations (5.3) and (5.4), giving the result we will call equation (5.6). The energy ϵ_f [equation (5.7)] is found by eliminating Y_f^2 between equations (5.5) and (5.6). The quantity γ_f [equation (5.8)] is obtained by inserting ϵ_f into equation (5.3), and Y_f [equation (5.9)] is obtained by inserting this result into equation (5.4). Substituting Y_f and ϵ_f in equation (5.1) will lead to equation (5.10) for $\cos\phi$.

5.3 Compton Scattering Cross Section

The differential scattering cross section $(d\Sigma/d\Omega_f)\ d\Omega_f$ is defined by means of the following relation:

$$dNh\nu_i = \frac{d\Sigma}{d\Omega_f} d\Omega_f \cdot I_{\nu i}\, dt\, d\nu_i\, d\Omega_i, \tag{5.12}$$

where $dN\,h\nu_i$ is the energy subtracted from the incident beam (and dN is the number of scatterings) during the time interval dt, within the frequency interval $d\nu_i$, and within the element of solid angle $d\Omega_i$ around the direction of the incident beam of intensity $I_{\nu i}$. The final values of energy $(h\nu_f)$ do not enter the definition of $(d\Sigma)/(d\Omega_f)$ since this definition is independent of the scattering mechanism. The differential scattering cross section is given for Compton scattering by the Klein-Nishina formula, which is derived on the basis of quantum mechanical considerations:

$$\frac{d\Sigma}{d\Omega_f} = \frac{3}{32\pi} \sigma_T \frac{\epsilon_f^2}{\epsilon_i^2} \left(\frac{\epsilon_i}{\epsilon_f} + \frac{\epsilon_f}{\epsilon_i} - 2 + 4 \cos^2 \psi \right), \tag{5.13}$$

where $\sigma_T = 8\pi/3\ (e^2/mc^2)^2 = 6.65 \times 10^{-25}$ cm^2 is the Thomson cross section and ψ is the angle between the directions of polarization of the initial and scattered photons. By the use of equation (5.7) this differential cross section can be represented as a function of the energy ϵ_i of the incident photon, the scattering angle θ, and the polarization angle ψ:

$$\frac{d\Sigma}{d\Omega_f} = \frac{3}{32\pi} \sigma_T \frac{1}{[1 + \epsilon_i(1 - \lambda)]^2} \left[\frac{\epsilon_i^2 (1 - \lambda)^2}{1 + \epsilon_i(1 - \lambda)} + 4 \cos^2 \psi \right]. \tag{5.14}$$

For nonrelativistic electrons $(\epsilon_i \ll 1)$ we have the formula for classical Thomson scattering,

$$\frac{d\Sigma}{d\Omega_f} = \frac{3}{8\pi} \sigma_T \cos^2 \psi. \tag{5.15}$$

We can describe the polarization of the scattered photon as a superposition of two linearly polarized components, $\perp$ and $\|$, perpendicular to the direction of polarization of the incident photon, and coplanar with it; or alternately by $(\perp)$ and $(\|)$, its components perpendicular and parallel to the scattering plane. The cross sections $(d\Sigma/d\Omega_f)_\perp$ and $(d\Sigma/d\Omega_f)_\|$ are given by the expressions in equation (5.14), in which $\cos \psi$ is replaced by 0 and $\sqrt{(1 - \sin^2 \theta \cos^2 \delta_i)}$, respectively. The angle between the plane of polarization of the incident photon and the scattering plane is δ_i. For $(d\Sigma/d\Omega_f)_{(\perp)}$ and $(d\Sigma/d\Omega_f)_{(\|)}$ the function $\cos \psi$ is replaced by $\sin \delta_i$ and $\cos \delta_i \sin \theta$, respectively (cf. Figure 5.2). For low-

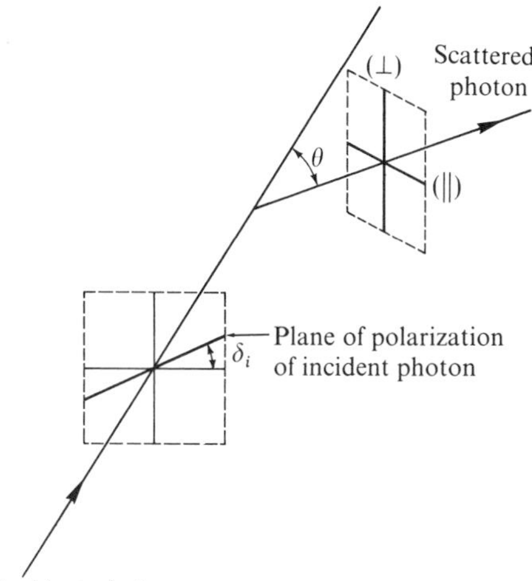

Fig. 5.2 Describing the polarization of a Compton scattered photon.

energy photons ($\epsilon_i \ll 1$, $\epsilon_i \approx \epsilon_f$) equation (5.14) yields the classical Thomson scattering formulae:

$$\left(\frac{d\Sigma}{d\Omega_f}\right)_\perp = 0, \quad \left(\frac{d\Sigma}{d\Omega_f}\right)_{\|} = \frac{3}{8\pi}\sigma_T(1 - \sin^2\theta\cos^2\delta_i), \tag{5.16}$$

which indicate that, if the incident photon is completely polarized, then the scattered photon is also completely polarized. The same result, equation (5.16), is obtained for extremely energetic photons ($\epsilon_i \gg 1$) in the region of small scattering angles, $\epsilon_i(1-\lambda) \ll 1$. In the region of large scattering angles, $\epsilon_i(1-\lambda) \gg 1$, the scattered radiation is unpolarized regardless of the polarization state of the incident radiation:

$$\left(\frac{d\Sigma}{d\Omega_f}\right)_\perp = \left(\frac{d\Sigma}{d\Omega_f}\right)_{\|} = \frac{3}{32\pi}\sigma_T\frac{1}{\epsilon_i(1-\lambda)}. \tag{5.17}$$

When the incident radiation is unpolarized, the total differential cross section can be obtained by adding the cross sections for the two polarizations and by averaging this total over the angle δ_i. The result is a function of ϵ_i and λ only:

$$\frac{d\Sigma}{d\Omega_f} = \frac{3}{16\pi}\sigma_T\frac{1}{[1+\epsilon_i(1-\lambda)]^2}\left[\frac{\epsilon_i^2(1-\lambda)^2}{1+\epsilon_i(1-\lambda)} + 1 + \lambda^2\right], \tag{5.18}$$

which for low-energy photons ($\epsilon_i \ll 1$) yields the formula for classical Thomson scattering,

$$\frac{d\Sigma}{d\Omega_f} = \frac{3}{16\pi}\sigma_T(1+\lambda^2). \tag{5.19}$$

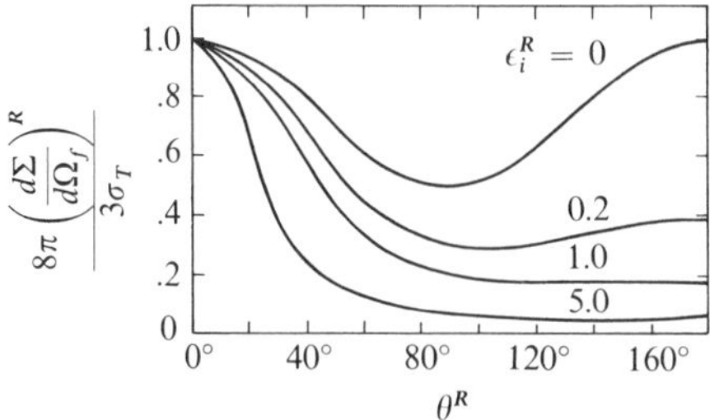

Fig. 5.3 The differential cross section for Compton scattering as a function of the scattering angle θ^R.

The dependence of $(d\Sigma/d\Omega_f)$ on θ is illustrated in Figure 5.3 for a few values of ϵ_i. We see that forward scattering becomes more important as the photon energy increases. The total cross section Σ for Compton scattering can be derived by integrating the differential scattering cross section of equation (5.18) over $d\Omega_f$. The result is

$$\Sigma = \frac{3}{4}\sigma_T\left\{\frac{1+\epsilon_i}{\epsilon_i^3}\left[\frac{2\epsilon_i(1+\epsilon_i)}{1+2\epsilon_i} - \ln(1+2\epsilon_i)\right] + \frac{1}{2\epsilon_i}\ln(1+2\epsilon_i) - \frac{1+3\epsilon_i}{(1+2\epsilon_i)^2}\right\}. \tag{5.20}$$

This expression can be approximated by

$$\Sigma = \sigma_T\left(1 - 2\epsilon_i + \frac{26}{5}\epsilon_i^2 + \cdots\right), \tag{5.21}$$

and by

$$\Sigma = \frac{3}{8}\sigma_T\frac{1}{\epsilon_i}\left(\ln 2\epsilon_i + \frac{1}{2}\right) \tag{5.22}$$

for low- and high-photon energies, respectively. The expression for the total cross section Σ for Compton scattering is illustrated in Figure 5.4 as a function of the initial photon energy ϵ_i. When the initial photon energy increases, the number of scattered photons decreases.

5.4 Electron Scattering in the Laboratory Frame

The Compton scattering described in previous sections is referred to as "inverse Compton scattering" when viewed in the reference frame in which the electron has a relativistic velocity $\beta \approx 1$, $\gamma \gg 1$ ("laboratory frame"). To obtain the formalism of inverse Compton scattering (or "electron scattering," as some authors call it), one has to transform the preceding formulae from the electron rest frame (R-frame) into the laboratory frame (L-frame).

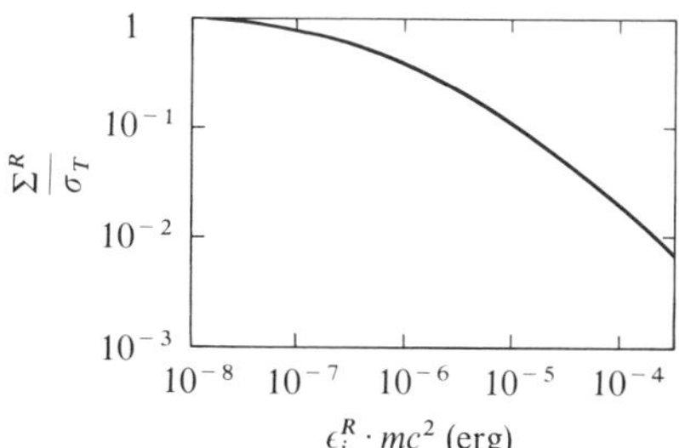

Fig. 5.4 The total cross section for Compton scattering as a function of the initial photon energy ϵ_i^R.

In this section we will make use of the Lorentz transformations of several quantities. A time interval dt transforms according to the relation

$$dt^{\mathrm{R}} = \gamma^{-1}\, dt^{\mathrm{L}}, \tag{5.23}$$

while the transformation of frequency (or energy $h\nu$) is given by

$$\nu^{\mathrm{R}} = \nu^{\mathrm{L}}\, \gamma(1 - \beta\mu^{\mathrm{L}}) \tag{5.24}$$

where μ is the cosine of the angle between the direction of motion and the direction to the observer. If μ is the cosine of the angle between a given direction and the direction of motion, then we have for the transformation of an angle

$$\mu^{\mathrm{R}} = \frac{\mu^{\mathrm{L}} - \beta}{1 - \beta\mu^{\mathrm{L}}}, \tag{5.25}$$

while $d\Omega$, the solid angle subtended around the direction making an angle $\cos^{-1}\mu$ with the direction of motion, transforms according to

$$d\Omega^{\mathrm{R}} = d\Omega^{\mathrm{L}}\, \frac{1}{\gamma^2(1 - \beta\mu^{\mathrm{L}})^2}. \tag{5.26}$$

The transformation given by equation (5.25) does not hold for an angle α between two arbitrary directions when neither of them coincides with the direction or motion. Let these two directions have direction cosines $(\mu, \sqrt{(1-\mu^2)}, 0)$ and $(\tilde{\mu}, m, n)$. Using notation evident from Figure 5.5, we have $\cos\alpha = \mu\tilde{\mu} + m\sqrt{(1-\mu^2)}$ and $n = m \tan\chi$. Since $1 = \tilde{\mu}^2 + m^2 + n^2 = \tilde{\mu}^2 + m^2(1 + \tan^2\chi)$, we have

$$m = \sqrt{\frac{1 - \tilde{\mu}^2}{1 + \tan^2\chi}} = \cos\chi\sqrt{1 - \tilde{\mu}^2}$$

and

$$\cos\alpha = \mu\tilde{\mu} + \cos\chi\sqrt{(1-\mu^2)(1-\tilde{\mu}^2)}, \tag{5.27}$$

where χ is in the plane perpendicular to $\boldsymbol{\beta}$, i.e., to the direction of motion,

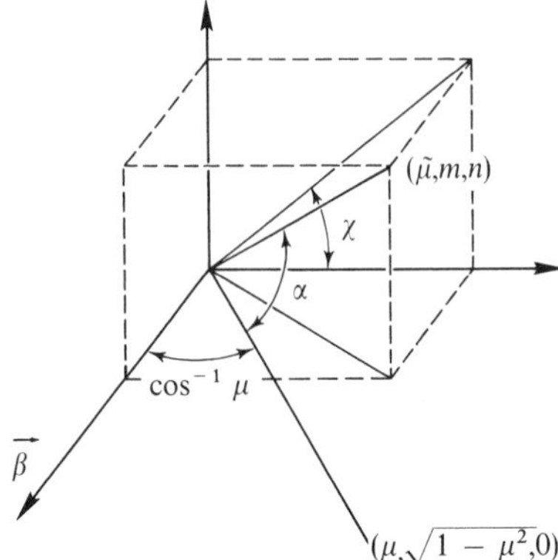

Fig. 5.5 Deriving the formula (5.27).

and is therefore Lorentz invariant. Writing equation (5.27) in the R-frame and in the L-frame and equating $\cos\chi$ between the two formulae, we obtain

$$\cos\alpha^{\mathrm{R}} = \frac{(1-\beta^2)(\cos\alpha^{\mathrm{L}} - \mu^{\mathrm{L}}\tilde{\mu}^{\mathrm{L}}) + (\mu^{\mathrm{L}} - \beta)(\tilde{\mu}^{\mathrm{L}} - \beta)}{(1-\beta\mu^{\mathrm{L}})(1-\beta\tilde{\mu}^{\mathrm{L}})} \tag{5.28}$$

after μ^{R} and $\tilde{\mu}^{\mathrm{R}}$ have been transformed to the L-frame with the aid of equation (5.25). Equation (5.28) is the Lorentz transformation of an angle α between the two arbitrary directions having direction cosines μ and $\tilde{\mu}$ with the direction of motion. Equation (5.28) reduces to equation (5.25) if one of the directions coincides with the direction of motion. Equation (5.28) can be written in a somewhat simpler form:

$$1 - \cos\alpha^{\mathrm{R}} = \frac{1 - \cos\alpha^{\mathrm{L}}}{\gamma^2(1-\beta\mu^{\mathrm{L}})(1-\beta\tilde{\mu}^{\mathrm{L}})}.$$

Now we will derive the transformation formula for intensity I_ν. The number of photons passing through a surface element $d\Sigma$ in the interval of time dt, having frequency within $d\nu$ around ν, and confined to a solid angle $d\Omega$ around a direction making an angle $\cos^{-1}\mu$ with the direction of motion, is, in the rest frame,

$$\left(\frac{1}{h\nu} I_\nu\, \mu\, d\Sigma\, d\Omega\, d\nu\, dt\right)^{\mathrm{R}}. \tag{5.29}$$

The same number of photons will be counted in the L-frame, and it is equal to

$$\left(\frac{1}{h\nu} I_\nu\, \mu\, d\Sigma\, d\Omega\, d\nu\, dt\right)^{\mathrm{L}} \tag{5.30}$$

if the surface $d\Sigma$ were stationary in the L-system. Since, however, the surface $d\Sigma$ is moving with the electron, the number of photons counted in the L-system will be $(\mu^{\mathrm{L}} - \beta)/\mu^{\mathrm{L}}$ times smaller than given by the expression (5.30) and, of course, equal to expression (5.29). We will then have

$$\frac{\mu^{\mathrm{L}} - \beta}{\mu^{\mathrm{L}}} \frac{I_\nu^{\mathrm{L}}}{h\nu^{\mathrm{L}}} \mu^{\mathrm{L}}\, d\Sigma^{\mathrm{L}}\, d\Omega^{\mathrm{L}}\, d\nu^{\mathrm{L}}\, dt^{\mathrm{L}} = \frac{I_\nu^{\mathrm{R}}}{h\nu^{\mathrm{R}}} \mu^{\mathrm{R}}\, d\Sigma^{\mathrm{R}}\, d\Omega^{\mathrm{R}}\, d\nu^{\mathrm{R}}\, dt^{\mathrm{R}}.$$

Remembering that $d\Sigma$ is perpendicular to $\boldsymbol{\beta}$ and applying the transformation equations (5.23)–(5.26) to the above expression, we obtain the transformation formula for intensity I_ν,

$$I_\nu^{\mathrm{R}} = I_\nu^{\mathrm{L}}\, \gamma^3 (1 - \beta\mu^{\mathrm{L}})^3, \tag{5.31}$$

where μ^{L} is the cosine of the angle between the direction of photons and the direction of motion.

Recalling the definition of the differential scattering cross section, $(d\Sigma/d\Omega_f)\, d\Omega_f$, in terms of the number of scatterings (which is Lorentz invariant), we have

$$\frac{I_{\nu_i}^{\mathrm{L}}}{h\nu_i^{\mathrm{L}}}\, d\nu_i^{\mathrm{L}}\, d\Omega_i^{\mathrm{L}} \left(\frac{d\Sigma}{d\Omega_f}\, d\Omega_f\right)^{\mathrm{L}} dt^{\mathrm{L}} = \frac{I_{\nu_i}^{\mathrm{R}}}{h\nu_i^{\mathrm{R}}}\, d\nu_i^{\mathrm{R}}\, d\Omega_i^{\mathrm{R}} \left(\frac{d\Sigma}{d\Omega_f}\, d\Omega_f\right)^{\mathrm{R}} dt^{\mathrm{R}},$$

from which the following transformation formula for the differential cross section results:

$$\left(\frac{d\Sigma}{d\Omega_f}\, d\Omega_f\right) = \left(\frac{d\Sigma}{d\Omega_f}\, d\Omega_f\right) \frac{1}{1 - \beta\mu_i^{\mathrm{L}}}. \tag{5.32}$$

We see that the cross section transforms like an area times $\mu^{\mathrm{L}}/(\mu^{\mathrm{L}} - \beta)$, since the correction $\mu^{\mathrm{L}}/(\mu^{\mathrm{L}} - \beta)$ is absorbed in the definition of the cross section.

Using equation (5.26) we can write equation (5.32) as

$$\left(\frac{d\Sigma}{d\Omega_f}\right)^{\mathrm{R}} = \left(\frac{d\Sigma}{d\Omega_f}\right)^{\mathrm{L}} \frac{(1 - \beta\mu_f^{\mathrm{L}})^2}{1 - \beta\mu_i^{\mathrm{L}}}\, \gamma^2, \tag{5.33}$$

where μ_i^{L} and μ_f^{L} are the direction cosines of the incident and scattered photons with respect to the direction of motion of the electron in the L-frame.

Let us assume that the electrons are highly relativistic, $\beta \approx 1$ $(\gamma \gg 1)$, and that the initial photons are of low energy, $\epsilon_i^{\mathrm{L}}\gamma \ll 1$. The equation of conservation of energy, equation (5.7), when transformed into the L-system will have the form

$$\epsilon_f^{L} = \epsilon_i^{L} \frac{1 - \beta\mu_i^{L}}{1 - \beta\mu_f^{L}} \cdot \frac{1}{1 + \epsilon_i^{L} \gamma(1 - \beta\mu_i^{L})(1 - \lambda^{L})}. \tag{5.34}$$

It will, however, be more convenient to have the above relation written with the aid of quantities, some of which are expressed in the L-system and some in the R-system. Transforming μ_f^{L} back into the R-system,

$$\frac{1}{1 - \beta\mu_f^{L}} = \gamma^2(1 + \beta\mu_f^{R}), \tag{5.35}$$

and expressing μ_f^{R} in terms of λ^{R}, μ_i^{R} and χ through a formula of the type of equation (5.27), we have

$$\frac{1}{1 - \beta\mu_f^{L}} = \gamma^2\{1 + \beta[\lambda^{R}\mu_i^{R} + \cos\chi\sqrt{[1 - (\lambda^{R})^2][1 - (\mu_i^{R})^2]}]\} \tag{5.36}$$

and, consequently,

$$\epsilon_f^{L} = \epsilon_i^{L}\gamma^2 \frac{(1 - \beta\mu_i^{L})\{1 + \beta[\lambda^{R}\mu_i^{R} + \cos\chi\sqrt{[1 - (\lambda^{R})^2][1 - (\mu_i^{R})^2]}]\}}{1 + \epsilon_i^{L}\gamma(1 - \beta\mu_i^{L})(1 - \lambda^{L})}. \tag{5.37}$$

When the electrons have ultrarelativistic velocities ($\beta \to 1$), the transformation of equation (5.25) yields

$$\mu_i^{R} = \frac{\mu_i^{L} - \beta}{1 - \beta\mu_i^{L}} \quad \to \quad -1; \tag{5.38}$$

in other words, all the collisions of photons with electrons appear to be head-on in the rest system. In this case the term in equation (5.37) containing the square root will vanish. Moreover, if $\epsilon_i^{L}\gamma \ll 1$, this expression will reduce to the form

$$\epsilon_f^{L} = \epsilon_i^{L}\gamma^2[(1 - \beta\mu_i^{L}) + \beta\lambda^{R}(\mu_i^{L} - \beta)]. \tag{5.39}$$

If we do not take into account overtaking and almost overtaking collisions in the laboratory system (there are very few such collisions since they occur within a very small solid angle when $\beta \approx 1$), we have $\beta(\mu_i^{L} - \beta) < 0$. Therefore, for a given value of the initial energy, the final energy increases when the cosine of the scattering angle increases. The minimum and maximum values of the final photon energy are $(\epsilon_f^{L})_{\text{min}} = \epsilon_i^{L}$ (this occurs for $\lambda_{\text{max}}^{R} = +1$, for any μ_i^{L}) and $(\epsilon_f^{L})_{\text{max}} = \epsilon_i^{L}(1 + \beta)^2\gamma^2$ (for $\lambda_{\text{min}}^{R} = -1$ and $\mu_i^{L} = -1$). For $\beta = 1$, $(\epsilon_f^{L})_{\text{max}} = 4\gamma^2\epsilon_i^{L}$ and

$$\epsilon_i^{\mathrm{L}} \leq \epsilon_f^{\mathrm{L}} \leq 4\gamma^2 \epsilon_i^{\mathrm{L}}. \tag{5.40}$$

For a fixed $\epsilon_f^{\mathrm{L}}/(\epsilon_i^{\mathrm{L}}\gamma^2)$ there is a limited range of μ_i^{L} (from -1 to $\mu_i^{\mathrm{L}*}$) for which there exist values of λ^{R} such that the energy equation (5.39) is satisfied. For $\mu_i^{\mathrm{L}} = \mu_i^{\mathrm{L}*}$, $\mu_i^{\mathrm{L}*} < \beta$, the only value of λ^{R} which will yield the desired $\epsilon_f^{\mathrm{L}}/\epsilon_i^{\mathrm{L}}\gamma^2$ is the value $\lambda^{\mathrm{R}} = -1$. Therefore $\mu_i^{\mathrm{L}*}$ can be obtained from equation (5.39) by inserting $\lambda^{\mathrm{R}} = -1$ and solving for μ_i^{L}. The result of such a procedure is

$$\mu_i^{\mathrm{L}*} = \frac{1 + \beta^2 - \dfrac{\epsilon_f^{\mathrm{L}}}{\epsilon_i^{\mathrm{L}}\gamma^2}}{2\beta},$$

and for $\beta = 1$ we have

$$-1 \leq \mu_i^{\mathrm{L}} \leq 1 - \frac{\epsilon_f^{\mathrm{L}}}{2\gamma^2 \epsilon_i^{\mathrm{L}}}. \tag{5.41}$$

We will now derive the expression for the scattering cross section in the laboratory frame. First, we notice that under the assumed approximation of $\epsilon_i^{\mathrm{L}}\gamma \ll 1$, the Klein-Nishina formula reduces to the classical Thomson formula for the cross section. Transforming the energy in the right-hand side of equation (5.18) (we will consider the unpolarized case), we have

$$\left(\frac{d\Sigma}{d\Omega_f}\right)^{\mathrm{R}} = \frac{3}{16\pi}\,\sigma_T \,\frac{1}{[1 + \epsilon_i^{\mathrm{L}}\gamma(1 - \beta\mu_i^{\mathrm{L}})(1 - \lambda^{\mathrm{R}})]} \cdot \left[\frac{(\epsilon_i^{\mathrm{L}})^2\gamma^2(1 - \beta\mu_i^{\mathrm{L}})^2(1 - \lambda^{\mathrm{R}})^2}{1 + \epsilon_i^{\mathrm{L}}\gamma(1 - \beta\mu_i^{\mathrm{L}})(1 - \lambda^{\mathrm{R}})} + 1 + (\lambda^{\mathrm{R}})^2\right], \tag{5.42}$$

which for $\epsilon_i^{\mathrm{L}}\gamma \ll 1$ gives

$$\left(\frac{d\Sigma}{d\Omega_f}\right)^{\mathrm{R}} = \frac{3}{16\pi}\,\sigma_T\,[1 + (\lambda^{\mathrm{R}})^2] \equiv \left(\frac{d\Sigma}{d\Omega_f}\right)^{\mathrm{R}}_{\mathrm{Thomson}} \tag{5.43}$$

It is easy to see that

$$\int_{4\pi}\left(\frac{d\Sigma}{d\Omega_f}\right)^{\mathrm{R}}_{\mathrm{Thomson}} d\Omega_f^{\mathrm{R}} = \sigma_T. \tag{5.44}$$

We will limit our consideration to isotropic distributions of both photons and electrons and we will compute the quantity

$$\sigma(\epsilon_f^{\mathrm{L}}, \epsilon_i^{\mathrm{L}}, \gamma) \equiv \frac{1}{4\pi}\iint \left(\frac{d\Sigma}{d\Omega_f}\right)^{\mathrm{L}} \delta[\epsilon_f^{\mathrm{L}} - \epsilon_f^{\mathrm{L}}(\epsilon_i^{\mathrm{L}}, \gamma, \mu_i^{\mathrm{L}}, \lambda^{\mathrm{R}})]\, d\Omega_i^{\mathrm{L}}\, d\Omega_f^{\mathrm{L}}, \tag{5.45}$$

which states the probability that a photon with the initial energy ϵ_i^{L} will have the final energy ϵ_f^{L} after being scattered off an electron of energy γ. The Dirac δ-function in the above expression for σ indicates that in order to evaluate σ we have to use values of μ_i^{L} and λ^{R} which, for given values of ϵ_f^{L}, ϵ_i^{L} and γ, fulfill the energy conservation condition of equation (5.39). Using equations (5.43), (5.33), and (5.26), and remembering that $d\Omega_i^{\mathrm{L}} = d\mu_i^{\mathrm{L}}\, d\tilde{\omega}_i^{\mathrm{L}}$ and $d\Omega_f^{\mathrm{L}} = d\mu_f^{\mathrm{L}}\, d\tilde{\omega}_f^{\mathrm{L}}$ (where $\tilde{\omega}_i^{\mathrm{L}}$, $\tilde{\omega}_f^{\mathrm{L}}$ are appropriate azimuthal angles and integration over each of them in the isotropic case yields simply 2π), we have from equation (5.45)

$$\sigma(\epsilon_f^{\mathrm{L}}, \epsilon_i^{\mathrm{L}}, \gamma) = \frac{3}{16}\sigma_T \int_{-1}^{+1}\int_{-1}^{\mu_i^{\mathrm{L}*}} (\beta\mu_i^{\mathrm{L}} - 1)[1 + (\lambda^{\mathrm{R}})^2]\, \delta[\epsilon_f^{\mathrm{L}} - \epsilon_f^{\mathrm{L}}(\epsilon_i^{\mathrm{L}}, \gamma, \mu_i^{\mathrm{L}}\lambda^{\mathrm{R}})]\, d\lambda^{\mathrm{R}}\, d\mu_i^{\mathrm{L}}. \tag{5.46}$$

In deriving equation (5.46) from equation (5.45) we expressed μ_f^{L} in terms of λ^{R} and used equation (5.36). This can be done rather simply since for $\beta \to 1$, $\mu_i^{\mathrm{R}} \approx -1$; $\mu_f^{\mathrm{R}} \approx -\lambda^{\mathrm{R}}$ derives from an equation of the type of equation (5.27), so that

$$\mu_f^{\mathrm{L}} \approx \frac{\beta - \lambda^{\mathrm{R}}}{1 - \beta\lambda^{\mathrm{R}}}, \quad d\mu_f^{\mathrm{L}} \approx \frac{-d\lambda^{\mathrm{R}}}{\gamma^2(1 - \beta\lambda^{\mathrm{R}})^2}. \tag{5.47}$$

Using the theorem concerning the two-dimensional Dirac δ-function,

$$\iint f(x, y)\, \delta[w - w(x, y)]\, dx\, dy = \int f[x, y_0(x)] \frac{1}{\left[\dfrac{\partial w(x, y)}{\partial y}\right]_{y=y_0(x)}} dx,$$

where $y_0(x)$ is the value of y fulfilling the condition $w(x, y) = 0$, we can write equation (5.46) in the form

$$\sigma(\epsilon_f^{\mathrm{L}}, \epsilon_i^{\mathrm{L}}, \gamma) = \frac{3}{16}\sigma_T \frac{1}{\epsilon_i^{\mathrm{L}}\gamma^2\beta^3} \int_{-1}^{\mu_i^{\mathrm{L}*}} \left[\beta^2 + \left(\frac{\epsilon_f^{\mathrm{L}}}{\epsilon_i^{\mathrm{L}}\gamma^2}\right)^2 \frac{1}{(\mu_i^{\mathrm{L}} - \beta)^2} + \frac{(1 - \beta\mu_i^{\mathrm{L}})^2}{(\mu_i^{\mathrm{L}} - \beta)^2} - 2\left(\frac{\epsilon_f^{\mathrm{L}}}{\epsilon_i^{\mathrm{L}}\gamma^2}\right) \frac{1 - \beta\mu_i^{\mathrm{L}}}{(\mu_i^{\mathrm{L}} - \beta)^2}\right] \frac{\beta\mu_i^{\mathrm{L}} - 1}{\mu_i^{\mathrm{L}} - \beta}\, d\mu_i^{\mathrm{L}}. \tag{5.48}$$

For $\beta = 1$ we have

$$\sigma(\epsilon_f^{\mathrm{L}}, \epsilon_i^{\mathrm{L}}, \gamma) = \frac{3}{16}\sigma_T \frac{1}{\epsilon_i^{\mathrm{L}}\gamma^2} \int_{-1}^{1-\epsilon_f^{\mathrm{L}}/(2\gamma^2\epsilon_i^{\mathrm{L}})} \left[2 + \left(\frac{\epsilon_f^{\mathrm{L}}}{\epsilon_i^{\mathrm{L}}\gamma^2}\right)\frac{2}{(\mu_i^{\mathrm{L}} - 1)} + \left(\frac{\epsilon_f^{\mathrm{L}}}{\epsilon_i^{\mathrm{L}}\gamma^2}\right)^2 \frac{1}{(\mu_i^{\mathrm{L}} - 1)^2}\right] d\mu_i^{\mathrm{L}}. \tag{5.49}$$

The integration in the above equation is simple and yields

$$\sigma(\epsilon_f^{\mathrm{L}}, \epsilon_i^{\mathrm{L}}, \gamma) = \frac{3}{32}\sigma_T \frac{1}{\epsilon_i^{\mathrm{L}}\gamma^2}$$

$$\left[8 + 2\left(\frac{\epsilon_f^{\mathrm{L}}}{\epsilon_i^{\mathrm{L}}\gamma^2}\right) - \left(\frac{\epsilon_f^{\mathrm{L}}}{\epsilon_i^{\mathrm{L}}\gamma^2}\right)^2 + 4\left(\frac{\epsilon_f^{\mathrm{L}}}{\epsilon_i^{\mathrm{L}}\gamma^2}\right)\ln\frac{1}{4}\left(\frac{\epsilon_f^{\mathrm{L}}}{\epsilon_i^{\mathrm{L}}\gamma^2}\right)\right]. \quad (5.50)$$

We recall that this expression is valid for very relativistic electrons ($\beta \cong 1$), for energies in the range

$$\epsilon_i^{\mathrm{L}} \leq \epsilon_f^{\mathrm{L}} \leq 4\gamma^2\epsilon_i^{\mathrm{L}},$$

for isotropic distributions of the initial photons and electrons, and when the polarization is neglected. Equation (5.50) is represented in Figures 5.6 and 5.7.

Under the assumptions of the preceding paragraph the emission coefficient $\mathcal{E}_\nu^C$ and the absorption coefficient κ_ν^C for inverse Compton scattering are

$$\mathcal{E}_\nu^C = \iint J(\nu_i)\,\sigma\left(\frac{h\nu}{mc^2}, \frac{h\nu_i}{mc^2}, \frac{E}{mc^2}\right) N(E)\,d\nu_i\,dE, \quad (5.51)$$

$$\kappa_\nu^C = \iint \sigma\left(\frac{h\nu_f}{mc^2}, \frac{h\nu}{mc^2}, \frac{E}{mc^2}\right) N(E)\,d\nu_f\,dE, \quad (5.52)$$

where σ is given by equation (5.50), and $N(E)$ is the distribution of electron energies (from now on all quantities will be expressed in the L-system so that we can drop superscripts without risking confusion). $J(\nu)$ is the average intensity of the radiation field. The expression for the absorption coefficient can be very much simplified if one performs the integration over $d\nu_f$. The result of integration is independent of ν_i when the limits of integration are ν_i and $4\gamma^2\nu_i$:

$$\kappa_\nu^C = \sigma_T \int f\left(\frac{E}{mc^2}\right) N(E)\,dE,$$

where

$$f(\gamma) = 1 - \frac{3}{4\gamma^2} - \frac{3}{16\gamma^4}\ln\frac{1}{4\gamma^2} + \frac{1}{32\gamma^6}.$$

The function $f(\gamma)$ is very close to unity for $\gamma \approx 10$ and larger, and therefore for $E/mc^2 \gtrsim 10$ we can write

$$\kappa_\nu^C = \sigma_T \cdot N, \quad (5.53)$$

where $N = \int N(E)\,dE$ is the total number density of electrons. If, in a region containing relativistic electrons and magnetic field, synchrotron radiation is present and inverse Compton scattering takes place, the

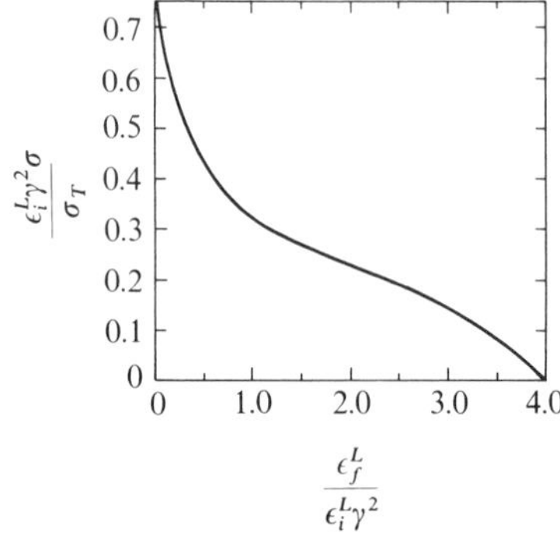

Fig. 5.6 The probability σ for inverse Compton scattering as a function of $\epsilon_f^L/\epsilon_i^L\gamma^2$.

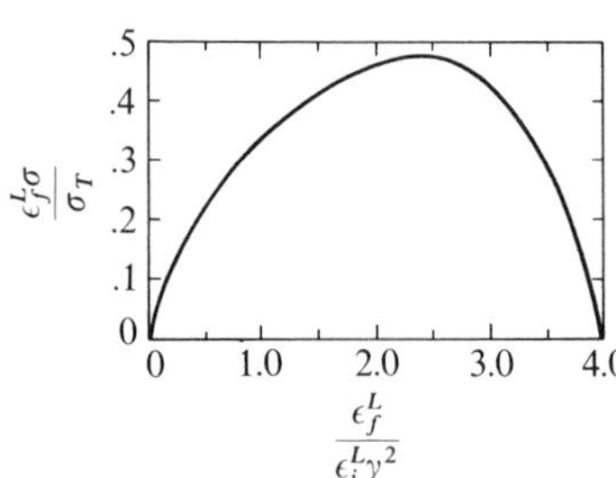

Fig. 5.7 The energy $\epsilon_f^L\sigma$ scattered by the inverse Compton process as a function of $\epsilon_f^L/\epsilon_i^L\gamma^2$.

transfer of radiation in such a region under our assumptions is described by the following equation:

$$\frac{dI_\nu}{ds} = -(\kappa_\nu{}^S + \kappa_\nu{}^C)\ I_\nu + \mathcal{E}_\nu{}^S + \mathcal{E}_\nu{}^C, \tag{5.54}$$

where $\kappa_\nu{}^S$ and $\mathcal{E}_\nu{}^S$ are the absorption and emission coefficients for synchrotron radiation (cf. Chapter 3) and s is the geometrical path. Since all the coefficients [except $\kappa_\nu{}^C$ in the approximation of equation (5.53)] depend on the electron energy distribution, and since the distribution will change as the result of scatterings in which electrons lose their energy as well as the result of synchrotron losses, we should solve the equation of transfer (5.54) simultaneously with an equation describing changes in the electron energy spectrum. This equation will be of the type of equation (6.10), but it must include a term describing losses due to the inverse Compton effect. The rate of loss of energy by an electron is

$$\left|\frac{d\gamma}{dt}\right| = 4\pi \int_{\epsilon_i=0}^{\infty} \int_{\epsilon_f=\epsilon_i}^{4\epsilon_i\gamma^2} \epsilon_f \frac{J(\epsilon_i)}{\epsilon_i} \sigma(\epsilon_i, \epsilon_f, \gamma)\ d\epsilon_i\ d\epsilon_f. \tag{5.55}$$

Under our assumptions and with σ of the form in equation (5.50) we have after one integration

$$\left|\frac{d\gamma}{dt}\right| = \frac{16\pi}{3}\,\sigma_T\gamma^2\int_0^\infty J(\epsilon_i)\,d\epsilon_i \tag{5.56}$$

for large γ. If $u_{\rm rad}$ is the energy density of the photon field in units of mc^2, we can write the equation for electron energy losses in the form

$$\left|\frac{d\gamma}{dt}\right| = \frac{4}{3}\,\sigma_T c u_{\rm rad}\gamma^2 = 2.66 \times 10^{-14}\,u_{\rm rad}\gamma^2.$$

In CGS units we have

$$\left|\frac{dE}{dt}\right| = \frac{32}{9}\,\frac{\pi c e^4}{(mc^2)^4}\,u_{\rm rad}E^2 = 3.97 \times 10^{-2}\,u_{\rm rad}E^2, \tag{5.57}$$

The lifetime of an electron against Compton losses is

$$\tau_C = \frac{E}{\left|\frac{dE}{dt}\right|} = \frac{25.2}{u_{\rm rad}E}. \tag{5.58}$$

The rate of energy loss depends on the inverse fourth power of the rest mass of the particle [equation (5.57)]. Proton scattering is therefore negligible compared with electron scattering. The ratio of synchrotron losses [equation (3.32)] to inverse Compton scattering losses can be written as

$$\frac{\left(\frac{dE}{dt}\right)_S}{\left(\frac{dE}{dt}\right)_C} = \frac{\frac{H^2}{8\pi}}{u_{\rm rad}}\cdot\frac{3}{2}\sin^2\vartheta, \tag{5.59}$$

where ϑ is the angle between the velocity of an electron and the local magnetic field. If the electron velocities are randomly oriented with respect to the magnetic field on the average, then $\langle\sin^2\vartheta\rangle = 2/3$ and

$$\frac{\left(\frac{dE}{dt}\right)_S}{\left(\frac{dE}{dt}\right)_C} = \frac{\text{magnetic energy density}}{\text{radiation energy density}}. \tag{5.60}$$

For a stationary case in a source of synchrotron photons scattered off their parent electrons, the above ratio of synchrotron to inverse Compton losses is not smaller than unity. If the ratio were smaller, the inverse Compton process—which increases the radiation energy density in the source by transferring the energy from electrons to photons—would quickly deplete the electrons' energy, which in turn would not be able to provide further synchrotron photons. The situation then would clearly not be stationary and would lead to a fast depletion of the energy contained in the relativistic electrons.

Bibliographical Notes to Chapter 5

5.1-5.3. Treatment of the inverse Compton scattering can be found in Ref. 35 of Chapter 2, and in many standard textbooks, such as the two following. The first also contains a derivation of the Klein-Nishina formula.

1. W. Heitler, *Quantum Theory of Radiation*, Oxford University Press, 1954.
2. A. I. Akhiezer and V. B. Berestetsky, *Quantum Electrodynamics*, Fizmatgiz, Moscow, 1959.

Astronomical applications of the inverse Compton process (to the problem of radio sources, in particular) may be found in the following papers.

3. F. Hoyle, G. R. Burbidge, and W. L. W. Sargent, "On the Nature of the Quasistellar Sources," *Nature* **209**, 751–753 (1966).
4. L. Woltjer, "Inverse Compton Radiation in Quasistellar Objects," *Astrophys. J.* **146**, 597–599 (1966).
5. J. Pfleiderer and M. Grewing, "Inverse Compton Effect: Some Consequences for Quasars," *Science* **154**, 1452–1453 (1966).
6. J. E. Felten and P. M. Morrison, "Omnidirectional Inverse Compton and Synchrotron Radiation from Cosmic Distributions of Fast Electrons and Thermal Photons," *Astrophys. J.* **146**, 686–708 (1968).

6

Interpretation of Spectra of Discrete Radio Sources

6.1 Introduction: Spectra of Discrete Radio Sources

Radio measurements of the flux of cosmic sources are very "monochromatic" compared with flux measurements in optical astronomy. The ratio of the bandwidths used to the frequency of observation usually ranges from 2×10^{-2} to 2×10^{-5} with the use of filters. Even multichannel receivers usually cover a narrow range of the spectrum corresponding to the Doppler-broadened profile of a radio line. Thus a radio measurement of the flux of a source furnishes one point on a flux-versus-frequency diagram. Other points can be obtained by separate measurements done with different receivers and often with different antennas. Therefore the important problem in continuum radio spectroscopy of cosmic sources is obtaining absolute intensity calibrations. The most frequently used method of calibrating a given antenna is to compare a measurement with one made with an antenna of small size, usually a pyramidal horn antenna, for which the gain can be calculated theoretically. The departure from theory for small horn antennas is of the order of 1% or smaller. By observing a strong source (usually the sun or a signal emitted by another antenna) with the horn and the given antenna, one can determine the gain of that antenna with an accuracy of about 2%. Another way of calibrating an antenna is by placing a black disk in its beam. This method of determining the antenna gain has an error of the order of 5–10%. A few radio sources (Cas A, Cyg A, Tau A) have had their absolute fluxes measured at several wavelengths. Observations of other radio sources at those and other wavelengths are made relative to the standards. The knowledge of the absolute fluxes of the standard sources permits one to reduce all the fluxes to the same scale and consequently to investigate the spectra of other sources.

Discrete radio sources identified with galactic ionized hydrogen (H II) regions and with most of the planetary nebulae are characterized by spectra which are flat at higher frequencies when plotted on a full logarithmic scale and decrease sharply toward lower frequencies forming a straight line with the slope of 2. Such spectra (sometimes referred to as Class T spectra), typical for thermal processes, are well explained in terms of the free-free mechanism of radio emission. About half of the well-investigated nonthermal spectra are of the form $F_\nu \propto \nu^{-\alpha}$ and are therefore represented by a straight line on a log F_ν–log ν diagram within the observable range of frequencies. The distribution of spectral indices α is Gaussian with a median value of about 0.75 and a standard deviation of 0.15 (the mean error in determining a single index α is 0.05). This type of spectrum cannot be described in terms of a reasonable superposition of thermally emitting regions. To produce a straight spectrum by the synchrotron mechanism, a power-law distribution of electron energies, $N(E) = N_0 E^{-(2\alpha+1)}$, within the source is required. The narrow dispersion of spectral indices suggests a similar narrow range of indices $\gamma = 2\alpha + 1$ of electron energy distribution among the discrete sources of radio radiation. Straight spectra are often referred to as Class S spectra.

The remaining spectra are of a more complex shape. Quite often several separate components can be identified in the spectrum of a radio source. The radiation of different components usually seems to originate in different regions of the source. The spectra of individual components of a complex source are often straight within a certain range of frequencies (if plotted on a full logarithmic scale) and then curved downward either at low frequencies (C_L spectrum) or at high frequencies (C_H spectrum), or at both. C_L spectra are characteristic of sources with a high brightness temperature. Possible reasons for the decrease of observed fluxes at low and high frequencies are discussed in forthcoming sections.

6.2 Discussion of Class T Spectra

Class T spectra of discrete radio sources are well interpreted in terms of thermal free-free radiation. If T_e is the electron kinetic temperature within the source, and N_e is the electron number density, the free-free absorption coefficient [cf. equation (2.86)] is approximately

$$\kappa_\nu = \frac{N_e{}^2}{T_e{}^{1.5}\ \nu^{2.1}} \tag{6.1}$$

in CGS units and the source function is Planckian; $S_\nu = B_\nu\,(T_e)$. Introducing the emission measure,

$$\mathscr{E} = \int N_e{}^2\, ds, \tag{6.2}$$

used frequently in optical astrophysics, we can write the optical depth τ_ν in the form

$$\tau_\nu = \int \kappa_\nu\, ds = T_e{}^{-1.5}\ \nu^{-2.1}\ \mathscr{E} \tag{6.3}$$

if T_e does not vary substantially within the source and if λ is the wavelength in centimeters. The equation of transfer of radiation within the source can then be integrated giving

$$I_\nu = B_\nu\,(T_e\,)(1 - e^{-\tau_\nu}). \tag{6.4}$$

The observed flux F_ν of radiation coming from the nebula is therefore

$$F_\nu = \frac{2k\nu^2}{c^2}\ T_e \int_\Omega (1 - e^{-\tau_\nu})\ d\Omega, \tag{6.5}$$

where Ω is the solid angle subtended by the source. At high frequencies, where the source is optically thin ($\tau_\nu \ll 1$), F_ν can be approximated by

$$F_\nu \cong \frac{2k\nu^2}{c^2}\ T_e \int_\Omega \tau_\nu\ d\Omega \propto \nu^{-0.1} \tag{6.6}$$

and is practically independent of frequency. At low frequencies, where the source is optically thick ($\tau_\nu \gg 1$), equation (6.5) yields

$$F_\nu \cong \frac{2k\nu^2}{c^2}\ T_e\ \Omega \propto \nu^2. \tag{6.7}$$

The shape of a thermal spectrum is illustrated in Figure 6.1, which presents the graph of the function

$$P(z) = z^2\ \frac{1}{1 - 1/e}\ (1 - e^{-z^{-2.1}}),$$

where $z = \nu/\nu_1$ and ν_1 is the frequency at which the optical depth is equal

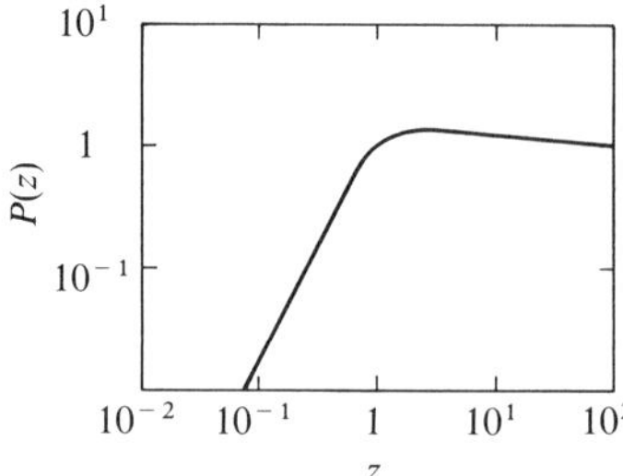

Fig. 6.1 The function $P(z)$ illustrating the shape of a thermal spectrum at radio frequencies.

to unity. The intensity of thermal radiation is therefore $I_\nu = I_{\nu_1} \cdot P(\nu/\nu_1)$ in terms of the $P(z)$ function.

Often a thermal radio source is seen superimposed on an appreciable background radiation of brightness temperature T_B. In this case the equation of transfer (A1.29) will yield the expression

$$F_\nu = \frac{2k\nu^2}{c^2}\left[T_e \int_\Omega (1 - e^{-\tau_\nu})\, d\Omega + T_B \int_\Omega e^{-\tau_\nu}\, d\Omega\right], \tag{6.8}$$

for the flux coming from the region occupied by the thermal source, where the second term describes the absorption of background radiation within the source (we of course assume, as before, that both the source and the background radiation are sufficiently uniform to take the appropriate quantities in front of the integral signs). Since the flux F_ν given by equation (6.8) is often compared with the background radiation coming from the immediate neighborhood of the source, the "apparent flux,"

$$F_{\nu A} = \frac{2k\nu^2}{c^2}(T_e - T_B)\int_\Omega (1 - e^{-\tau_\nu})\, d\Omega, \tag{6.9}$$

is frequently used to describe the radiation coming from the thermal source. The apparent flux is the difference between the flux density coming from the source plus the transmitted part of the background radiation equation (6.8) and the background flux which would be coming from the area occupied by the source if there were no source. We see from equation (6.9) that, depending on the difference of temperatures T_e and T_B, the source can be seen in emission if $T_e > T_B$ or in absorption if $T_e < T_B$. If the observations are carried out at a number of frequencies in both the optically thick and optically thin regions, the electron temperature T_e and emission measure $\mathscr{E}$ can both be determined provided that the size and distance are known. Such determinations agree fairly well with optical data.

6.3 Synchrotron Spectra: Energy Distribution of Relativistic Electrons

A discussion of the spectrum of an ensemble of electrons emitting synchrotron radiation requires a knowledge of the distribution of energies of the electrons at a given point of the source and at a given time, i.e., of the function $N(E, \vec{k}, \vec{r}, t)$. Given a specific distribution $N(E, \vec{k}, \vec{r}, t_0)$ at some "initial" instant t_0, further changes in the distribution function can be determined provided that both electron energy losses and gains dE/dt, as well as electron sources $q(E, \vec{k}, \vec{r}, t)$ and sinks $p(E, \vec{k}, \vec{r}, t)$, are known. In general, all the functions mentioned above depend on spatial coordinates, direction, and time. However, for simplicity (and because the dependence of the distribution function on the position within the source can be neglected for the description of the principal features in the observed spectra of radio sources) we will assume in this chapter that the problem is uniform and isotropic; i.e., all of the functions: $N(E, t)$, $q(E, t)$, and $p(E, t)$ depend only on time (and, of course, on electron energy). There are, however, some indications that for certain sources (like quasars) the assumption that $N(E, t)$ is isotropic may not be correct. The isotropic and uniform distribution function of electrons $N(E, t)$ fulfills the following equation:

$$\frac{\partial N(E,t)}{\partial t} + \nabla_E \cdot \left[N(E,t)\,\frac{dE}{dt}\right] = q(E,t) - p(E,t), \qquad (6.10)$$

which is in fact the continuity equation for the number density of radiating electrons in a one-dimensional energy space. $N(E, t)\,(dE/dt)$ is the flux of electrons with energies passing through the value E in the unit of time (dE/dt is the velocity in energy space) as the result of losses and gains of energy by the electrons. The source function $q(E, t)$ describes the number of electrons of energy E injected into the radiating region at the time t per unit time and per unit energy interval. The number of electrons of energy E removed from the radiating region as the result either of nuclear collisions or of escape from the region is given by $p(E, t)$; it can also be written as $(1/T)\ N(E, t)$, where T is the electron lifetime with respect to these catastrophic losses. We will assume here that $p(E, t) = 0$ and that $dE/dt = \varphi(E)$ depending on electron energy only, and that the region containing electrons is stationary. We will limit our consideration to the case in which the function $\varphi(E)$ has the form,

$$\varphi(E) = -\zeta - \eta E - \xi E^2, \tag{6.11}$$

which represents the losses of electron energy due to ionization of the surrounding medium, free-free radiation, synchrotron radiation, and the inverse Compton effect.

Energy losses of relativistic electrons caused by the *ionization of the surrounding medium* are described by $dE/dt = \zeta_I$, where

$$\zeta_I \approx 3.66 \times 10^{-20}\, n\left(6.27 + \ln \frac{E}{mc^2}\right) \tag{6.12}$$

if the medium consists of atomic hydrogen of number density n, and if $(E/mc^2) < 3 \times 10^{11}\, n^{-1/2}$; or where

$$\zeta_I \approx 1.22 \times 10^{-20}\, n\left(73.4 + \ln \frac{E}{mc^2} - \ln n\right) \tag{6.13}$$

if the medium is a completely ionized gas with a nonrelativistic electron number density n. In this latter case the equation takes into account all energy losses due to Cherenkov emission of plasma waves, and so on, rather than due to the excitation and ionization of neighboring atoms. In both cases the logarithmic dependence of ζ_I on E can be neglected, and ionization losses can be considered independent of the electron energy for relativistic electrons.

The losses due to the formation of photons through interactions with the nuclei of the surrounding medium, *free-free radiation*, are roughly proportional to the electron energy:

$$\frac{dE}{dt} = -\eta E. \tag{6.14}$$

In neutral hydrogen of number density n

$$\eta \approx 8.0 \times 10^{-16}\, n, \tag{6.15}$$

and in fully ionized hydrogen

$$\eta \approx 1.37 \times 10^{-16}\, n\left(0.36 + \ln \frac{E}{mc^2}\right). \tag{6.16}$$

The electron energy losses for free-free radiation are not continuous since the energy of the photon emitted in this process is comparable to the electron energy. The electron therefore loses practically all of its energy in a single interaction with a nucleus, but the probability that this will occur while the electron traverses a medium of density (integrated along the electron path) l, is $1 - e^{l/L}$ (where $L = 62$ g/cm^2 for hydrogen).

In a large ensemble of electrons these losses can be treated as continuous on the average, the energy of every electron being reduced by the factor of e after passing through a layer L. In a mixture of 90% hydrogen and 10% helium, the losses for free-free radiation are 20% greater than in pure hydrogen.

The losses of energy suffered by electrons through both *synchrotron radiation* and the *inverse Compton effect* are proportional to the square of the electron energy:

$$\frac{dE}{dt} = -\xi E^2 = -(\xi_S + \xi_C) E^2. \tag{6.17}$$

Synchrotron radiation losses are given by equation (3.32) as

$$\xi_S = 2.37 \times 10^{-3} H_\perp{}^2, \tag{6.18}$$

where $H_\perp$ is the component of the magnetic field in the source perpendicular to the electron velocity. The inverse Compton scattering losses are given by equation (5.57),

$$\xi_C = 3.97 \times 10^{-2} u_{\mathrm{rad}}, \tag{6.19}$$

where u_{rad} is the radiation energy density in the source. The relative importance of these two processes in the depletion of the electron energy is discussed in Chapter 5. To review – inverse Compton losses are important in compact radio sources of high brightness, but in a stationary source of synchrotron radiation they are smaller than the synchrotron losses.

The relative importance of the ionization losses, free-free radiation losses, and synchrotron radiation losses is represented in Figure 6.2. Generally speaking, at high frequencies synchrotron losses are the most important, while at low frequencies ionization losses are predominant, and free-free radiation losses are most important at intermediate frequencies. Under our assumptions the equation for the distribution function, $N(E, t)$, is

$$\frac{\partial N(E,t)}{\partial t} + \frac{\partial}{\partial E}[N(E,t)\,\varphi(E)] = q(E,t).$$

In a steady state $[(\partial N/\partial t) = 0,\ q(E,t) = q(E),\ N(E,t) = N(E)]$ its solution is

$$N(E) = \varphi^{-1} \int q(E)\, dE.$$

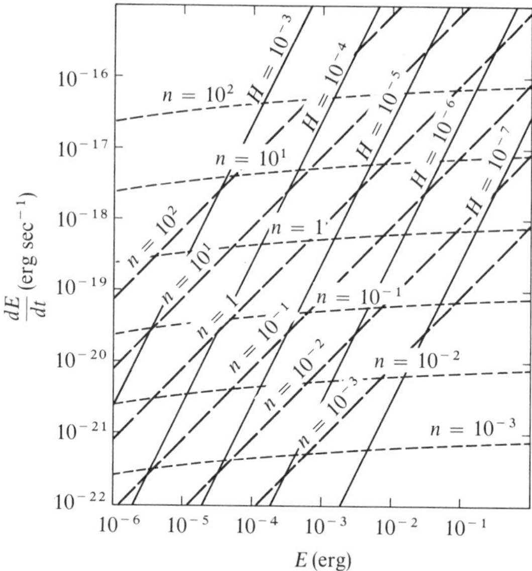

Fig. 6.2 Electron energy loss rate as a function of electron energy in a region containing neutral hydrogen of density $n(\mathrm{cm}^{-3})$ and a magnetic field of intensity H. A point line indicates ionization losses, a broken line free-free radiation losses, and a solid line represents synchrotron losses.

When the source function has the form $q(E) = q_0 E^{-\gamma}$, we have

$$N(E) = q_0(\gamma - 1)^{-1} E^{-\gamma} (\zeta E^{-1} + \eta + \xi E)^{-1}.$$

For the region of energies in which the losses independent of energy predominate, $N(E) \propto E^{-(\gamma-1)}$. For intermediate energies $[N(E) \propto E^{-\gamma}]$ the exponent in the electron distribution function remains the same as for the injected particles, $q(E)$. Finally, for large energies the losses proportional to the square of the electron energy are the most important and the electron distribution function becomes more steep: $N(E) \propto E^{-(\gamma+1)}$. The situation is represented in Figure 6.3. In the same figure the synchrotron radiation spectrum (broken line) corresponding to the distribution function (solid line) is shown. The synchrotron spectrum was obtained from equation (3.40) by a substitution of the appropriate $N(E)$. The indices of the electron energy distribution (γ) and the radiation spectrum (α) are related by $\gamma = 2\alpha + 1$.

We will now examine the time-dependent electron distribution when synchrotron radiation losses are the only factor affecting the electron energy. Equation (6.17) for the rate of the energy loss due to synchro-

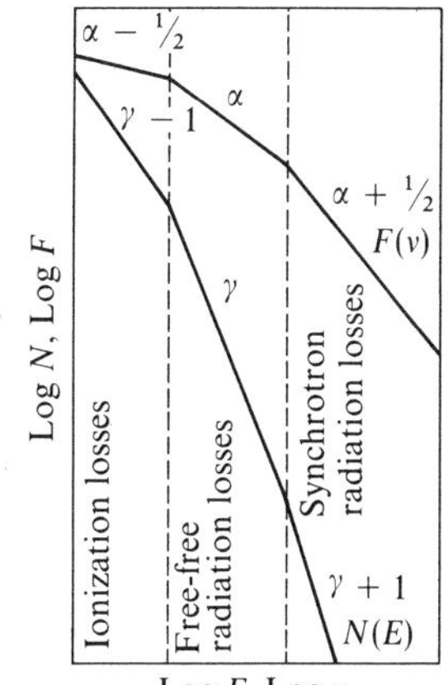

Fig. 6.3 The distribution function of electrons, $N(E)$, and their synchrotron spectrum $F(\nu)$ for a steady-state distribution of electrons.

tron radiation can be easily integrated (with the aid of the substitution $z = 1/E$), yielding

$$E = \frac{E_0}{1 + \xi_S (t - t_0) E_0}, \tag{6.20}$$

where $E_0 = E(t_0)$ is the initial energy (energy at the time t_0). If the initial distribution of electrons (i.e., at some initial time t_0) is

$$N(E_0, \vartheta, 0)\ dE_0 = N_0 E_0^{-\gamma}\ dE_0. \tag{6.21}$$

and all the electrons are directed at the same angle ϑ relative to the magnetic field, then the distribution of electrons at some later time t will be

$$N(E, \vartheta, t)\ dE = N_0\ E^{-\gamma}(1 - \xi_S E t)^{\gamma-2}\ dE \tag{6.22}$$

for $E < E_T$ and $N(E, \vartheta, t) = 0$ for $E > E_T$. This can be obtained from equation (6.21) by substituting E_0 from equation (6.20) and $dE = dE_0(1 - \xi_S E t)^{-2}$ from the differentiation of equation (6.20). The distribution function, $N(E, \vartheta, t)$, is characterized by the presence of a cutoff energy, $E_T = 1/\xi_S t$, above which there are no electrons; even an electron with infinitely large energy will have its energy reduced to the value $1/\xi_S t$ within some finite time (Figure 6.4). The cutoff energy E_T is a function of the angle ϑ between the electron velocity and the magnetic field. The quantity ξ_S depends on ϑ through $\xi_S \equiv \tilde{\xi}_S \sin^2\vartheta \equiv c_2 H^2 \sin^2\vartheta$. However, the angle ϑ does not change with time since the radiation is emitted along the velocity vector. For electrons moving close to the direction of the magnetic field the cutoff energy is very high even for large $\tilde{\xi}_S t$. If the initial power-law distribution of electrons is isotropic, the distribution at some later time t can be obtained by averaging equation (6.22) over all directions:

$$N(E,t) = 4\pi\, N_0\, E^{-\gamma} \int_0^{\pi/2} (1 - \tilde{\xi}_S \sin^2\vartheta\, E\, t)^{\gamma-2} \sin\vartheta\, d\vartheta. \quad (6.23)$$

For low energies, $E \ll \tilde{E}_T$ (and therefore $E \ll E_T$), where $\tilde{E}_T = 1/(\tilde{\xi}_S t)$, we can neglect the second term in the parentheses when compared to unity. In this case we have a stationary power-law distribution,

$$N(E,t) = 4\pi\, N_0\, E^{-\gamma}. \quad (6.24)$$

For high energies ($E \gg \tilde{E}_T$, but still $E < E_T$) we need to integrate within the range of ϑ from 0 only up to $\tilde{\vartheta}$, where $\tilde{\vartheta}$ is defined by

$$\sin^2\tilde{\vartheta} = \frac{1}{E\tilde{\xi}_S t} = \frac{\tilde{E}_T}{E} \equiv \tilde{\epsilon},$$

since there are no electrons with large energies between $\tilde{\vartheta}$ and $\pi/2$. The electron energy spectrum is then given by

$$\begin{aligned} N(E,t) &= 4\pi\, N_0\, E^{-\gamma} \int_{\cos\tilde{\vartheta}}^{1} [\tilde{\xi}_S Et \cos^2\vartheta - (\tilde{\xi}_S Et - 1)]^{\gamma-2}\, d(\cos\vartheta) \\ &\approx 4\pi\, N_0\, E^{-\gamma}\, \tilde{\epsilon}^{-\gamma+2} \int_0^{\tilde{\epsilon}/2} (\tilde{\epsilon} - 2\epsilon)^{\gamma-2}\, d\epsilon, \end{aligned}$$

where we have made the substitution $\epsilon = 1 - \cos\vartheta$. Since $\tilde{\epsilon} \ll 1$, we have $\epsilon \ll 1$ and ϵ ranges from 0 to $\pi/2$. Performing the above integration is straightforward, and we finally obtain the electron distribution,

$$N = \frac{2\pi N_0}{\tilde{\xi} t(\gamma - 1)}\, E^{-(\gamma+1)}. \quad (6.25)$$

For an initially isotropic distribution of electrons there will be a change in the distribution index from γ to $\gamma + 1$ around some value of the energy, rather than a cutoff in the electron energy distribution.

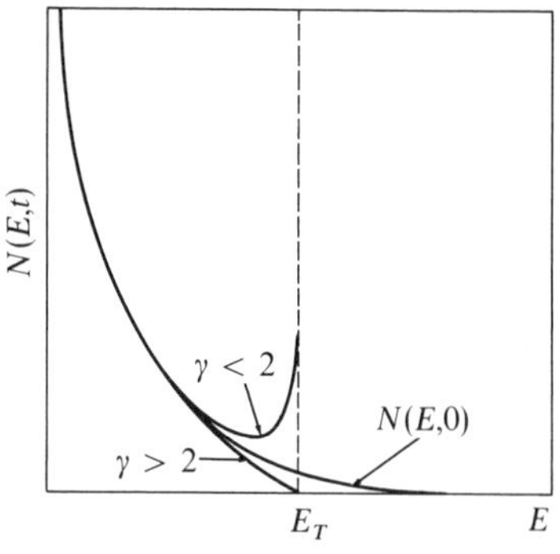

Fig. 6.4 The distribution function, given by equation (6.22), of electrons moving at the same angle ϑ with respect to the magnetic field. For all values of the exponent γ there is a cutoff in the distribution occuring at $E_C = 1/\xi_S t$. For $\gamma > 2$ the high energy tail of the distribution falls down with time; for $\gamma < 2$ the tail rises with time in such a way that electrons accumulate just below E_C. There are no electrons with energies higher than E_C.

The synchrotron radiation spectrum of such a homogeneous and isotropic distribution of electrons in a homogeneous magnetic field can be obtained in the case of an optically thin medium in the following way [cf. equation (3.40)]:

$$I_\nu(t) = \int_{4\pi} I_\nu(\vartheta, t)\, d\tilde{\Omega} = s \int_{4\pi} \mathcal{E}(\vartheta, t)\, d\tilde{\Omega}$$

$$= s \int_{4\pi} c_3\, H \sin\vartheta \int_0^\infty F(x)\, N(E, \vartheta, t)\, dE\, d\tilde{\Omega},$$

where s is the extent of the source along the line of sight. We will integrate the above expression using the following approximations in the regions where $\nu \ll \nu_T$ and $\nu \gg \nu_T$, respectively:

$$\nu \ll \nu_T,\quad N(E, \vartheta, t) \cong N_0\, E^{-\gamma},$$

$$\nu \gg \nu_T,\quad N(E, \vartheta, t) = N_0\, E^{-\gamma}(1 - \tilde{\xi}_S \sin^2\vartheta\, Et)^{\gamma-2},$$

where

$$\nu_T = \nu_C\left(E = \frac{1}{\tilde{\xi}_S t}\right) = c_1\, H \sin\vartheta \left(\frac{1}{\tilde{\xi}_S t}\right)^2 \approx c_7\, H^{-3}\, t^{-2}, \tag{6.26}$$

and c_7 is equal to $c_1/c_2^2 = 1.12 \times 10^{24}$. The integral in the low-frequency region becomes

$$I_\nu(t) = 4\pi\, N_0\, sc_3 \int_0^{\pi/2} H \sin\vartheta \int_0^\infty E^{-\gamma}\, F(x)\, dE \sin\vartheta\, d\vartheta$$

$$= 2\pi\, N_0\, sc_3\, c_1^{(\gamma-1)/2}\, c_8(\gamma)\, c_9(\gamma)\, H^{(\gamma+1)/2}\, \nu^{(1-\gamma)/2}, \tag{6.27}$$

while the integral in the high-frequency region becomes

$$I_\nu(t) = 4\pi\, N_0\, sc_3 \int_0^{\vartheta_0} H \sin\vartheta$$

$$\int_0^\infty E^{-\gamma}(1 - \tilde{\xi}_S \sin^2\vartheta\, Et)^{\gamma-2}\, F(x)\, dE \sin\vartheta\, d\vartheta$$

$$= 2\pi N_0\, sc_1^{(2\gamma+1)/3}\, c_2^{-(\gamma+5)/3}\, c_{10}(\gamma)\, c_{11}(\gamma)\, H^{-2}\, \nu^{-(2\gamma+1)/3}\, t^{-(\gamma+5)/3}. \tag{6.28}$$

The constants,

$$c_8(\gamma) = \int_0^\infty x^{(\gamma-3)/2}\, F(x)\, dx,$$

$$c_9(\gamma) = \int_0^{\pi/2} (\sin\vartheta)^{(\gamma+3)/2}\, d\vartheta,$$

$$c_{10}(\gamma) = \int_0^\infty x^{(2/3)(\gamma-1)} F(x)\, dx,$$

$$c_{11}(\gamma) = \int_0^1 (1 - x^{3/2})^{\gamma-2} x^{(\gamma+3)/2}\, dx, \tag{6.29}$$

are tabulated in Appendix 2. We see that around ν_T there is a break in the spectrum as a result of the synchrotron losses, and for $\nu \gg \nu_T$ the spectrum becomes steeper. The frequency ν_T shifts with time toward lower frequencies. The determination of ν_T in the spectrum of a synchrotron source permits one to estimate the lifetime of the source t if the magnetic field can be determined independently. The lifetime of the source is understood here as the time which has elapsed since the initial moment at which the electrons had a power-law distribution, $N_0 E^{-\gamma}$, at all energies.

6.4 Discussion of C_L Spectra

The low-frequency curvature in synchrotron spectra of components of radio sources can be due to several factors. In emission the presence of a low energy cutoff in the distribution of electron energies will affect the power-law synchrotron spectrum in such a way that around the critical frequency ν_L, corresponding to the cutoff energy E_L, a maximum of emitted radiation will be observed. Below that frequency the slope of the synchrotron spectrum will have an index $\alpha = -1/3$ because the radiation of a single electron below its critical frequency is characterized by a spectrum with this index (see Section 3.4 for the asymptotic expressions of the function $F(x)$ for $x \to 0$). The intensity of synchrotron radiation from an optically thin source with a power-law electron distribution for energies larger than E_L (that is, with $N(E) = N_0 E^{-\gamma}$ for $E > E_L$ and $N(E) = 0$ for $E < E_L$), when all electrons are moving under the same angle ϑ to the magnetic field, is

$$I_\nu(\vartheta) = \frac{s}{2} c_3 c_1^{(\gamma-1)/2} N_0 (H \sin\vartheta)^{(\gamma+1)/2} \nu_L^{(1-\gamma)/2} \cdot L(x_L, \gamma), \tag{6.30}$$

where s is the extent of the source and

$$L(x_L, \gamma) = x_L^{(1-\gamma)/2} \int_0^{x_L} F(z)\, z^{(\gamma-3)/2}\, dz, \tag{6.31}$$

$$x_L = \frac{\nu}{\nu_L}, \tag{6.32}$$

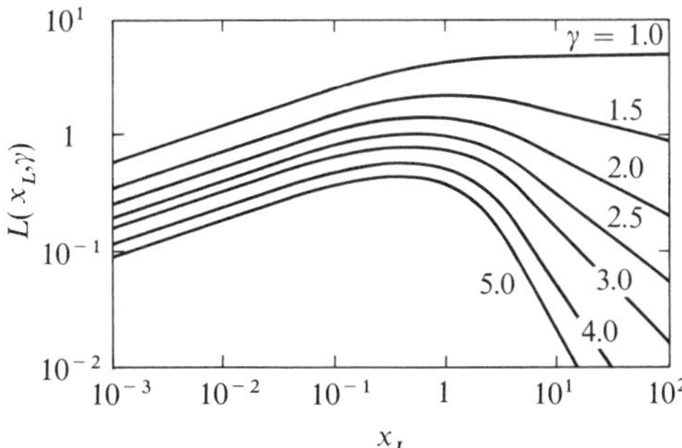

Fig. 6.5 The function $L(x_L, \gamma)$.

and

$$\nu_L = c_1 \, H \sin \vartheta \, E_L{}^2. \tag{6.33}$$

The function $L(x_L, \gamma)$ is illustrated in Figure 6.5. For small x_L the asymptotic expression for $L(x_L, \gamma)$ is

$$L(x_L, \gamma) \approx \frac{12.9}{3\gamma - 1} x_L{}^{1/3}. \tag{6.34}$$

For isotropic distribution of electrons we have to integrate equation (6.30) over the solid angle $\tilde{\Omega}$.

It should be noted that the low-frequency slope of most sources with a C_L-spectrum is steeper than one third and therefore cannot be accounted for by assuming the appropriate low-energy cutoff in the electron energy distribution. The other factor affecting the emission of synchrotron radiation is the presence of thermal electrons within the source, which cause the departure from unity of the refractive index of the medium. In this case (calculated for a homogeneous source), as indicated in Figure 4.2, the spectrum is very steep at low frequencies. However, the basic difficulty in attributing the low-frequency curvature of synchrotron spectra of discrete radio sources to the plasma effect is the rather high concentration of electrons within the source required for the refractive index of the medium to be significantly different from unity at radio frequencies. The frequency at which this departure from unity becomes significant [cf. equation (4.10)] is

$$\nu_S \approx 20 \frac{N_e}{H}, \tag{6.35}$$

where N_e is the number density of thermal electrons.

The low-frequency curvature in synchrotron spectra can be due to an absorption process also. If a layer of ionized hydrogen is located between the source and the observer, the power-law synchrotron spectrum seen by the observer will be modified by thermal absorption within the cloud of ionized hydrogen:

$$F_\nu \propto \nu^{-\alpha} e^{-\tau_\nu^{(T)}} \tag{6.36}$$

where $\tau_\nu^{(T)}$ is given by equation (6.3). Significant departures from the power-law spectrum will therefore be seen at frequencies close to and below the frequency at which $\tau_\nu^{(T)} \approx 1$,

$$\nu_1^{(T)} \approx 10^{-3} N_e \sqrt{s}, \tag{6.37}$$

where s is the linear size of the cloud along the line of sight and N_e is the number density of thermal electrons in the cloud, and where we have assumed that the temperature of the cloud is 10^4 °K. The emission measure $\mathscr{E}$ [equation (6.2)] of the cloud can be determined by fitting equation (6.36) to the observed spectrum.

The most likely cause for spectral curvature at low frequencies seems to be synchrotron self-absorption within the source. The synchrotron spectrum of a power-law distribution of electrons, represented in Figure 3.8, is curved downward below the frequency $\nu_1^{(S)}$ at which the source becomes optically thick; this frequency is given by equation (3.53), which can be transformed to a form containing only directly measurable quantities and the magnetic field by combining it with an expression for the flux of radiation F_ν at any frequency ν where the source is optically thin:

$$(\nu_1^{(S)})^{(\gamma+4)/2} = c_{14}(\gamma)\ (H \sin\vartheta)^{1/2} \frac{F_\nu\ \nu^{(\gamma-1)/2}}{\Omega}, \tag{6.38}$$

where

$$c_{14}(\gamma) = (2c_1)^{5/2} \frac{c_6}{c_5} \tag{6.39}$$

is tabulated in Appendix 2 (Table 7). In the derivation of equation (6.38), equations (A1.15) and (3.50) were used. In equation (6.38) Ω is the solid angle of the source in steradians; and if Ω is measurable for a given source, then equation (6.38) permits us to estimate the strength of the magnetic field.

6.5 Discussion of C_H Spectra

The shape of the high-frequency part of a synchrotron spectrum of a component of a radio source from an initial power-law distribution of electrons depends mainly on the balance of the rate of synchrotron (and eventually Compton) energy losses and the rate of injection of new particles into the source. Synchrotron (and eventually Compton) energy losses are the ones particularly important at high frequencies since their rates increase with the square of the electron energies. In the case of an extended source the Compton losses are small compared with synchrotron losses (this need not be true in the cases of compact sources like quasars).

Before we discuss the effects of high-energy sources and sinks of electrons resulting in a high-frequency curvature in the spectrum, we will examine the spectrum from a steady state electron distribution with a *high-energy cutoff* at E_H (that is, with $N(E) = 0$ for $E > E_H$). If all of the electrons are moving at the same angle ϑ with respect to the direction of a (uniform) magnetic field, the observed intensity of synchrotron radiation is

$$I_\nu(\vartheta) = \frac{s}{2} c_3 c_1{}^{(\gamma-1)/2} N_0 (H \sin\vartheta)^{(\gamma+1)/2} \nu_H{}^{(1-\gamma)/2} A(x_H, \gamma), \tag{6.40}$$

where

$$A(x_H, \gamma) = x_H{}^{(1-\gamma)/2} \int_{x_H}^{\infty} F(z)\, z^{(\gamma-3)/2}\, dz, \tag{6.41}$$

$$x_H = \frac{\nu}{\nu_H}, \tag{6.42}$$

and

$$\nu_H = c_1 H \sin\vartheta\, E_H{}^2. \tag{6.43}$$

For an isotropic distribution of electrons,

$$I_\nu = \int I_\nu(\vartheta)\, d\tilde{\Omega} = 2\pi s\, c_3 c_1{}^{(\gamma-1)/2} N_0\, H^{(\gamma+1)/2}\, \tilde{\nu}_H{}^{(1-\gamma)/2} \tilde{A}(\tilde{x}_H, \gamma) \tag{6.44}$$

with

$$\tilde{A}(\tilde{x}_H, \gamma) = \int_0^{\pi/2} \sin^2\vartheta\, A(\tilde{x}_H/\sin\vartheta, \gamma)\, d\vartheta, \tag{6.45}$$

$$\tilde{x}_H = \frac{\nu}{\tilde{\nu}_H}, \tag{6.46}$$

$$\tilde{\nu}_H = c_1 H E_H{}^2. \tag{6.47}$$

The functions $A(x_H, \gamma)$ and $\tilde{A}(\tilde{x}_H, \gamma)$ illustrating the shape of a power-law synchrotron spectrum with a high-energy cutoff are represented in Figures 6.6 and 6.7. We can see that the spectrum becomes steeper

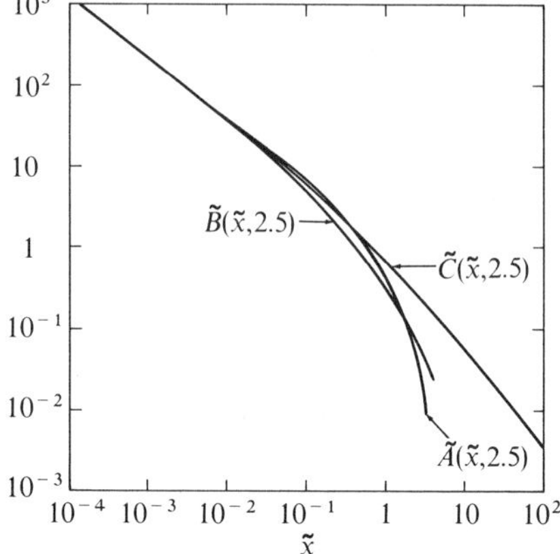

Fig. 6.6 The functions $\tilde{A}$, $\tilde{B}$ and $\tilde{C}$ for the value of γ equal to 2.5.

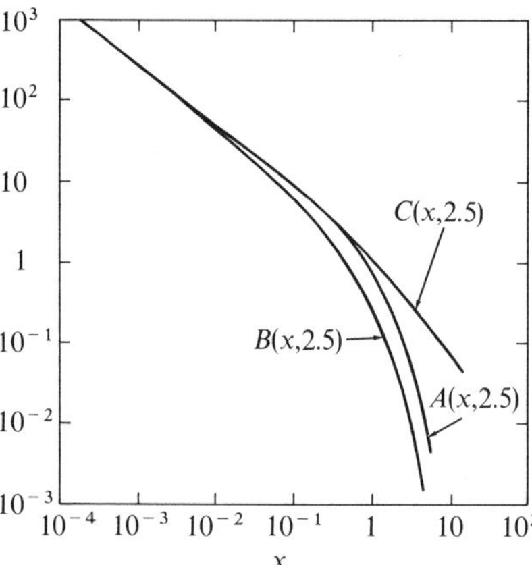

Fig. 6.7 The functions A, B and C for the value of γ equal to 2.5.

around the frequency ν_H (or $\tilde{\nu}_H$). Let us compare this spectrum with the nonstationary spectrum resulting from synchrotron energy losses in the two following cases: first, with an injection of electrons (characterized by a source function of the form $N_0 E^{-\gamma}$) terminated t seconds ago; and second, with a continuous steady injection of electrons described by a source function of the same form. The first case is the one discussed at the end of Section 3. We will write here the intensity of radiation coming from a monodirectional distribution of electrons (all having velocities inclined at the same angle ϑ with respect to the magnetic field):

$$I_\nu(\vartheta) = \frac{s}{2} c_3 c_1^{(\gamma-1)/2} N_0 (H \sin \vartheta)^{(\gamma+1)/2} \nu_T^{(1-\gamma)/2} B(x_T, \gamma), \tag{6.48}$$

where

$$B(x_T, \gamma) = x_T^{(1-\gamma)/2} \int_{x_T}^{\infty} F(z)\, z^{-1/2} (z^{1/2} - x_T^{1/2})^{\gamma-2}\, dz, \tag{6.49}$$

$$x_T = \frac{\nu}{\nu_T}, \tag{6.50}$$

and

$$\nu_T = c_1\, H \sin\vartheta\, E_T^2 = \frac{c_1}{c_2^2\, H^3 \sin^3\vartheta\, t^2}. \tag{6.51}$$

If the distribution of electrons were initially isotropic, the intensity is

$$I_\nu = \int I_\nu(\vartheta)\, d\tilde{\Omega} = 2\pi\, s\, c_3 c_1^{(\gamma-1)/2}\, N_0\, H^{(\gamma+1)/2}\, \tilde{\nu}_T^{(1-\gamma)/2}\, \tilde{B}(\tilde{x}_T, \gamma), \tag{6.52}$$

with

$$\tilde{B}(\tilde{x}_T, \gamma) = \int_0^{\pi/2} (\sin\vartheta)^{2\gamma}\, B(\tilde{x}_T \sin^3\vartheta, \gamma)\, d\vartheta, \tag{6.53}$$

$$\tilde{x}_T = \frac{\nu}{\tilde{\nu}_T}, \tag{6.54}$$

and

$$\tilde{\nu}_T(t) = \frac{c_1}{c_2^2\, H^3\, t^2}. \tag{6.55}$$

In the above expressions t is the time which has elapsed since the termination of the injection of relativistic particles into the radio source.

When the injection of relativistic electrons is continuous and described by the source function $qE^{-\gamma}$, we have at a time t' the following distribution of electron energies resulting from equation (6.10):

$$N(E, \vartheta, t') = \begin{cases} \dfrac{qE^{-(\gamma+1)}}{(\gamma-1)\,\xi_S}\,[1 - (1 - \xi_S\, t' E)^{\gamma-1}] & E < E_T \\[2ex] \dfrac{qE^{-(\gamma+1)}}{(\gamma-1)\,\xi_S} & E \geq E_T, \end{cases}$$

where t' is the time which has elapsed since the injection of the relativistic particles began. Consequently, for a unidirectional distribution of electrons

$$I_\nu(\vartheta) = \frac{s}{2}\, c_3 c_1^{(\gamma-1)/2}\, qt'\, (H \sin\vartheta)^{(\gamma+1)/2}\, \nu_T^{(1-\gamma)/2}\, C(x_T, \gamma); \tag{6.56}$$

and for an initially isotropic distribution of electrons

$$I_\nu = \int I_\nu(\vartheta)\, d\tilde{\Omega} = 2\pi\, s\, c_3 c_1^{(\gamma-1)/2}\, qt'\, H^{(\gamma+1)/2}\, \tilde{\nu}_T^{(1-\gamma)/2}\, \tilde{C}(\tilde{x}_T, \gamma), \quad (6.57)$$

where

$$C(x_T, \gamma) = \frac{1}{\gamma - 1}\, x_T^{(1-\gamma)/2}$$
$$\left\{ \int_0^\infty F(z)\, z^{(\gamma-2)/2}\, dz - \int_{x_T}^\infty F(z)\, z^{-1/2}\, [z^{1/2} - x_T^{1/2}]^{\gamma-1}\, dz \right\}, \quad (6.58)$$

and

$$\tilde{C}(\tilde{x}_T, \gamma) = \int_0^{\pi/2} (\sin\vartheta)^{2\gamma}\, C(\tilde{x}_T \sin^3\vartheta, \gamma)\, d\vartheta. \quad (6.59)$$

E_T, x_T, $\tilde{x}_T$, ν_T and $\tilde{\nu}_T$ refer here to the time t'. The functions B, $\tilde{B}$ and C, $\tilde{C}$ are plotted in Figures 6.6 and 6.7. We can see that deviations from the power-law spectrum occur at frequencies larger than ν_T (or $\tilde{\nu}_T$). If the observed C_H spectrum of a component of a radio source is well determined, particularly at higher frequencies, one can determine ν_T (or $\tilde{\nu}_T$) for a given source together with the information on the character of the injection process. The few better known C_H spectra of radio source components are best approximated by the function $\tilde{B}(\tilde{x}_T, \gamma)$ indicating that the injection mechanism ceased to work some t years ago. The values of t' determined from $\tilde{\nu}_T$ are of the order of 10^7 years when the magnetic field is estimated from the energy equipartition condition (see Chapter 7).

It must be borne in mind that this discussion of the processes leading to the curvature in synchrotron spectra of initially power-law distributions of electrons is a simplified one covering only the basic processes affecting the energy distribution of electrons in a homogeneous stationary source; but it can rather easily be generalized to cover more complex (and at the same time more realistic) cases. For example, without the assumption that the source is stationary we must take into account that the rates of energy losses due to the described mechanisms will vary significantly with the radius R of the expanding source. Assuming that the magnetic flux remains conserved during the expansion of the source, the rate of synchrotron losses varies as $R^{-1} E^2$, the rate of Compton losses varies as $R^{-8} E^2$, the rate of free-free radiation losses varies as $R^{-3} E$, and the rate of ionization losses varies as $R^{-3.}$ To these we must add the energy losses due to the expansion of the source (their rate varies as $R^{-1} E$). The energy gains by the Fermi statistical acceleration process depend on $R^{-4} E$. If the energy of every relativistic particle decreases as R^{-1} during the expansion of the synchrotron-emitting region, we can see that the rates of energy losses and gains will depend on various powers of the radius, from minus two for expansion losses to minus ten for inverse Compton effect losses. Therefore during an evolution of the component of a source the relative contribution of different processes may also undergo changes. All of this will, of course, have to be taken into account when discussing the evolution of spectra of expanding components. Some of the sources like quasars show changes of the flux in time at different frequencies. The general character of these variations can be roughly described in terms of a model of an expanding source which is optically thin at higher frequencies and thick at lower frequencies.

6.6 Discussion of Class S Spectra

The observed statistical distribution of spectral indices of S-type spectra of radio sources (Section 6.1) can be accounted for by a simple picture of recurrent bursts of injections of relativistic particles with an initial distribution characterized by $\gamma = 1.5 \pm 0.4$. At lower frequencies, where synchrotron losses are not important, the sources will have a spectral index corresponding to the initial value of γ, i.e., $\alpha = (\gamma - 1)/2 = 0.25$, which is the lowest range of observed indices. If the frequency of the bursts is such that the time between bursts T is smaller than the lifetime of an electron against energy losses at intermediate frequencies, then the injection of particles can be considered continuous at these frequencies; and the spectrum will be characterized by the index of 0.75 [cf. equation (6.57)]. This will take place at frequencies between $\tilde{\nu}(t')$ and $\tilde{\nu}(t)$. Finally, at high frequencies, where electron energy losses are large, the injection cannot be considered continuous since the injected electrons will lose most of their energy shortly after every burst. That spectrum will have a still steeper index of 1.33 [cf. equation (6.52)]; this value is characteristic for the steepest spectra observed. Since $t \approx T \ll t'$, the value of $\tilde{\nu}(t)$ depends mainly on the frequency of the bursts. Since the frequency $\tilde{\nu}(t')$ decreases with the age of the source (decreasing in proportion to the square of the time elapsed since the moment when the first burst of particles took place), only very young sources have flat spectra, and after a sufficiently long time the entire observable spectrum is characterized by the index of 0.75.

Bibliographical Notes to Chapter 6

6.1. Absolute intensity calibrations are reviewed by Findlay:

1. J. W. Findlay, "Absolute Intensity Calibrations in Radio Astronomy," *Ann. Rev. Astron. Astrophys.* **4**, 77–94 (1966).

Reviews of spectra of discrete radio sources are presented in Refs. 2–20.

2. G. R. Whitfield, "The Spectra of Radio Stars," *Monthly Notices Roy. Astron. Soc.* **117**, 680–691 (1957).
3. R. G. Conway, K. I. Kellermann, and R. J. Long, "The Radio Frequency Spectra of Discrete Radio Sources," *Monthly Notices Roy. Astron. Soc.* **125**, 261–284 (1963).
4. K. I. Kellermann, "A Compilation of Radio Sources Flux Densities," *Publ. Owens Valley Rad. Obs.* **1**, No. 1, 1–27 (1964).
5. K. I. Kellermann, "The Spectra of Nonthermal Radio Sources," *Astrophys. J.* **140**, 969–991 (1964).
6. W. C. Erickson and W. M. Cronym, "The Spectra of Radio Sources at Decametric Wavelengths," *Astrophys. J.* **142**, 1156–1170 (1965).
7. W. E. Howard, T. R. Dennis, S. P. Maran, and H. D. Aller, "A Uniform Flux-density System for Observations of Discrete Radio Sources," *Astrophys. J. Supplement.* **10**, 331–349 (1965).
8. C. Hazard, "The Radio Spectrum of Normal Extragalactic Nebulae," *Monthly Notices Roy. Astron. Soc.* **126**, 489–498 (1963).
9. W. E. Howard, T. R. Dennis, S. P. Maran, and H. D. Aller, "Curvature in Spectra of Non-Thermal Radio Sources," *Nature* **202**, 862–864 (1964).
10. W. A. Dent and F. T. Haddock, "A New Class of Radio Source Spectra," *Nature* **205**, 487–488 (1965).
11. J. W. M. Baars, P. G. Mezger, and H. Wendeker, "A Radio Investigation of NGC 1256 and NGC 1275," *Nature* **205**, 488–489 (1965).
12. J. W. M. Baars, P. G. Mezger, and H. Wendeker, "The Spectra of the Strongest Non-Thermal Radio Sources in the Centimeter Wavelength Range," *Astrophys. J.* **142**, 122–134 (1965).
13. W. A. Dent and F. T. Haddock, "The Extension of Non-Thermal Radio-Source Spectra to 8000 Mc/s," *Astrophys. J.* **144**, 568–586 (1966).
14. I. I. K. Pauliny-Toth and K. I. Kellerman, "Variations in the Radio Frequency Spectra of 3C 84, 3C 273, 3C 279 and Other Radio Sources," *Astrophys. J.* **146**, 634–645 (1966).
15. V. A. Hughes and R. V. Potter, "Spectrum of the Radio Source 4C 50.11/NRAO 150," *Nature* **217**, 832–833 (1968).
16. R. J. Long, M. A. Smith, P. Stewart, and P. J. S. Williams, "The Radio Spectra of Sources in the Fourth Cambridge Catalogue," *Monthly Notices Roy. Astron. Soc.* **134**, 371–388 (1966).
17. P. J. S. Williams and P. Stewart, "The Radio Spectra of Sources in the Fourth Cambridge Catalogue. II," *Monthly Notices Roy. Astron. Soc.* **135**, 319–328 (1967).
18. P. J. S. Williams, R. A. Collins, J. L. Caswell, and D. J. Holden, "The Radio Spectra of Sources in the Fourth Cambridge Catalogue. III," *Monthly Notices Roy. Astron. Soc.* **139**, 289–311 (1968).
19. P. J. S. Williams and A. H. Bridle, "The Spectral Indices of Radio Sources," *Observatory* **87**, 280–286 (1967).
20. K. I. Kellermann, I. I. K. Pauliny-Toth, and W. C. Tyler, "Measurements

of the Flux Density of Discrete Radio Sources at Centimeter Wavelengths. I. Observations at 2695 MHz (11.3 cm)," *Astron. J.* **73**, 298–309 (1968).

6.2. Thermal spectra are discussed in

21. C. M. Wade, "On the Radio Emission of Hydrogen Nebulae," *Australian J. Phys.* **11**, 388–399 (1958).

The next two papers report surveys of galactic sources made at 22 cm and 11 cm, respectively. Most of the sources are thermal.

22. G. Westerhout, "A Survey of the Continuous Radiation from the Galactic System at a Frequency of 1390 Mc/s," *Bull. Astron. Inst. Netherlands* **14**, 215–260 (1958).
23. W. Altenhöff, P. G. Mezger, H. Wendeker, and G. Westerhout, "Die Durchmusterung der Milchstrasse und die Quellen-Durchmusterung bei 2.7 GHz," *Veröff. Sternwarte Bonn* **59**, 48–98 (1960).

Observations of H II regions at 6 cm and 2 cm were reported in the following two papers. See also Refs. 26 and 27.

24. P. G. Mezger and A. P. Henderson, "Galactic H II Regions. I. Observations of their continuum at the frequency 5 GHz," *Astrophys. J.* **147**, 471–489 (1967).
25. J. W. M. Baars, P. G. Mezger, and H. Wendeker, "The Flux Density of the Strongest Thermal Radio Sources at the Frequency 14.5 GHz," *Z. Astrophys.* **61**, 134–143 (1965).
26. Y. Terzian, "Radio Emission from H II Regions," *Astrophys. J.* **142**, 135–147 (1965).
27. M. Ryle and D. Downes, "High Resolution Radio Observations of an Intense H II Region in Cygnus X," *Astrophys. J.* **148**, L17–21 (1967).

The following paper is a catalog of 80 sources in the galactic plane in the longitude range 180°–40°, recorded at 408 MHz with the Molonglo Cross telescope:

28. M. J. L. Kesteven, "A Catalogue of Galactic Radio Sources," *Australian J. Phys.* **21**, 369–376 (1968).

Observations of planetary nebulae were carried out at 1400 MHz and 3000 MHz by Lynds; at 1410 MHz and 750 MHz by Menon and Terzian; and at 408 MHz by Ficarra, Barbieri and Ficarra, and Slee and Orchiston.

29. C. R. Lynds, "Observations of Planetary Nebulae at Centimeter Wavelengths," *Publ. Natl. Rad. Astron. Obs.* **1**, 85–97 (1961).

30. T. K. Menon and Y. Terzian, "Radio Observations of Planetary Nebulae," *Astrophys. J.* **141**, 745–749 (1965).
31. A. Ficarra, "Radio Emission from Fourteen Planetary Nebulae at 408 MHz," *Nuovo Cimento* **52 B**, 267–269 (1967).
32. C. Barbieri and A. Ficarra, "Observations of Planetary Nebulae at 408 MHz," *Laboratorio Nazionale di Radioastronomia Preprint,* December, 1967.
33. O. B. Slee and D. W. Orchiston, "A Preliminary Radio Survey of Planetary Nebulae South of Declination 24 Degrees," *Australian J. Phys.* **18**, 187–191 (1965).

6.3. For discussion of the distribution of the electron energies in sources of synchrotron radiation, see these four papers:

34. H. Tunmer, "The Relation of Cosmic Radio Emission to the Electronic Component of Cosmic Rays," *Monthly Notices Roy. Astron. Soc.* **119**, 184–193 (1959).
35. N. S. Kardashev, A. D. Kuzmin, and S. I. Syrovatsky, "The Nature of the Emission from the Radio Galaxy Cygnus A," *Astron. Zh.* **39**, 216–221 (1962).
36. N. S. Kardashev, "Nonstationariness of Spectra of Young Sources of Nonthermal Radio Emission," *Astron. Zh.* **39**, 393–409 (1962).
37. N. S. Kardashev, "Nature of the Radio Galaxy Cygnus A," *Astron. Zh.* **40**, 965–971 (1963).

Ref. 36 contains solutions for the coordinate independent equation for the electron energy distribution, taking into account many deceleration and acceleration processes. The coordinate dependent problem of the electron energy distribution and the equation of diffusion of electrons in a source are discussed by Syrovatsky:

38. S. I. Syrovatsky, "The Distribution of Relativistic Electrons in the Galaxy and the Spectrum of Synchrotron Radio Emission," *Astron. Zh.* **36**, 17–32, (1959).

Figure 6.2 follows a figure in Ref. 34.

6.4. C_L spectra are discussed in Refs. 27–29 of Chapter 3, and in the following papers.

39. R. J. Lamden and A. C. B. Lovell, "The Low Frequency Spectrum of the Cygnus (19N4A) and Cassiopeia (23N5A) Radio Sources," *Phil. Mag.* Ser. 8, **1**, 725–738 (1956).

40. A. C. B. Lovell and H. W. Wells, "The Spectrum of the Cygnus (19N4A) and Cassiopeia (23N5A) Radio Sources Below 30 Mc/s," *Monthly Notices Roy. Astron. Soc.* **121**, 111–114 (1960).
41. G. R. A. Ellis, "Extra-Galactic Radio Emission at 4.8 Mc/s," *Nature* **193**, 258–259 (1962).
42. K. I. Kellerman, R. J. Long, L. R. Allen, and M. Moran, "A Correlation between the Spectra of Non-Thermal Radio Sources and their Brightness Temperatures," *Nature* **195**, 692–693 (1962).
43. J. M. Hornby and P. J. S. Williams, Radio Sources Having Spectra with a Low Frequency Cut-Off," *Monthly Notices Roy. Astron. Soc.* **131**, 237–246 (1966).
44. P. J. S. Williams, "Magnetic Field within some Quasistellar Radio Sources," *Nature* **210**, 285–286 (1966).
45. A. H. Bridle, "New Limits to the Magnetic Field Strengths within Some Radio Sources," *Observatory* **87**, 263–267 (1967).
46. J. G. Bolton, F. F. Gardner, M. B. Mackey, "A Radio Source with a Very Unusual Spectrum," *Nature* **199**, 682–683 (1963).
47. K. I. Kellerman, "The Radio Source 1934–63," *Australian J. Phys.* **19**, 195–207 (1966).
48. P. A. G. Scheuer, "Radio Structure of 3C 273 and Spectra of Radio Sources," *in* I. Robinson, A. Schild, and E. L. Schucking, eds., *Quasi-stellar Sources and Gravitational Collapse.* University of Chicago Press, 1965. Chapter 28.
49. P. J. S. Williams, "The Spectra of the Radio Sources 3C 343 and 343.1," *Observatory* **86**, 67–68 (1966).
50. B. M. Andrew, "The Flux Densities of Twenty Radio Sources at 13.1 Mc/s," *Astrophys. J.* **147**, 423–432 (1967).
51. A. H. Bridle and C. R. Purton, "Observations of Radio Sources at 10.03 MHz," *Astron. J.* **73**, 717–726 (1968).
52. I. I. K. Pauliny-Toth and K. I. Kellerman, "Measurements of the Flux Density and Spectra of Discrete Radio Sources at Centimeter Wavelengths, II. The Observations at 5 GHz (6 cm)," *Astron. J.* **73**, 953–969 (1968).

6.5. The presentation of material in Section 5 loosely follows that in Ref. 37.

6.6. Interpretation of S-spectra in terms of recurrent injections of a power-law distribution of electrons was suggested and developed in this paper by Kellerman:

53. K. I. Kellerman, "On the Interpretation of Radio-Source Spectra and the Evolution of Radio Galaxies and Quasi Stellar Sources," *Astrophys. J.* **146**, 621–633 (1966).

7

Physical Conditions in Radio Sources

7.1 Introduction

In the previous chapter we described the observed spectra of radio sources and discussed in some detail the implications of the interpretation of the spectra in terms of synchrotron radiation from a cloud containing relativistic particles and a magnetic field. In the present chapter we will present briefly the results of observations concerning radio sources and then, we will discuss the physical conditions in radio sources and estimates of the parameters describing these conditions insofar as they can be deduced from the seemingly well-established assumption of the synchrotron character of radiation of radio sources, without recourse to any drastic additional postulates. Since there are still some doubts as to whether the synchrotron mechanism is indeed responsible for the bulk of the radiation (infrared and millimeter) from quasi-stellar sources (quasars) and from certain peculiar galaxies, and since the nature of the radiating mechanism in the newly discovered pulsating sources (pulsars) is as yet entirely unknown, our considerations will necessarily be limited to sources associated mostly with elliptical galaxies and only in some aspects to galaxies with peculiar spectral characteristics (Seyfert galaxies) and quasars. We will not present or discuss here any detailed model of radio sources since any such discussion in radio astronomy at the time of this writing would be premature both from the observational and theoretical standpoint; we are far from understanding the most fundamental questions pertaining to radio sources—the character of the primary source of energy in radio sources, the process of conversion of this energy into the form of relativistic particles (the particle acceleration mechanism), or the origin of magnetic fields in sources. Indeed, our present understanding of the structure and evolution of extragalactic radio sources is reminiscent of our understanding of the structure and evolution of stars early in this century. At that time a certain amount of observational data concerned mainly with the integral properties of stars had been accumulated, and the mechanism of emission of radiation was believed to be thermal; but for the explanation of the origin of that radiative energy nothing better than the Kelvin–Helmholtz contraction was suggested. There was a long way to go from that stage to the contemporary models of stellar interiors and to our present understanding of stellar evolution. Similarly, we have accumulated today a certain amount of data on integral properties of radio sources. We have several over-all correlations between the observed properties of sources, and it is hoped by some astronomers that these correlations might assume a role similar to that of the Hertzsprung–Russell diagram in the theory of stellar evolution. We do seem to have reached an understanding of the mechanism of emission of radiation from at least some classes of radio sources. As for the mechanisms supplying the energy to radio sources and the mechanisms of particle acceleration, we are not much beyond the corresponding Kelvin–Helmholtz phase in stellar physics, although it would not be surprising if in the future we find that some of the suggested processes are present at particular stages of the evolution of radio sources or in particular sources. It is definitely not the purpose of this book to describe even briefly all the theories and speculations presented to date which attempt to answer these fundamental questions concerning the character and evolution of radio sources. The bibliography contains several reviews of these problems, some of which are in book form. We recommend them to the reader interested in these questions.

7.2 Identification of Radio Sources with Optical Objects; the Structure and Polarization of Radio Sources

The identification of radio sources with optical objects is based principally on positional coincidence. When more than one optical object can be distinguished by means of present-day techniques within the region delineated by errors in the radio position determination, or when the source is extended with a complex brightness distribution, the object with optical characteristics similar to those of optical objects previously identified with radio sources is usually assumed to be the correct identification. This procedure, of course, may lead to errors.

Several classes of discrete radio sources can be distinguished. Among galactic sources with continuous radiation spectra we have sources identified with *supernovae remnants* (for example, the Crab Nebula associated with a supernova of type I, and Cassiopeia A associated with a supernova of type II), which are characterized by nonthermal synchrotron spectra; *ionized hydrogen regions* (H II regions) and *planetary nebulae*, both of which have thermal spectra (Section 6.2); *flare stars* like UV Ceti, which exhibit sporadic increases in brightness by a factor of ten or so with some similarity to solar flares, but with the radio emission 10^4 times larger; and recently discovered *pulsating radio sources* (pulsars), which emit short pulses (or a series of up to three pulses) at very stable intervals of the order of 0.03 to 4 seconds. Among extragalactic radio sources we will consider normal spiral, elliptical, irregular, and peculiar galaxies, the nuclei of Seyfert galaxies, N-type galaxies, and the quasi-stellar sources.

In *normal spiral* and *irregular galaxies* the radio radiation is usually characterized by a straight synchrotron spectrum. Their radiation comes from the region coincident with the region emitting optical radiation, or they may exhibit a halo-core radio structure centered on the optical object. Normal galaxies are weak radio emitters.

Peculiar galaxies are strong radio emitters. Their radio structure is usually double or multiple with two or more extended regions located outside the optical galaxy at distances up to 100 kpc. In some better-investigated cases the radio emitting regions exhibit fine structure with steep brightness gradients, and local maxima ("hot spots"), within each region. The radio spectra are of S, C_H or C_L types. The optical forms associated with these radio sources are the peculiar ellipticals (indicating, for example, jetlike structures); the D galaxies, which have an elliptical nucleus immersed in an extensive envelope; and the "dumbbells," characterized by two separated nuclei in a common envelope.

The nuclei of *Seyfert galaxies* are usually weak radio emitters (with a few exceptions) at centimeter and longer wavelengths, and they seem to have a halo-core radio structure with a compact core which is brighter than that of other spiral galaxies. There is optical evidence of violent activity taking place in the Seyfert nuclei. This activity manifests itself by the emission of broad spectral lines characterized by Doppler velocities of the order of several thousand km/sec from material in a high state of excitation. The emission of a strong infrared continuum seems to be a characteristic of Seyfert nuclei. In some cases the radio spectrum seems to have a complex structure with different curved components; in at least one case it is variable. The optical and possibly infrared flux is also variable in a few cases. Strong radio sources seem to be associated with N galaxies. These objects are spectroscopically very similar to Seyfert galaxies but have faint envelopes around their bright compact nuclei rather than the extended outer structure with spiral characteristics. The radio source may be double or complex and may have bright compact components. The radio radiation of the *quasi-stellar sources* (quasars) is often associated with an optical starlike object characterized by variable light and by a large ultraviolet and (in the cases where it is measurable) infrared flux of radiaton. The starlike objects identified with quasars are spectroscopically similar to the nuclei of Seyfert galaxies, the principal difference being the presence of a large redshift of the spectral lines. The redshift z, is defined through

$$1 + z = \frac{\lambda^L}{\lambda^R} = \frac{\nu^R}{\nu^L}, \tag{7.1}$$

where λ and ν are the wavelength and frequency of a spectral feature, and where the superscript R refers to the rest frame of the emitter and the superscript L to the observer's frame. This redshift is larger than 2 in a number of sources. If interpreted as a Doppler shift due to the expansion of the universe, it implies that quasars are the most distant and luminous astronomical objects known. The radio structure of quasars is in some cases complex (sometimes double with a jet present), but the component associated (coincident) with the starlike optical object is very bright and compact (usually unresolved) at radio wavelengths. It is further characterized by a multicomponent spectrum prominent at centimeter (and in measurable cases millimeter) wavelengths, and exhibits large flux variations.

The presence of easily measurable linear polarization in radio sources of the order of several percent (in some of the cases of better resolved sources up to 20% or 30% locally), besides confirming the synchrotron character of radiation, indicates a rather high degree of ordering of the magnetic fields present in those sources since most of the measurements refer to the radiation integrated over the (usually unresolved) source and since a depolarization by Faraday rotation within the source may also take place. The existing polarization data are not sufficient to permit us to separate the Faraday effects (rotation and depolarization by rotation) occuring in the interstellar medium and in the intergalactic medium from those taking place within the radio source or in its immediate neighborhood. This circumstance and the fact that the radiation observed is usually integrated over the extent of a source are probably responsible for the lack of an established correlation between the polarization and the other properties of radio sources. On the other hand, Faraday rotation seems to exhibit correlations with galactic coordinates (and is assumed therefore to be mostly of an interstellar origin), which leads to results generally compatible with the results of the interpretation of the optical interstellar polarization of starlight. In this way radio observations of extragalactic sources yield information on interstellar magnetic fields and electron densities.

7.3 Characteristics of Discrete Radio Sources

In this section we will discuss a number of the properties of radio sources which are obtained more or less directly from observations. These properties will be concerned with the location and geometry of the source (the distance, the angular and the linear sizes) and with its radiation characteristics (the flux, spectrum, luminosity, and surface brightness). We will also discuss some properties related to the structure and evolution of radio sources (the minimum total energy, the magnetic field, and the lifetime). These characteristics can be determined from observations of synchrotron radiation emitted by the sources.

The *fluxes and spectra* of radio sources were discussed in some detail in Chapter 6. The catalogues of radio fluxes of discrete radio sources are discussed in detail in Appendix 4. Appendix 3 contains several useful nomograms; Figure A.3 gives a scale for conversion of frequencies into wavelengths and vice versa, and Figure A.4 presents a nomogram permitting a determination of the flux at one frequency when the value of flux at another frequency and the value of the spectral index are given. Under the assumption of a power-law spectrum Figure A.4 also permits the finding of the spectral index when fluxes at two frequencies are known.

Angular sizes of discrete radio sources can be determined in many cases from interferometric observations or, for smaller sources, from lunar occultations of sources and by scintillation methods (Chapter 1). Conversion of the angular size of a source into the linear size requires, of course, a knowledge of its distance. Figure A.5 facilitates the conversion of angular into linear sizes and vice versa when the distance is known. For very compact sources the size can be indirectly inferred from the location of the maximum in the spectrum, assuming that the source is optically thick for synchrotron radiation at frequencies below that of maximum (Chapter 6). Knowledge of the magnetic field within a radio source is required to make this estimate of its size possible; however, the procedure is rather insensitive to the accepted value of the magnetic field. Finally, for compact sources with variable flux at radio frequencies we can set an upper limit to the size of the radiating region from the time scale of these variations; this limiting size is equal to the distance traveled by light within a time of the order of the time scale of variations. This size limit leads to difficulties in confronting some of the observed properties of certain sources like quasars and the nuclei of Seyfert galaxies when a distance deduced from the cosmic redshift is accepted for quasars (the distances to Seyfert galaxies are not so large as the distances to quasars and there seems to be no reason for questioning the former).

There are no direct radio astronomical methods of determining the *distances* to radio sources at the present time. Distances are determined by optical means for objects identified with radio sources. For extragalactic sources this determination comes mainly from the redshifts of lines in the optical spectrum, which are assumed to be of Doppler origin. In several particular cases there is the possibility of setting a limit on the distance to a source based on radio data. These cases involve observations of the 21-cm line in absorption, dispersion by the interstellar plasma, and the surface brightness of supernovae remnants.

The presence of the 21-cm line in absorption in the spectrum of a radio source may set a lower limit on the distance to that source (see Section 8.2). For example, the interstellar 21-cm line in the spectrum of the quasi-stellar radio source 3C 273 is of comparable intensity to that in the source 3C 274 (neighboring in the sky), which is rather definitely identified with a peculiar galaxy NGC 4468 in the Virgo cluster (Virgo A) thus indicating that 3C 273 is outside our galactic system. Upper and lower limits can be set on the distances to pulsating radio sources (pulsars) because the interstellar plasma causes a dispersion of electromagnetic waves arriving from the source. This dispersion manifests itself in an observed drift in frequency of the pulse:

$$\frac{d\nu}{dt} = -\frac{c\nu^3}{\int \nu_0^2\, ds} \tag{7.2}$$

where ν_0 is the plasma frequency. By measuring $d\nu/dt$ and by assuming certain minimum and maximum electron densities N_e of the interstellar medium in the direction to the pulsar, one can set limits on the distance.

For supernovae remnants it is possible to derive a relation between radio surface brightness, apparent diameter, and distance to an expanding radio nebula, assuming that its radiation is of synchrotron origin. This method, however, requires a knowledge of the amount of energy released in a supernova explosion and of the initial magnetic field. The assumption of a small range of values of these two unknown quantities among supernovae remnants does not seem to be justified, and therefore this method of determining distances seems to yield only a very rough approximation.

The radio *luminosities* of sources can be computed from their fluxes and spectra if the distances are known. If F_ν is the flux at a frequency ν, the luminosity L is

$$L = 4\pi D^2 \int_{\nu_1}^{\nu_2} F_\nu \, d\nu = 4\pi D^2 F, \tag{7.3}$$

where D is the distance to the source and ν_2 and ν_1 are the upper and lower cutoff frequencies, respectively. With $\nu_1 = 10^7$ Hz and $\nu_2 = 10^{11}$ Hz, the luminosities of normal galaxies are lower than 10^{40} erg/sec, those of peculiar galaxies are between 10^{40} and 10^{45} erg/sec, and the luminosities of quasars are between 10^{44} and 10^{46} erg/sec.

The *surface brightness* of radio sources can be determined when the flux and the angular size of a source are known. For unresolved quasi-stellar sources the lower limits on brightness obtained from interferometric or scintillation studies are of the order of 10^8 to 10^9 f.u. per square second of arc at centimeter and meter wavelengths.

In what follows we will discuss parameters characterizing the physical conditions within radio sources that can be determined from observations of synchrotron radiation emitted by the source. The *minimum total energy*, E_{total}, stored within the source in the form of relativistic particles and a magnetic field can be estimated in the following way: the total energy emitted by the electrons with the energy distribution $\mathcal{N}(E) = \mathcal{N}_0 E^{-\gamma}$ between E_1 and E_2 (the luminosity) is

$$L = -\int_{E_1}^{E_2} \frac{dE}{dt} \mathcal{N}(E) \, dE = \mathcal{N}_0 \, c_2 \, H^2 \sin^2 \vartheta \int_{E_1}^{E_2} E^{-\gamma+2} \, dE, \tag{7.4}$$

where dE/dt is given by equation (3.32). The total energy of the electrons is

$$E_e = \int_{E_1}^{E_2} E \mathcal{N}(E) \, dE = \mathcal{N}_0 \int_{E_1}^{E_2} E^{-\gamma+1} \, dE. \tag{7.5}$$

Eliminating $\mathcal{N}_0$ between equations (7.4) and (7.5) and solving for E_e, after performing the above integrations, we have

$$E_e = c_2^{-1} L(H \sin \vartheta)^{-2} \frac{(\gamma - 3)}{(\gamma - 2)} \frac{(E_1^{-\gamma+2} - E_2^{-\gamma+2})}{(E_1^{-\gamma+3} - E_2^{-\gamma+3})}. \quad (7.6)$$

Since each electron radiates most of its energy in the neighborhood of the critical frequency, for the purpose of this estimate we can replace the cutoff energies E_1 and E_2 by the appropriate critical frequencies ν_1 and ν_2 in equation (7.6). Using equation (3.28) we will then have

$$\begin{aligned} E_e &= c_2^{-1} c_1^{1/2} \tilde{c}(\alpha, \nu_1, \nu_2) (H \sin \vartheta)^{-3/2} L \\ &= c_{12}(\alpha, \nu_1, \nu_2) (H \sin \vartheta)^{-3/2} L \end{aligned} \quad (7.7)$$

with the spectral index $\alpha = -(1 - \gamma)/2$ and

$$\tilde{c}(\alpha, \nu_1, \nu_2) = \frac{2\alpha - 2}{2\alpha - 1} \frac{\nu_1^{(1-2\alpha)/2} - \nu_2^{(1-2\alpha)/2}}{\nu_1^{1-\alpha} - \nu_2^{1-\alpha}}. \quad (7.8)$$

The function c_{12} is tabulated in Appendix 2. Equation (7.7) permits one to estimate the energy of the relativistic electrons, provided that the magnetic field is known. We will define the total energy E_{total} within a radio source as

$$E_{\text{total}} = E_e + E_p + E_H, \quad (7.9)$$

where E_p and E_H are the energies of the heavy particles and of the magnetic field. We will suppose that the heavy particle energy is k times the electron energy, with the ratio k depending on the mechanism of generation of the relativistic electrons. Since this mechanism is unknown at the present time, the value k cannot be determined. It can range from $k \approx 1$, if the annihilation of matter and antimatter is the source of electrons and positrons, up to $k \approx 2000$ for an induction-type acceleration mechanism, which gives the protons M/m times more energy than the electrons. If electrons and positrons originate as secondary particles following collisions of a primary proton flux with the gas and dust within a radio source, k will be of the order of 100. The magnetic energy within a radio source of radius R is

$$E_H = \frac{H^2}{8\pi} \phi \frac{4}{3} \pi R^3 = \frac{H^2 \phi R^3}{6} \quad (7.10)$$

if ϕ is the fraction of the source's volume occupied by the magnetic field and by the relativistic particles. For the purpose of this estimate we can identify H with $H \sin \vartheta$ and write equation (7.9) in the form

$$E_{\text{total}} = (1 + k)\, c_{12}\, H^{-3/2}\, L + \frac{H^2 \phi R^3}{6}. \tag{7.11}$$

The above expression considered as a function of the magnetic field H attains its minimum when the magnetic energy is approximately equal to the total particle energy (equipartition situation):

$$E_H = \frac{3}{4}\, (1 + k)\, E_e. \tag{7.12}$$

The minimum value of the total energy is

$$E_{\text{total}}^{(\text{min})} = \frac{7}{4}(1 + k)\, E_e = \frac{7}{4}(1 + k)\, c_{12}\, H^{-3/2}\, L. \tag{7.13}$$

This value is attained for the value of the magnetic field equal to

$$H^{(\text{min})} = (4.5)^{2/7}\, (1 + k)^{2/7}\, c_{12}{}^{2/7}\, \phi^{-2/7}\, R^{-6/7}\, L^{2/7}. \tag{7.14}$$

Introducing equation (7.14) into equation (7.13), we have

$$E_{\text{total}}^{(\text{min})} = c_{13}(1 + k)^{4/7}\, \phi^{3/7}\, R^{9/7}\, L^{4/7}, \tag{7.15}$$

with $\log c_{13} = -0.036 + (4/7) \log c_{12}$. The function c_{13} is tabulated in Appendix 2. The estimates of the total energy and of the field through equations (7.14) and (7.15) are relatively insensitive to the values of k and of ϕ but depend most strongly on the radius of the emitting region. The minimum total energies for radio sources estimated in this manner are very large, amounting to 10^{58} to 10^{61} ergs. These values are equivalent to the hydrogen-burning energy from stars of from 10^7 to 10^{10} solar masses.

The estimate of the magnetic field from the energy equipartition condition [equation (7.15)] is the only way of estimating the magnetic fields in many sources such as those associated with normal galaxies and in most of those associated with peculiar galaxies. The values of the magnetic field obtained in this way are of the order of 10^{-5} to 10^{-3} gauss. If a radio source ejected from a parent galaxy has a magnetic field of such a value after expanding for a certain time into the intergalactic space, its original magnetic field before the expansion began must have been considerably larger. For quasars and other sources with curved components in their spectra, the magnetic field can be determined from the low frequency spectral curvature assumed to result from synchrotron absorption (Section 6.4), provided that the size of the source is known. For extended sources with C_L spectra this determination of the magnetic field yields results which are compatible with the assumption of equipartition of energy. For quasars, usually only an upper limit on the size is set by observations. Measurements of X-rays due to inverse Compton scattering of photons with known energy off relativistic electrons in a synchrotron source (see Section 5.4) give information about the electron distribution, $N(E)$, within the source. This, combined with observations of the synchrotron emission, permits an estimate of the magnetic field. An upper limit on the magnetic field intensity can be imposed by the observed polarization. The existence of measurable polarization sets a limit on the amount of depolarization by Faraday rotation within the source (see Section 3.5), and this in turn puts a limit on the magnetic field. The limiting value of the field obtained in this way is, however, a function of the electron content of the source, and this is an unknown quantity for emitting regions located outside the galaxies. A lower limit on the magnetic field can be inferred from considerations of the inverse Compton losses in compact sources, since in a stationary source the inverse Compton scattering losses cannot exceed the synchrotron losses (see Section 5.4).

The *lifetimes* of radio sources, t and t', (defined as the time t which has elapsed since the acceleration of the relativistic electrons was terminated in a radio source and the duration t' of the period of production of the particles, if this production is continuous), were discussed in Section 6.5; these time scales can be determined from the high-frequency curvature of radio spectra. The following time scale, defined as

$$\tau = \frac{E_e}{L} = c_{12} \, H_\perp^{-3/2}, \tag{7.16}$$

can be estimated with the aid of the equipartition condition. It is a measure of the time scale of replenishment of the relativistic electrons or of the lifetime of the source itself if no replenishment occurs. This time τ decreases with an increasing magnetic field. The time scales mentioned above are of the order of 10^7 to 10^9 years for extended radio sources. Statistical types of arguments can provide an estimate of the lifetime of radio sources. For example, if N_E is the space density of elliptical galaxies (1.3×10^{-4} Mpc^{-3}) and N_R is the number of elliptical galaxies which are strong radio sources (7×10^{-6} Mpc^{-3}), and if all the elliptical galaxies were formed T_E years ago (10^{10} years), then the duration T_R of the radio source stage of an elliptical galaxy is

$$T_R = \frac{N_R}{N_E} \, T_E \approx 5 \times 10^8 \text{ years} \tag{7.17}$$

if all the ellipticals go through the radio stage and if the probability of radio emission is independent of time.

For extended radio sources located outside their parent galaxies the above mentioned ways of determining the parameters characterizing the physical conditions within sources yield fairly consistent results. Serious difficulties arise, however, in the case of quasi-stellar sources (if they are assumed to be at cosmological distances) and of the nuclei of Seyfert galaxies. The upper limits on the sizes of these objects, usually set by the observed time scale of the variations of flux, are rather low and lead to very high lower limits on surface brightness. This in turn implies high electron energies and low fields if the source is to be optically thin at frequencies at which it has a variable flux. Moreover, a high surface brightness implies that inverse Compton scattering takes place in the source and that Compton losses are very high—higher than synchrotron losses—since the Compton losses depend critically on the size of the source, while synchrotron losses depend strongly on the magnetic field.

Bibliographical Notes to Chapter 7

7.1-7.2. Papers on identifications of radio sources with optical objects are listed in Appendix 3. Radio radiation from supernovae remnants is discussed to some extent in the following review paper by Minkowski. See also Refs. 2–7.

1. R. Minkowski, "Supernovae and Supernovae Remnants," *Ann. Rev. Astron. Astrophys.* **2**, 247–266 (1963).
2. I. S. Shklovsky, "The Nature of Supernovae," *Astron. Zh.* **37**, 369–610 (1960).
3. D. S. Heeschen and B. L. Meredith, "Secular Variations of the Flux Density of the Radio Source Cassiopeia A," *Nature* **190**, 705–706 (1961).
4. C. H. Mayer, T. P. McCullough, R. M. Sloanaker, and F. T. Haddock, "Secular Variation of the λ9.4-cm Radio Emission from Discrete Sources," *Astrophys. J.* **141**, 867–872 (1965).
5. D. E. Harris, "The Radio Spectrum of Supernova Remnants," *Astrophys. J.* **135**, 661–678 (1962).
6. D. E. Hogg, "The Radio Structure of IC 443," *Astrophys. J.* **140**, 992–1001 (1964).
7. E. R. Hill, "Some Observations of Shell-Type Galactic Radio Sources," *Australian J. Phys.* **20**, 297–307 (1967).

The radio method of determining distances to supernovae remnants is suggested in Ref. 2. Refs. 21–33 of Chapter 6 refer to thermal radio sources. Continuous galactic radiation is reviewed in the following paper by Mills, and radiation in the direction of the galactic center in the paper by Burke. Further bibliographies on this subject can be found in these references.

8. B. Y. Mills, "Nonthermal Radio Frequency Radiation from the Galaxy," *Ann. Rev. Astron. Astrophys.* **2**, 185–212 (1963).
9. B. F. Burke, "Radio Radiation from the Galactic Nuclear Region," *Ann. Rev. Astron. Astrophys.* **3**, 275–296 (1964).

Radio radiation from flare stars was reviewed by Lovell, whose paper lists further references on the subject.

10. A. C. B. Lovell, "Radio Stars in the Galaxy," *Observatory* **84**, 191–210 (1964).

The discovery of pulsars was reported in the following paper.

11. A. Hewish, S. J. Bell, J. D. H. Pilkington, P. F. Scott and R. A. Collins, "Observation of a Rapidly Pulsating Radio Source," *Nature* **217**, 709–713 (1968).

The literature published on the subject of pulsars during the first half of 1968 was listed by Maran and Cameron.

12. S. P. Maran and A. G. W. Cameron, "Pulsars," *Phys. Today* **21**, 41–49 (1968).

For a description of the optical forms associated with extra-galactic radio sources, see

13. T. A. Matthews, W. W. Morgan, and M. Schmidt, "A Discussion of Galaxies Identified with Radio Sources," *Astrophys. J.* **140**, 35–49 (1964).

Investigations of radio radiation from NGC galaxies were reported in the following six papers (see also Ref. 8 of Chapter 6 and the bibliography contained therein).

14. D. S. Heeschen, "Radio Observation of Galaxies," *Publ. Nat. Rad. Astron. Obs.* **1**, 129–154 (1961).
15. D. S. Heeschen and C. M. Wade, "A Radio Survey of Galaxies," *Astron. J.* **69**, 277–287 (1964).
16. H. M. Tovmassian, "On the Radio Emission from Some Peculiar Galaxies," *Australian J. Phys.* **19**, 565–572 (1966).
17. K. I. Kellerman and I. I. K. Pauliny-Toth, "A Search for Radio Emission from Blue Stellar Objects and Seyfert Galaxies," *Nature* **212**, 781–782 (1966).

18. M. L. De Jong, "Radio Observations of Galaxies," *Astrophys. J.* **150**, 1–8 (1967).
19. H. M. Tovmassian, "Radio Emission of 158 Galaxies," *Australian J. Phys.* **21**, 193–199 (1968).

For an extensive and up-to-date review of problems related to quasi-stellar radio sources, and for a large bibliography on the subject, see

20. G. Burbidge and M. Burbidge, *Quasi-stellar Objects*, W. H. Freeman and Company, San Francisco, 1967.

Problems associated with Seyfert nuclei, N galaxies, and other related objects, are reviewed in the next paper, which also contains an extensive bibliography.

21. A. G. Pacholczyk and R. J. Weymann, eds., "Proceedings of the Conference on Seyfert Galaxies and Related Objects," *Astron. J.* **73**, 836–918 (1968).

Investigations of the structure of extragalactic radio sources are reviewed, and a bibliography is given, in the following paper by Moffet.

22. A. T. Moffet, "The Structure of Radio Galaxies," *Ann. Rev. Astron. Astrophys.* **4**, 145–170 (1966).

For more recent scintillation studies of the diameters of radio sources, see the bibliography to Chapter 1. A review of the results of polarization studies of radio sources, and a large bibliography of the subject, is given in

23. F. F. Gardner and J. B. Whiteoak, "The Polarization of Cosmic Radio Waves," *Ann. Rev. Astron. Astrophys.* **4**, 245–292 (1966).

Intensity variations of extragalactic radio sources are summarized and discussed in the following paper, which also provides an extensive list of references.

24. K. I. Kellerman and I. I. K. Pauliny-Toth, "Variable Radio Sources," *Ann. Rev. Astron. Astrophys.* **6**, 417–448 (1968).

A relatively large bibliography exists on the subject of expanding models of extended radio sources. There follow fifteen references on the subject.

25. F. Hoyle, "Radio-Source Problems," *Monthly Notices Roy. Astron. Soc.* **120**, 338–359 (1960).

26. I. S. Shklovsky, "Secular Variation of the Flux and Intensity of Radio Emission from Discrete Radio Sources," *Astron. Zh.* **37**, 256–264 (1960).
27. I. S. Shklovsky, "Radio Galaxies," *Astron. Zh.* **37**, 945–1152 (1960).
28. I. S. Shklovsky, "On the Nature of Radio Galaxies," *Astron. Zh.* **39**, 591–606 (1962).
29. I. S. Shklovsky, "Nature of Jets in Radio Galaxies," *Astron. Zh.* **7**, 972–981, (1963).
30. I. S. Shklovsky, "A Possible Secular Change in the Flux and Spectrum of the Radio Source 1934–63," *Astron. Zh.* **42**, 30–32 (1965).
31. H. van der Laan, "Radio Galaxies. I. The Interpretation of Radio Source Data," *Monthly Notices Roy. Astron. Soc.* **126**, 519–533 (1963).
32. H. van der Laan, "Radio Galaxies. II. A Model of Extended Sources," *Monthly Notices Roy. Astron. Soc.* **126**, 535–552 (1963).
33. I. I. K. Pauliny-Toth and K. I. Kellermann, "Variations in the Radio Frequency Spectra of 3C 84, 3C 273, 3C 279, and Other Radio Sources," *Astrophys. J.* **146**, 634–645 (1966).
34. H. van der Laan, "The Structure of Radio Galaxies," *Z. Astrophys.* **64**, 17–26 (1966).
35. H. van der Laan, "A Model for Variable Extragalactic Radio Sources," *Nature* **211**, 1131–1133 (1966).
36. A. G. Pacholczyk, "Evolution of Extended Radio Sources," *Astrophys. J.* **142**, 1141–1148 (1965).
37. M. Ryle and M. S. Longair, "A Possible Method for Investigating the Evolution of Radio Galaxies," *Monthly Notices Roy. Astron. Soc.* **136**, 123–140 (1967).
38. D. S. Heeschen, "The Absolute Radio Luminosity and Surface Brightness of Extragalactic Radio Sources," *Astrophys. J.* **146**, 517–522 (1966).
39. M. Simon and F. D. Drake, "An Evolutionary Sequence for Strong Radio Sources," *Nature* **215**, 1457–1459 (1967).

The method of estimating the minimum total energy stored within a radio source was developed by Burbidge.

40. G. R. Burbidge, "On Synchrotron Radiation from Messier 87," *Astrophys. J.* **124**, 416–429 (1956).

For a discussion of statistical lifetimes of radio sources, see

41. M. Schmidt, "Lifetimes of Extragalactic Radio Sources," *Astrophys. J.* **146**, 7–12 (1966).

8

Spectral Radio Lines

8.1 Introduction

Many types of spectral lines are being observed at present by radio astronomical methods. The 21-cm line formed by a transition between the two hyperfine levels of the ground state of hydrogen was detected first: this line is responsible for much of our knowledge of interstellar neutral hydrogen. Next, the four 18-cm lines of the hydroxyl molecule were detected. They are formed by transitions between the hyperfine levels of the Λ doublet of the ground state of OH. The mechanism of their excitation still remains very puzzling. The recently discovered recombination lines are formed in hot, highly ionized regions of interstellar space. They are observed from hydrogen, helium, and possibly carbon. Ammonia was discovered at wavelengths of 1.27–1.20 cm corresponding to the inversion transitions of the $J = K$ ($J = 1, 2, 3, 4$ and 6) rotational levels in vibrational ground state of the molecule. The 5.0- and 6.3-cm Λ doublets of hydroxyl in the excited state ${}^2\Pi_{3/2}$, $J = 5/2$, and in the state ${}^2\Pi_{1/2}$, $J = 1/2$, were also observed. The rotational transition of water molecules at a wavelength of 1.35 cm, and the 6.22-cm ground state rotational transition of formaldehyde were recently detected.

It is difficult to foresee what lines will be discovered next. It seems probable that recombination lines of other elements will be detected, and perhaps lines arising from transitions between the Λ doublets of CH, SiH, and SH, and possibly some molecular rotational transitions of CO, NO, and CS may be observed, although unsuccessful attempts to detect the 10-cm Λ-doubling line of CH and the 92-cm hyperfine transition line of deuterium were reported.

In the present chapter the discussion of spectral radio lines will be limited to basic information on the line formation. The observational results of line spectroscopy of the interstellar medium (and of nearby galaxies) will not be described in detail as they are beyond the scope of this book.

8.2 The 21-cm Hydrogen Line

The 21-cm neutral hydrogen line is formed by a forbidden transition between the two hyperfine levels $F = 1$ and $F = 0$ of the ground state of hydrogen. The frequency of the line is 1420.4058 MHz. In the $F = 1$ level the magnetic moments of the proton and the electron are antiparallel, whereas in the $F = 0$ level they are parallel. The transition between these levels is a magnetic dipole transition with a very low probability; the Einstein coefficient, $A_{21} = 2.84 \times 10^{-15}$ sec^{-1}, which corresponds to the radiative lifetime of the upper level equal to 3.5×10^{14} sec or 1.1×10^{7} years. In the interstellar medium the intervals between atomic collisions are much shorter than the lifetime of the upper level; and therefore most of the transitions, both upward and downward, between these two levels are collisional, and only a few downward transitions are radiative. The number of downward collisional transitions is about 10^3 times larger than the number of radiative transitions. The population of the $F = 1$ state is maintained in equilibrium by collisions at the expense of the internal energy of the interstellar medium; the 21-cm line radiation is therefore thermal. The excitation (or spin) temperature T, defined by

$$\frac{N_2}{N_1} = \frac{g_2}{g_1} \exp\left(-\frac{h\nu}{kT}\right),$$

where N_2 and N_1 are the populations of the upper and lower levels, and g_2 and g_1 their statistical weights, respectively, is close to the kinetic temperature T_k of the interstellar gas. In a first approximation one can put $T = T_k$ for most of galactic 21-cm line work except under conditions of low density or high radiation intensity, that is, for absorption lines formed in clouds near or within very bright radio sources. The absorption coefficient $\tilde{\kappa}_{\nu L}$ within the line is

$$\tilde{\kappa}_{\nu L} = \frac{N_1\, h\nu}{4\pi}\, B_{12}\, f(\nu),$$

where $f(\nu)\, d\nu$ is the probability that the transition $1 \to 2$ occurs in the frequency range between ν and $\nu + d\nu$, and B_{12} is the Einstein coefficient. When corrected for stimulated emission (cf. Appendix 1) it becomes

$$\kappa_{\nu L} = \tilde{\kappa}_{\nu L}(1 - e^{(h\nu/kT)}) \approx \tilde{\kappa}_{\nu L}\, \frac{h\nu}{kT}$$

in the radio region, if the excitation (spin) temperature T is larger than a few degrees ($h\nu/k \approx 0.07\,°\mathrm{K}$ at 21 cm). Since

$$B_{12} = B_{21}\, \frac{g_2}{g_1},$$

and

$$B_{21} = A_{21}\, \frac{c^2}{2h\nu^3},$$

we have the absorption coefficient equal to

$$\kappa_{\nu L} = \frac{3N_1}{8\pi}\, \frac{hc^2}{kT\nu}\, A_{21}\, f(\nu) = \frac{3}{32\pi}\, N\, \frac{hc^2}{kT\nu}\, A_{21}\, f(\nu)$$

$$= 2.58 \times 10^{-15}\, \frac{N}{T}\, f(\nu), \qquad (8.1)$$

since $g_2/g_1 = 3$ for the 21-cm line (N is the number density of all the hydrogen atoms). The total absorption coefficient ($\kappa_{\nu L}$ integrated over the line) is

$$\kappa_L = 2.58 \times 10^{-15}\, \frac{N}{T}, \qquad (8.2)$$

since $\int f(\nu)\, d\nu = 1$ and the frequency dependence of the denominator in equation (8.1) is neglected within the line. Because the natural line width of the 21-cm line is very small and collisional broadening is unimportant because of the low densities of the interstellar matter, the line profile $f(\nu)$ is determined by the Doppler effect. If $F(v)$ is the fraction of atoms having radial velocity between v and $v + dv$ (and therefore emitting within the frequency interval from ν to $\nu + d\nu$ such that $\nu = \nu_0(1 - v/c)$, where ν_0 is the rest frequency), we can write

$$f(\nu)\, d\nu = -F(v)\, dv;$$

and since $d\nu = -\nu_0/c\; dv$,

$$\kappa_{\nu L} = \frac{3}{32\pi} N A_{21} \frac{hc^3}{kT\nu^2} F(v) = 5.44 \times 10^{-14} \frac{N}{T} F(v). \tag{8.3}$$

The total absorption coefficient

$$\kappa_L = \int \kappa_{\nu L} \, d\nu = 5.44 \times 10^{-14} \frac{N}{T} \int F(v) \, d\nu = 2.58 \times 10^{-15} \frac{N}{T},$$

in agreement with equation (8.2). Let $\kappa_{\nu L}$ and $\kappa_{\nu K}$ be the absorption coefficients within the line and in the adjacent continuum, respectively. $\kappa_{\nu L}$, of course, is strongly frequency dependent, and this dependence is determined by the Doppler effect. $\kappa_{\nu K}$ has a large-scale dependence on frequency, but in the immediate neighborhood of the line this dependence can be neglected. Furthermore, let $\mathcal{E}_{\nu K}$ be the emission coefficient in the continuum (assumed to be frequency independent in the vicinity of the line) and $\kappa_{\nu L} \, B_\nu(T)$ be the emission coefficient in the line ($B_\nu(T)$ is the Planck function). Since we specified clearly the frequency dependence of the coefficients we will omit the subscript ν in the following discussion. The absorption coefficients are corrected for stimulated emission. Since we are in the radio spectral region, we can use the Rayleigh-Jeans approximation for the Planck function, $B \approx 2\nu^2 \, kT/c^2$. The equation of transfer within the line is

$$\frac{dI_L}{ds} = -\kappa_L \, I - \kappa_K \, I + \kappa_L \, B + \mathcal{E}_K. \tag{8.4}$$

In the continuum adjacent to the line, where κ_L is practically zero, we have

$$\frac{dI_K}{ds} = -\kappa_K \, I + \mathcal{E}_K.$$

In terms of the brightness temperature, $T_B = Ic^2/2k\nu^2$, and with the use of the Rayleigh-Jeans approximation for B these equations of transfer can be written in the following integral form:

$$T_{BL} = \frac{c^2}{2k\nu^2} \int_0^{s^*} \left(\mathcal{E}_K + \kappa_L \frac{2\nu^2}{c^2} kT \right) e^{-(\tau_K + \tau_L)} \, ds \tag{8.5}$$

and

$$T_{BK} = \frac{c^2}{2k\nu^2} \int_0^{s^*} \mathcal{E}_K \, e^{-\tau_K} \, ds, \tag{8.6}$$

where

$$\tau_L = \int_0^s \kappa_L \, ds$$

and

$$\tau_K = \int_0^s \kappa_K \, ds$$

are the optical depths in the line and in the continuum, respectively, and s^* is the extent of the entire region. Since the interstellar medium is transparent to decimeter radio radiation in the continuum, we can assume that $\exp(-\tau_K) \approx 1$ and rewrite the second equation in the form

$$T_{BK} = \frac{c^2}{2k\nu^2} \int_0^{s^*} \varepsilon_K \, ds. \tag{8.7}$$

For the 21-cm hydrogen line $\kappa_L \gg \kappa_K$, so that κ_K can be neglected in comparison with κ_L. We can simplify equation (8.5):

$$T_{BL} = \frac{c^2}{2k\nu^2} \int_0^{s^*} \varepsilon_K \, e^{-\tau_L} \, ds + \int_0^{s^*} T\kappa_L \, e^{-\tau_L} \, ds. \tag{8.8}$$

Introducing a mean optical depth $\langle\tau\rangle$

$$e^{-\langle\tau\rangle} = \frac{\int_0^{s^*} e^{-\tau_L} \, \varepsilon_K \, ds}{\int_0^{s^*} \varepsilon_K \, ds}$$

(note that $\langle\tau\rangle$ is of the same order of magnitude as τ_L) and assuming that the line-forming region is homogeneous (i.e., its properties, like the absorption coefficient, do not depend on position), we have equation (8.8) with the aid of equation (8.7) in the form,

$$T_{BL} = T_{BK} \, e^{-\langle\tau\rangle} + T(1 - e^{-\tau_L^*}). \tag{8.9}$$

The difference ΔT_B of the brightness temperature in the line and in the adjacent continuum is

$$\Delta T_B = T_{BL} - T_{BK} = (1 - e^{-\tau_L^*})T - (1 - e^{-\langle\tau\rangle})T_{BK}. \tag{8.10}$$

Since τ_L^* and $\langle\tau\rangle$ are of the same order, we see from equation (8.10) that the line will be visible in emission if $T \gg T_{BK}$ and in absorption if $T \ll T_{BK}$. Since in the interstellar medium $T \approx T_k \gg T_{BK}$, the 21-cm line is seen in emission. Because of the inequality $T \gg T_{BK}$ in the interstellar medium, we can neglect T_{BK} as compared with T and write simply

$$\Delta T_B = T(1 - e^{-\tau_L^*}).$$

In an optically thin case ($\tau_L^* \ll 1$) we have

$$\Delta T_B = T\tau_L^* = 5.44 \times 10^{-14} \int_0^{s^*} N(v)\, ds = 5.44 \times 10^{-14}\, N_H(v), \quad (8.11)$$

independent of temperature, where $N_H(v)dv$ is the number density of hydrogen atoms with velocities between v and $v + dv$. If we observe the 21-cm line on the background of a strong radio source, the line is seen in absorption superimposed on the spectrum of the discrete source, as in the case of the optical interstellar lines. If we neglect the brightness temperature of the interstellar continuum radiation, T_{BK}, in comparison with the kinetic temperature T_k and with the brightness temperature of the background radio source T_B, and if we neglect the continuum absorption coefficient κ_K in comparison with the line absorption coefficient κ_L, we can write the transfer equations in the line and in the continuum as

$$T_{BL}{}^S = T_B\, e^{-\tau_L^*} + T(1 - e^{-\tau_L^*})$$

$$T_{BK}{}^S = T_B\, e^{-\tau_K^*} \simeq T_B$$

when looking at the discrete source, and

$$T_{BL}{}^N = T(1 - e^{-\tau_L^*})$$

$$T_{BK}{}^N \simeq 0$$

when looking just off the discrete radio source. The difference of the brightness temperatures in the line and in the adjacent continuum is therefore

$$\Delta T^S = T_{BL}{}^S - T_{BK}{}^S = (T - T_B)(1 - e^{-\tau_L^*})$$

when the antenna is pointing at the source, and

$$\Delta T^N = T_{BL}{}^N - T_{BK}{}^N = T(1 - e^{-\tau_L^*})$$

when it is pointing off the source. Eliminating T between the above equations and solving for τ_L^* yields

$$\tau_L^* = -\ln\left(1 - \frac{\Delta T^N - \Delta T^S}{T_B}\right). \quad (8.12)$$

In the above expression for τ_L^* all the right-hand values are known from measurements, and

$$\tau_L{}^* = \int_0^{s^*} \kappa_L \, ds$$

can therefore be computed: s^* is the extent of the interstellar matter up to the (galactic) source considered. Equation (8.12) is sometimes useful for estimating a lower limit on the distance to a discrete radio source.

The importance of observations of the 21-cm line of neutral hydrogen derives from the fact that it provides the only method of direct observation of neutral hydrogen in the ground state. Optical observations of Balmer lines give information on the population of higher levels, although through the assumption of local thermodynamic equilibrium one can estimate the population of the ground level. In many interesting cases, however, matter and radiation are far from being in equilibrium. The regions of neutral hydrogen in the interstellar matter, where practically all of the atoms are in the ground state, cannot be observed by means of optical astronomy. The 21-cm line is therefore an important tool in the investigation of interstellar hydrogen, most of which is in the form of H I regions. Moreover, the radio observations are not affected by interstellar dust, and therefore the most remote parts of the galaxy can be observed with radio methods.

We will not discuss in detail the investigation of the structure of the galaxy by means of the hydrogen-line studies, because this book covers primarily the physics of extragalactic radio sources, but we will mention a few of the important aspects of study. The 21-cm observations permit the determination of the galactic rotation at distances from the center which are smaller than the sun's distance. The determination is made by measuring a maximum radial velocity in a given direction and assuming that it arises from a neutral hydrogen cloud located at the point where the radius vector from the galactic center is perpendicular to the line of sight. Assuming further that the rotation is circular and that the sun's distance from, and velocity about, the galactic center are known, we can in principle obtain the galactic rotation curve. At distance larger than the sun's distance the rotation curve has to be derived from dynamical considerations.

The most important contribution of the 21-cm line studies to the knowledge of galactic structure is the determination of the distribution of neutral hydrogen in the plane of the galaxy. A line profile obtained by observation in a particular direction in the galactic plane yields the radial velocities of the principal concentrations of neutral hydrogen. With the knowledge of the galactic rotation curve the radial velocities can be converted into the distances to neutral hydrogen regions. On the other hand, the integrated feature in the line profile, corresponding to a given region with particular radial velocity, yields information on the integrated density N_H of neutral hydrogen. The hydrogen density at a given distance can be computed from N_H if an estimate of the size of the observed region is made from the shape of the line profile. Many factors introduce uncertainties into this procedure for the determination of the neutral hydrogen distribution in the galaxy. Any large-scale deviations from circular rotation as well as local systematic deviations from the general galactic rotation cause a distortion of the neutral hydrogen distribution. Moreover, there is an ambiguity in the conversion of radial velocity into distance for distances from the galactic center smaller than the sun's distance. The random motions within the hydrogen regions or their complexes broaden the line profiles and are an additional source of errors in determining the density distribution.

Observations of the 21-cm hydrogen line also provide a means of investigating the structure and masses of nearby external galaxies.

8.3 Molecular Lines

The 18-cm hydroxyl (OH) radio lines were the first molecular lines detected by radio-astronomical methods. The lines are formed by the transitions between the hyperfine structure of the two levels corresponding to the Λ doubling of the lowest electronic, rotational, and vibrational energy state of the OH molecule. The lowest energy levels of hydroxyl are represented in Figure 8.1. The ground state of the hydroxyl molecule is the $J = 3/2$ rotational state of the $^2\Pi_{3/2}$ electronic state. In this state two different orientations of the electron distribution in the molecule (the molecule has an odd number of electrons) relative to the molecular rotation axis are possible: one along the rotation axis, the other in the plane of rotation (Figure 8.2). Therefore the $J = 3/2$ rotational state of $^2\Pi_{3/2}$ splits into two levels. This phenomenon is called Λ doubling. The transition between these two levels gives rise to the 18-cm radio line. Each level of the Λ doublet has a hyperfine structure and is split into two states in which the hydrogen atom spin and the molecule's magnetic moment are parallel ($F = 2$) or antiparallel ($F = 1$) to each other. Between these levels four electric dipole transitions are allowed. These transitions are described in Table 8.1 together with Λ-doubling transitions in excited states. The relative intensities of the lines are given for the case of equally

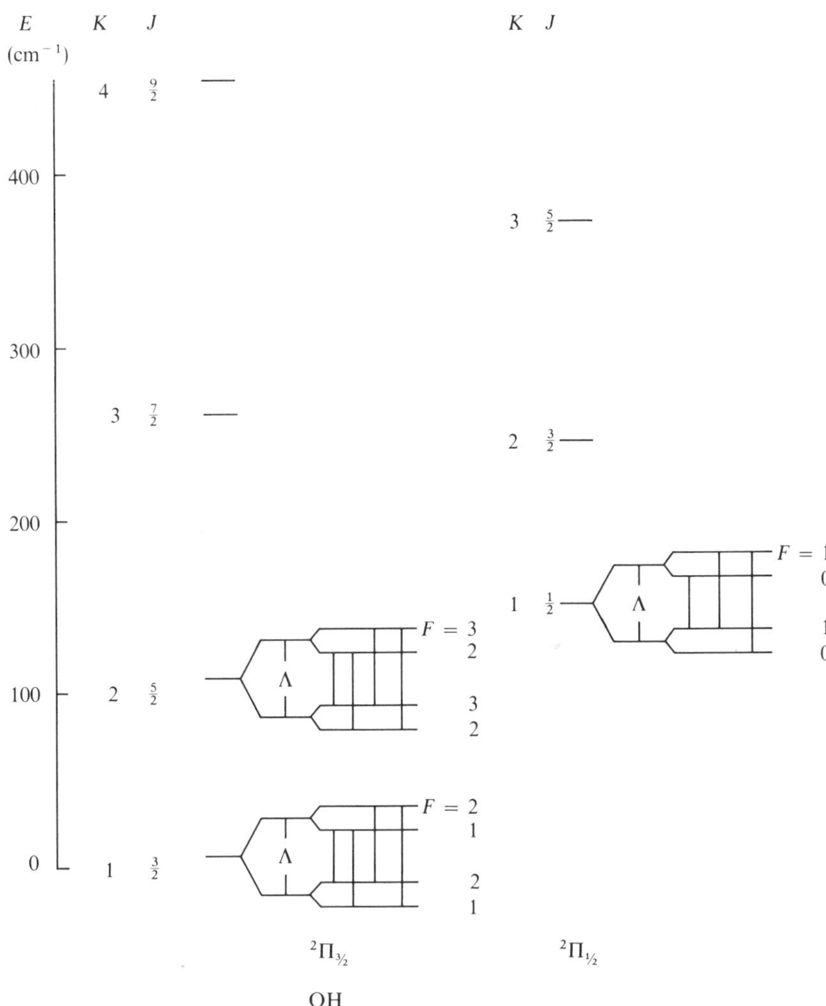

Fig. 8.1 Lowest energy levels of hydroxyl. The Λ-doubling levels and the hyperfine structure levels are not to scale.

populated levels and an optically thin source. They are derived from the values of the Einstein coefficient A and from the statistical weights $g_F = 2F + 1$ of the levels. If the source is optically thick the relative intensities of all the lines are nearly equal to unity. Since the 18-cm OH lines arise from a redistribution of electric charge in the molecule (electric dipole transitions) and the 21-cm line of H arises from a redistribution of the magnetic moment of the atom (magnetic dipole transition), the intensity of OH lines would be 10^4 times larger than that of the H line, all

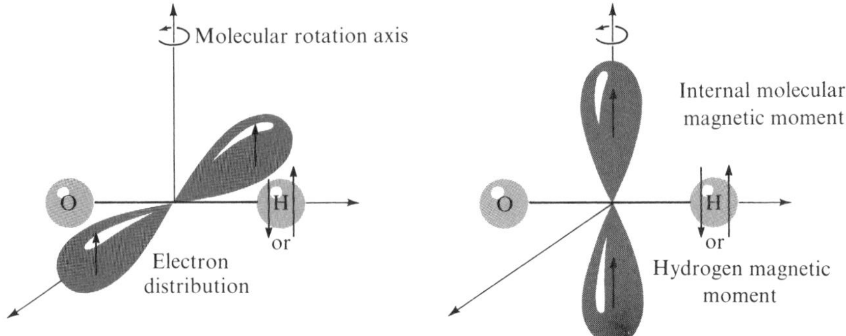

Fig. 8.2 The two different orientations of the electron distribution in the OH molecule leading to Λ-doubling.

other things being equal, because the line intensities depend on the square of dipole moments and the electric dipole moment is two orders of magnitude larger than the magnetic one. Therefore the effect of a 10^{-7} times lower abundance of OH in the interstellar medium relative to H is partially offset by the 10^4 times larger line intensity of OH, and the interstellar hydroxyl can then still be detected despite its much lower abundance. The Einstein coefficient A_{21} of the $F = 2$–2 transition is 8×10^{-11} sec^{-1}.

The hydroxyl 18-cm line was first detected in absorption in a few sources including the galactic center. The Doppler widths of these lines correspond to temperatures of the order of 100° K, but there are anomalies in the line strength, some of which cannot be explained in terms of large optical depth alone. The Doppler shifts of OH absorption lines are often different from those of hydrogen 21-cm lines. In some cases an anomalous abundance of OH was noted (10^{-4} that of atomic hydrogen).

The 18-cm emission of OH comes from regions exhibiting very fine structure with components of angular diameter smaller than 0.02 seconds of arc, characterized by very high brightness temperatures. The upper limits on brightness temperature of the stronger components are of the order of 10^{12} °K. The OH emission seems to be located near the edges of a region of ionized hydrogen (H II region). The spectra of the OH emission regions are rather complex. They exhibit many components that are relatively narrow (sometimes less than 2 kHz). The intensity ratios of the four hyperfine components of the Λ doubling are very different from those predicted by the theoretical line strengths, and the intensity of the 1665 MHz component is almost always stronger than that of the 1667 MHz

Table 8.1 Λ-doubling transitions in the lowest states of the OH molecule

State	F number for levels		Frequency (MHz)	Relative intensity
	upper	lower		
$^2\Pi_{3/2}, J = \frac{3}{2}$	1	2	1612.231	1
	1	1	1665.401	5
	2	2	1667.358	9
	2	1	1720.533	1
$^2\Pi_{3/2}, J = \frac{5}{2}$	2	3	6016.746	1
	2	2	6030.739	14
	3	3	6035.085	20
	3	2	6049.084	1
$^2\Pi_{1/2}, J = \frac{1}{2}$	0	1	4660.242	2
	1	1	4750.656	1
	1	0	4765.562	1

line. The spectra at the four frequencies do not appear to be related. The line intensity varies with time in some sources, with variations of intensity by a factor of two or three occuring with a time scale of a few months. The OH emission, which is strongly polarized, also seems to be time dependent. Completely linearly polarized lines, as well as completely circularly polarized ones, have been observed.

Similar Λ-doubling transitions were observed in the $^2\Pi_{3/2}$, $J = 5/2 (K = 2)$ state of OH. Each level of this doublet is split into two levels by hyperfine interaction, these levels have total angular momenta characterized by $F = 3$ and $F = 2$. Between these levels four transitions described in Table 8.1 can take place. The most intense $F = 3$–3 and $F = 2$–2 lines were detected in the source W3, from which the anomalous Λ-doubling $^2\Pi_{3/2}$, $J = 3/2$ emission was previously observed. Observations indicate anomalous excitation, the lines appear to be circularly polarized and the observed ratio of the $F = 3$–3 to the $F = 2$–2 intensities is about 3, implying that hydroxyl is not in local thermodynamical equilibrium.

The emission from the $^2\Pi_{1/2}$, $J = 1/2$ $(K = 1)$ state of hydroxyl was detected in the direction of the galactic source W3. The $^2\Pi_{1/2}$, $J = 1/2$ state is split by Λ-doubling into two levels which show hyperfine structure corresponding to the total angular momentum of $F = 1$ and $F = 0$. In sum, the $^2\Pi_{1/2}$, $J = 1/2$ state is split into four levels, just like the $^2\Pi_{3/2}$, $J = 3/2$ state, but the number of allowed transitions between the hyperfine levels is only three since the $F = 0$–0 transition is forbidden. The $F = 1$–0 transition was observed, but no polarization was detected; the $F = 1$–1 transition was not seen although in local thermodynamical equilibrium it should be at least as strong as the $F = 1$–0 transition. This implies a non-thermal origin of the observed emission.

The observed properties of OH emission suggest that a maser type mechanism involving pumping at one frequency and stimulated emission of radiation at the observed radio frequencies must be the mechanism responsible for the OH emission in cosmic sources. Indeed, it is difficult to account for the observed anomalous line intensities without simulated emission. Furthermore, polarization can be understood in terms of stimulated emission, whereas thermal emission would not produce polarization unless a Zeeman effect with a rather high magnetic field was invoked. A line width less than the thermal width can be produced by maser action. Several schemes of a maser mechanism of radio emission of the interstellar hydroxyl were proposed with various pumping processes (optical, infrared, radio, collisional), but none of them are yet in full agreement with all the observational data.

The hydroxyl lines, like the 21-cm hydrogen line, constitute a useful tool for investigating the interstellar medium—not only because they provide a way of determining the abundance of oxygen relative to hydrogen; or because under certain conditions they allow differentiation between thermal and turbulent broadening, since OH has a molecular weight different from that of hydrogen—but because OH is excited by a mechanism different from that which excites hydrogen, a mechanism that very probably involves stimulated emission.

Another molecule detected in the interstellar medium by radio-astronomical methods is that of ammonia (NH_3). The inversion transitions of ammonia in its ground vibrational state and its rotational states (J, K) of $(1, 1)$, $(2, 2)$, $(3, 3)$, $(4, 4)$, and $(6, 6)$ were observed in emission. The rest frequencies of these transitions are: 23,694.48, 23,722.71, 23,870.11, 24,139.39, and 25,056.04 MHz. Figure 8.3 represents the lowest energy levels in the ground vibrational state of ammonia. The $(4, 3)$, $(3, 1)$ and $(2, 1)$ inversion transitions were not detected. This can be understood by noting that the $J = K$ levels are metastable with respect to infrared transitions, but that the $J \neq K$ levels are not. If collisions are not frequent

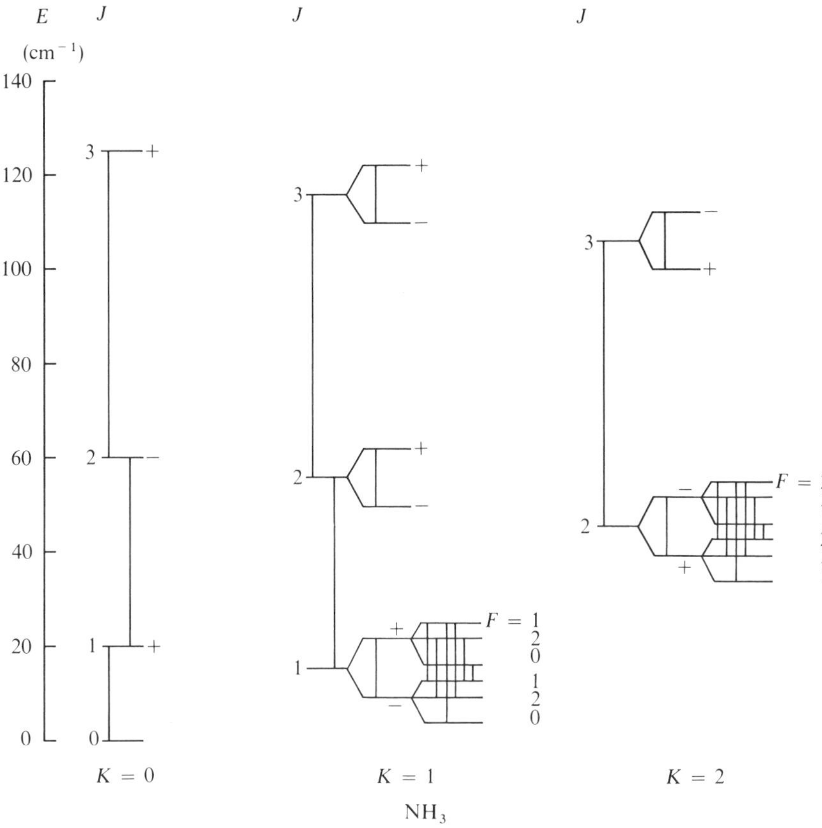

Fig. 8.3 Energy levels of ammonia in its ground vibrational state. The inversion levels and the hyperfine structure levels are not to scale.

enough to populate the $J \neq K$ levels significantly, but occur often enough to maintain thermal equilibrium in metastable levels and in their individual inversion levels, we will not see emission from the $J \neq K$ levels. The observed intensities of NH_3 emission in Sagittarius B2 can be explained in terms of two radiating regions at different temperatures.

Water (H_2O) was observed in emission from the 22,235.22 MHz 6_{16}–5_{23} rotational transition in the direction of a number of galactic sources including Sagittarius B2, W3, and Orion Nebula. The sources show many spectral features, some of which are polarized and some variable with a time scale of a few weeks. The sources are compact—less than a minute of arc in diameter—and have very high brightness temperatures. The positions and range of Doppler velocities of the hydroxyl and

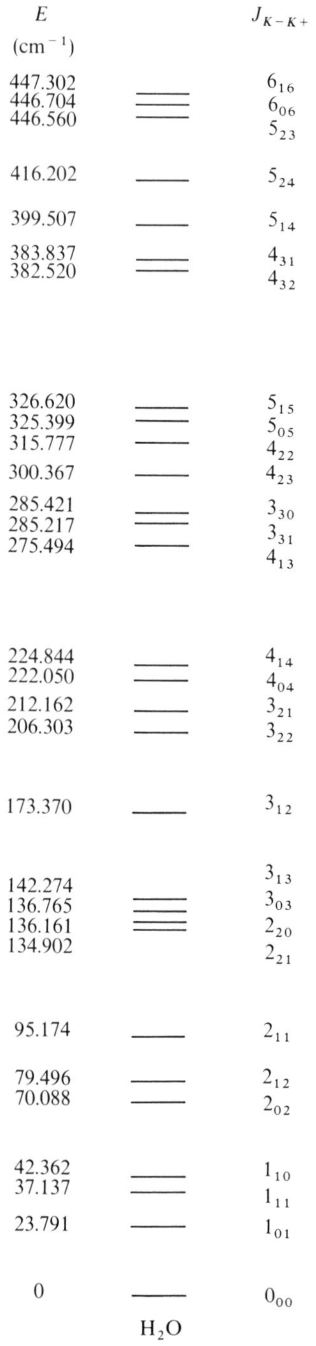

E (cm^{-1})	$J_{K_-K_+}$
447.302	6_{16}
446.704	6_{06}
446.560	5_{23}
416.202	5_{24}
399.507	5_{14}
383.837	4_{31}
382.520	4_{32}
326.620	5_{15}
325.399	5_{05}
315.777	4_{22}
300.367	4_{23}
285.421	3_{30}
285.217	3_{31}
275.494	4_{13}
224.844	4_{14}
222.050	4_{04}
212.162	3_{21}
206.303	3_{22}
173.370	3_{12}
142.274	3_{13}
136.765	3_{03}
136.161	2_{20}
134.902	2_{21}
95.174	2_{11}
79.496	2_{12}
70.088	2_{02}
42.362	1_{10}
37.137	1_{11}
23.791	1_{01}
0	0_{00}

H_2O

Fig. 8.4 Lowest energy levels of water.

water sources agree in general, although there is not much similarity in detailed spectral features. The 6_{16}–5_{23} water line, involving rotational levels of energy of more than 450 cm^{-1} (see Figure 8.4) with a lifetime of about ten seconds, requires moderately high temperatures and frequent excitations either by collisions or by radiation to produce the observed line intensity. It is therefore surprising that radiation from the NH_3 states that are not metastable was not observed (in particular in Sagittarius B2, where both NH_3 and H_2O molecules are present) unless the excitation mechanism for water and ammonia was different. Indeed, very high brightness temperatures of water sources; presence of narrow lines with widths corresponding to temperatures of only about 100 °K, clearly not in equilibrium with radiation temperatures and with excitation temperatures; and the enormous masses of the emitting regions (5×10^4 solar masses) required to account for the microwave emission if assumed isotropic; all suggest that the radiation is produced by stimulated emission.

The first organic polyatomic molecule detected in the interstellar matter is the recently observed formaldehyde (H_2CO) molecule. The 4829.649 MHz 1_{11}–1_{10}, $F = 2$–2 transition (Figure 8.5) was seen in absorption against a number of sources including Sagittarius A and B2, and W3. The presence of molecules like H_2CO together with H_2O and NH_3 indicates that the chemical evolution of interstellar matter is more complex than had been previously thought on basis of optical observations of interstellar lines.

It will certainly take some time and much more observational study to produce a clear and coherent picture of the mechanism of radiation of interstellar molecules and of chemical processes in the interstellar medium.

8.4 Recombination Lines

When an electron is recaptured by an ion into a level other than the ground level, subsequent downward transitions will give rise to a series of spectral lines with frequencies

$$\nu = Z^2 R\left(\frac{1}{n_1^2} - \frac{1}{n_2^2}\right), \tag{8.13}$$

where n_1 and n_2 are the principal quantum numbers of the lower and upper energy levels, respectively. Z is the effective nuclear charge and R is the

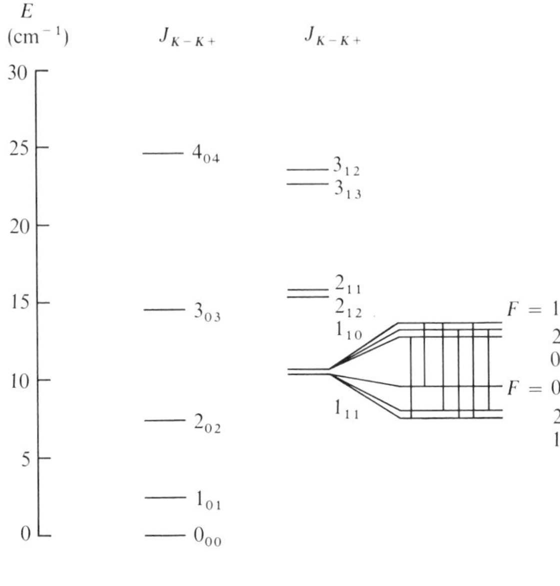

Fig. 8.5 Lowest energy levels of formaldehyde. The hyperfine structure levels are not to scale.

Rydberg constant. The values of the Rydberg constant are given below for several elements:

Hydrogen	$R = 3.288052 \times 10^{15}$ Hz
Helium II	$R = 3.289391 \times 10^{15}$ Hz
Carbon VI	$R = 3.289927 \times 10^{15}$ Hz.

In a region of hot ionized interstellar hydrogen the energy levels are populated mainly by recombination accompanied by cascade transitions toward the ground state. The lines formed by such transitions are called recombination lines. The transitions between the level $n + 1$ and n have the highest transition probability. The transition probabilities and some other data on $n + 1 \rightarrow n$ recombination lines are given in Table 8.2. For low principal quantum numbers the lines are located in the optical region. In the radio range the recombination lines of hydrogen have been observed between 404 MHz, the H253α line, and 8872.5 MHz, the H90α

Table 8.2 Radio recombination lines

Wavelength (cm)	Frequency (MHz)	For hydrogen $n\alpha$ recombination lines: n	Distance between neighboring lines (MHz)	Einstein coefficient ($\sec^{-1}$)	Frequency difference between helium and hydrogen line (MHz)
0.1	3×10^5	28	32,000	2.9×10^2	122
1	3×10^4	60	1,500	6.6	12.2
10	3×10^3	130	69	1.5×10^{-1}	1.22
100	3×10^2	280	3.2	3.0×10^{-3}	0.122

line. In this notation α denotes the transition from $n+1$ to n, and as in optical spectra, the number preceding α refers to the principal quantum number n of the lower state. A few recombination lines of helium and carbon have also been observed. Observations yield the following four parameters characterizing the line: $\nu_L - \nu_R$, the Doppler shift of the observed central frequency ν_L from its rest frequency ν_R; $\Delta\nu_L$, the line width between half-intensity points; ΔT_B, the difference between the brightness temperature in the line center and in the adjacent continuum; and T_B, the brightness temperature in the continuum. The line width is due principally to the Doppler broadening: both levels are very close and the collisions disturb both upper and lower levels in a similar way; therefore the line is not substantially collisionally broadened. In the case of Doppler broadening we can insert into equation (8.3) the function $F(v)$ of the form

$$F(v) = \sqrt{\frac{M}{2\pi kT}} \exp\left(-\frac{Mv^2}{2kT}\right), \tag{8.14}$$

which describes the Maxwellian distribution of velocities. We therefore have the following expression for the line absorption coefficient:

$$\begin{aligned} \kappa_L &= \frac{3}{8\pi} N_n \frac{hc^3}{kT\nu^2} A_{n\alpha} \sqrt{\frac{M}{2\pi kT}} \exp\left(-\frac{M}{2kT} v^2\right) \\ &= \frac{3}{8\pi^{3/2}} N_n A_{n\alpha} \frac{hc^2}{kT\nu} \frac{1}{\Delta\nu_D} \exp\left[-\left(\frac{\Delta\nu}{\Delta\nu_D}\right)^2\right], \end{aligned} \tag{8.15}$$

where

$$\Delta\nu = \nu - \nu_L = \frac{\nu_L}{c}\, v,$$

and

$$\Delta\nu_D = \frac{\nu_L}{c}\sqrt{\frac{2kT}{m}} = 4.3 \times 10^{-7}\, T^{1/2}\, \nu_L. \tag{8.16}$$

N_n is the population of the nth state, and M is the mass of the hydrogen atom; turbulent velocities are neglected here compared with thermal ones. The equilibrium population of the nth state of hydrogen for large n, found from the Saha equation, is

$$N_n = 4.2 \times 10^{-16}\, n^2 \frac{N_e^2}{T^{3/2}}, \tag{8.17}$$

where N_e is the number density of electrons; the transition probability $A_{n\alpha}$ for large n is

$$A_{n\alpha} = 5.2 \times 10^9\, n^{-5}, \tag{8.18}$$

and from equation (8.13) we find $\nu_L \simeq 2Rn^{-3}$ for large n. In the optically thin case we therefore have at the line center (ignoring the frequency dependence over the line)

$$\frac{\Delta T_B}{T_B} = \frac{T\tau_L{}^*}{T\tau_K{}^*} = 2.3 \times 10^{-6} \frac{\nu^{1.1}}{T^{3/2}}, \tag{8.19}$$

since (cf. Section 6.2)

$$T_B = \frac{\mathscr{E}}{T^{1/2}\, \nu^{2.1}}, \tag{8.20}$$

where $\mathscr{E}$ is the emission measure (in cgs units). Equation (8.19) is obtained by the use of equations (8.15), (8.17), (8.18), and (8.20). Equation (8.19) permits the determination of the kinetic temperature T of a region of ionized hydrogen from the observations of recombination lines. If $\Delta\nu_L$ is measured, $\Delta\nu_D$ can be determined and used for the determination of T.

The kinetic temperature of ionized hydrogen regions determined from equation (8.19) are lower by a factor of two than the temperatures usually attributed to those regions. This is because the departures from local thermodynamic equilibrium are not taken into account in equation (8.19). The nonequilibrium corrections for the populations of energy levels for large principal quantum numbers are very close to unity; however the differences in the corrections for two neighboring levels are large in comparison with $h\nu/kT$ ($=2.4 \times 10^{-5}$ for H109α line) at radio frequencies. This indicates overpopulation of each level relative to the level below it, which leads to an increase of stimulated emission and to a maser-type enhancement of the line. When these corrections are taken into account, the kinetic temperatures obtained from the intensities of recombination lines agree with those obtained by optical means. The hydrogen recombination line intensities are affected relatively weakly by the departures from thermodynamic equilibrium. For heavier elements the enhancement of recombination lines can be large when the process of dielectric recombination, in which the recapture of an electron occurs through an intermediate, doubly excited state, is predominantly responsible for the population of levels with large principal quantum numbers. This enhancement makes possible observations of recombination lines of heavier elements, such as carbon. When lines of more heavy elements are observed, the recombination line technique may become an important way of determining relative abundances in ionized hydrogen regions.

Bibliographical Notes to Chapter 8

8.1. The possibilities of galactic radio spectroscopy in lines other than those already detected are considered in these six references:

1. I. S. Shklovsky, "Problems of Galactic Radiospectroscopy," in his *Cosmic Radio Waves*, Chap. 17, Gostechizdat, Moscow, 1956; and Harvard University Press, 1960.
2. A. H. Barrett, "Spectral Lines in Radio Astronomy," *Proc. IRE* **46**, 250–259 (1958).
3. A. E. Douglas and G. A. Elliott, "Laboratory Investigations of the Interstellar Radio-Frequency Lines of CH and Other Molecules," *Canadian J. Phys.* **43**, 496–502 (1965).
4. G. Herzberg, "Molecular Spectroscopy and Astrophysical Problems," *J. Opt. Soc. Am.* **55**, 229–238 (1965).
5. W. Miller Goss, "A New Determination of the Frequency of the Interstellar Radio Line of CH," *Astrophys. J.* **145**, 707–714 (1966).
6. B. J. Robinson, "Radio Observations of Interstellar Molecules," *in* H. van Woerden, ed., *Radio Astronomy and the Galactic System* (I. A. U. Symposium No. 31), pp. 49–64, Academic Press, London, 1967.

8.2. It is impossible, here, to give a complete bibliography of the 21-cm line observations; therefore, only a few major historical works and several recent review papers will be cited. The possibility of observing the 21-cm line of neutral hydrogen in interstellar space was suggested by Bakker and van der Hulst. The line was first detected in 1951: Refs. 8–10 report the observations.

7. C. J. Bakker and H. C. van der Hulst, "Radiogolven uit het wereldruim," *Nederlands Tijds. Nat.* **11**, 201–221 (1945).
8. H. I. Ewen and E. M. Purcell, "Radiation from Galactic Hydrogen at 1,420 Mc/sec.," *Nature* **168**, 356 (1951).
9. C. A. Muller and J. H. Oort, "The Interstellar Hydrogen Line at 1,420 Mc/sec. and an Estimate of Galactic Rotation," *Nature* **168**, 357–358 (1951).
10. W. Christiansen and J. Hindman, "A Preliminary Survey of 1420 Mc/s Line Emission from Galactic Hydrogen," *Australian J. Sci. Res.* **5**, 437–455 (1952).

The fundamental work on the distribution of neutral hydrogen in the galactic plane was reported in the following papers.

11. H. C. van der Hulst, C. A. Muller, and J. H. Oort, "The Spiral Structure of the Outer Part of the Galactic System Derived from Hydrogen Emission at 21 cm Wavelength," *Bull. Astron. Inst. Netherlands* **12**, 117–149 (1954).
12. G. Westerhout, "The Distribution of Atomic Hydrogen in the Outer Parts of the Galactic System," *Bull. Astron. Inst. Netherlands* **13**, 201–246 (1957).
13. M. Schmidt, "Spiral Structure in the Inner Parts of the Galactic System Derived from the Hydrogen Emission at 21 cm Wavelength," *Bull. Astron. Inst. Netherlands* **13**, 247–268 (1957).
14. C. A. Muller and G. Westerhout, "A Catalogue of 21 cm Line Profiles," *Bull. Astron. Inst. Netherlands* **13**, 155–195 (1957).
15. F. J. Kerr, J. V. Hindman, and C. S. Gum, "A 21 cm Survey of the Southern Milky Way," *Australian J. Phys.* **12**, 270–292 (1959).

Determinations of the galactic rotation from 21-cm observations were done by Kwee, Muller, and Westerhout, and by Kerr.

16. K. K. Kwee, C. A. Muller, and G. Westerhout, "The Rotation of the Inner Parts of the Galactic System," *Bull. Astron. Inst. Netherlands* **12**, 211–222 (1954).
17. F. J. Kerr, "Galactic Velocity Models and the Interpretation of 21-cm Surveys," *Monthly Notices Roy. Astron. Soc.* **123**, 327–345 (1962).

The excitation of the 21-cm line is discussed in the following papers.

18. J. P. Wild, "The Radio Frequency Line Spectrum of Atomic Hydrogen and its Application in Astronomy," *Astrophys. J.* **115**, 206–221 (1952).

19. S. A. Wouthuysen, "On the Excitation Mechanism of the 21 cm Interstellar Hydrogen Emission Line," *Astron. J.* **57**, 31–32 (1952).
20. E. M. Purcell and G. B. Field, "Influence of Collisions Upon Population of Hyperfine States in Hydrogen," *Astrophys. J.* **124**, 542–549 (1956).
21. G. B. Field, "Excitation of the Hydrogen 21 cm Line," *Proc. IRE* **46**, 240–250 (1958).

Reviews of the 21-cm line studies of neutral hydrogen in the galaxy were written by Heeschen, and by Kerr and Westerhout.

22. D. S. Heeschen, "Galactic Hydrogen Line Studies," *in* H. P. Palmer, R. D. Davies, and M. I. Large, eds., *Radio Astronomy Today*, Chap. 9, Harvard University Press, Cambridge, 1963.
23. F. J. Kerr and G. Westerhout, "Distribution of Interstellar Hydrogen," *in* A. Blaauw and M. Schmidt, eds., *Galactic Structure*, Chap 9, pp. 167–202, University of Chicago Press, 1965.

The expanding inner arm about 3 kpc from the galactic center was discovered by van Woerden, Rougoor, and Oort, and an extensive investigation of the central regions of the galaxy was made by Rougoor and Oort.

24. H. van Woerden, G. W. Rougoor, and J. H. Oort, "Expansion d'une structure spirale dans le noyau du Système Galactique, et position de la radiosource Sagittarius A," *Compt. Rend.* **244**, 1691–1695 (1957).
25. G. W. Rougoor and J. H. Oort, "Distribution and Motion of Interstellar Hydrogen in the Galactic System with Particular Reference to the Region within 3 Kiloparsecs of the Center," *Proc. Natl. Acad. Sci. U.S.* **46**, 1–13 (1960).

Recent reviews of the distribution and motions of neutral hydrogen in the galaxy were published by Lindblad, for regions away from the center, and Kerr, for the central region. The distribution of neutral hydrogen in nearby galaxies was reviewed by Roberts.

26. P. O. Lindblad, "Distribution and Systematic Motions of Neutral Hydrogen," I. A. U. Symposium No. 31, pp. 143–160 (see Ref. 6).
27. F. J. Kerr, "Interstellar Gas in the Central Region of the Galaxy," I. A. U. Symposium No. 31, pp. 239–251 (see Ref. 6).
28. M. S. Roberts, "The Hydrogen Distribution in Galaxies," I. A. U. Symposium No. 31, pp. 189–197 (see Ref. 6).

The volume of the proceedings of the I. A. U. Symposium No. 31 (see Ref. 6) contains many more articles on the recent 21-cm galactic studies.

8.3. The possibility of observing the 18-cm hydroxyl line in interstellar space was first mentioned by Shklovsky, and Barrett and Lilley made the first unsuccessful attempt to observe it.

29. I. S. Shklovsky, "Possibility of Observing the Monochromatic Radiation from Interstellar Molecules," *Dokl. Akad. Nauk SSSR* **92**, 25–28 (1953).
30. A. H. Barrett and A. E. Lilley, "A Search for the 18-cm Line of OH in Interstellar Medium," *Astron. J.* **62**, 5–6 (1957).

The interstellar OH radio line was discovered by Weinreb, Barrett, Meeks, and Henry. Their paper reported the detection of the two stronger OH lines in absorption in the source Cas A. Subsequently, other investigators observed OH (in absorption) in the galactic center (Refs. 32 and 33). Further observation of OH in the Galactic Center and in Cas A may be found in Refs. 34–37.

31. S. Weinreb, A. H. Barrett, M. L. Meeks, and J. C. Henry, "Radio Observations of OH in the Interstellar Medium," *Nature* **200**, 829–831 (1963).
32. J. G. Bolton, K. J. van Damme, F. F. Gardner, and B. J. Robinson, "Observation of OH Absorption Lines in the Radio Spectrum of the Galactic Centre," *Nature* **201**, 279–281 (1964).
33. S. J. Goldstein Jr., E. J. Gundermann, A. A. Penzias, and A. E. Lilley, "OH Absorption Spectra in Sagittarius," *Nature* **203**, 65 (1964).
34. N. H. Dieter and H. I. Ewen, "Radio Observations of the Interstellar OH Line at 1,667 Mc/s," *Nature* **201**, 279–281 (1964).
35. H. F. Weaver and D. R. W. Williams, "OH Absorption Profile in the Direction of Sagittarius A," *Nature* **201**, 380 (1963).
36. A. H. Barrett, M. L. Meeks, and S. Weinreb, "High-resolution Microwave Spectra of H and OH Absorption Lines in Cassiopeia A," *Nature* **202**, 475–476 (1964).
37. B. J. Robinson, F. F. Gardner, K. J. van Damme, and J. G. Bolton, "An Intense Concentration of OH Near the Galactic Centre," *Nature* **202**, 989–991 (1964).

The discovery of OH (in emission) in the source W49 was reported in the following paper. The authors reported anomalous intensities of the hyperfine component lines, implying a very exotic excitation mechanism.

38. H. F. Weaver, D. R. W. Williams, N. H. Dieter, and W. T. Lum, "Observations of a Strong Unidentified Microwave Line and of Emission from the OH Molecule," *Nature* **208**, 29–31 (1965).

OH emission was then found to be highly linearly polarized (Ref. 39) and variable (Ref. 40). Subsequent work (see Refs. 41–44) confirmed these findings.

39. S. Weinreb, M. L. Meeks, J. C. Carter, A. H. Barrett, and A. E. E. Rogers, "Observations of Polarized OH Emission," *Nature* **208**, 440–441 (1965).
40. N. H. Dieter, H. F. Weaver, and D. R. W. Williams, "Secular Variations in the Radio Frequency Emission of OH," *Astron. J.* **71**, 160 (1966).
41. B. Zuckerman, A. E. Lilley, and H. Penfield, "OH Emission in the Direction of Radio Source W49," *Nature* **208**, 441–443 (1965).
42. R. X. McGee, B. J. Robinson, F. F. Gardner, and J. G. Bolton, "Anomalous Intensity Ratios of the Interstellar Lines of OH in Absorption and Emission," *Nature* **208**, 1193–1195 (1965).
43. H. F. Weaver, D. R. W. Williams and N. H. Dieter, "OH Radio-Frequency Emission Near Very Bright H II Regions," *Astron. J.* **71**, 184 (1966).
44. D. R. W. Williams, N. H. Dieter, and H. F. Weaver, "The Linear Polarization of the OH Emission," *Astron. J.* **71**, 186 (1966).

Circular polarization in OH emission was observed by Davies, de Jager, and Verschuur, and by Barrett and Rogers.

45. R. D. Davies, G. de Jager, and G. L. Verschuur, "Detection of Circular Polarization in the OH Emission Sources Near W3 and W49," *Nature* **209**, 974–977 (1966).
46. A. H. Barrett and A. E. E. Rogers, "Observations of Circularly Polarized OH Emission and Narrow Spectral Features," *Nature* **210**, 188–190 (1966).

The following papers report further work on the polarization of the OH radio lines.

47. M. L. Meeks, J. A. Ball, and J. C. Carter, "The Polarization Parameters for OH Emission from W3," *Astron. J.* **71**, 392–393 (1966).
48. M. L. Meeks, J. A. Ball, J. C. Carter, and R. P. Ingalls, "Stokes Parameters for 1665-Megacycles-per-second Emission from OH near Source W3," *Science* **153**, 978–981 (1966).
49. A. E. E. Rogers, and J. M. Moran, P. P. Crowther, B. F. Burke, M. L. Meeks, J. A. Ball, and G. M. Hyde, "Interferometric Study of Cosmic Line Emission at OH Frequencies," *Phys. Rev. Letters* **17**, 450–452 (1966).
50. F. F. Gardner, R. X. McGee and B. J. Robinson, "18 cm OH-Line Radiation from NGC 6334," *Australian J. Phys.* **20**, 309–324 (1967).

Investigations of the fine structure of OH emission regions are reported in the following papers.

51. A. E. E. Rogers, J. M. Moran, P. P. Crowther, B. F. Burke, M. L. Meeks, J. A. Ball, and G. M. Hyde, "The Positions and Angular Extent of OH Emission Associated with the H II Regions W3, W24, W49 and NGC 6334," *Astrophys. J.* **147**, 369–377 (1967).

52. D. D. Cudaback, R. B. Read, and G. W. Rougoor, "Diameters and Positions of Three Sources of 18-cm OH Emission," *Phys. Rev. Letters* **17**, 452–455 (1966).
53. R. D. Davies, B. Rowson, R. S. Booth, A. J. Cooper, H. Gent, R. L. Adgie, and J. H. Crowther, "Measurements of OH Emission Sources with an Interferometer of High Resolution," *Nature* **213**, 1109–1110 (1967).
54. J. M. Moran, P. P. Crowther, B. F. Burke, A. H. Barrett, A. E. E. Rogers, J. A. Ball, J. C. Carter, and C. C. Bare, "Spectral Line Interferometry with Independent Time Standards at Stations Separated by 845 Kilometers," *Science* **157**, 676–677 (1967).
55. P. Palmer and B. Zuckerman, "Observations of Galactic OH," *Astrophys. J.* **148**, 727–744 (1967).
56. V. A. Hughes and R. Butler, "Radio Source W49 and Anomalous OH Emission," *Nature* **215**, 941–942 (1967).
57. W. Miller Goss, "OH Absorption in the Galaxy," *Astrophys. J. Supplement* **15**, 131–202 (1968).
58. H. F. Weaver, N. H. Dieter, and D. R. W. Williams, "Observations of OH Emission in W3, NGC 6334, W49, W51, W75, and Ori A," *Astrophys. J. Supplement* **16**, 219–274 (1968).

Normal OH emission in a cloud of interstellar dust was detected by Heiles, and by Ball and Meeks.

59. C. E. Heiles, "Normal OH Emission and Interstellar Dust Clouds," *Astrophys. J.* **151**, 919–934 (1968).
60. J. A. Ball and M. L. Meeks, "Observations of Galactic OH Emission," *Astrophys. J.* **153**, 577–594 (1968).

The following five papers and Ref. 6 review the observations of interstellar OH at radio frequencies.

61. B. J. Robinson, "Hydroxyl Radicals in Space," *Sci. Am.* **213**, 26–33 (1965).
62. N. M. Dieter, H. F. Weaver, and D. R. W. Williams, "The Interstellar Hydroxyl Radio Emission," *Sky and Telescopes* **31**, No. 3, 2–6 (1966).
63. N. H. Dieter and W. Miller Goss, "Recent Work on the Interstellar Medium," *Rev. Mod. Phys.* **38**, 256–297 (1966).
64. A. H. Barrett, "Radio Observations of Interstellar Hydroxyl Radicals," *Science* **157**, 881–889 (1967).
65. B. J. Robinson and R. X. McGee, "OH Molecules in the Interstellar Medium," *Ann. Rev. Astron. Astrophys.* **5**, 183–212 (1967).

The frequencies of Λ-doubling transitions in the $J = 3/2$ rotational state of the $^2\Pi_{3/2}$ electronic state of the OH radical were computed and observed in the laboratory by Ehrenstein, Townes, and Stevenson.

66. G. Ehrenstein, C. H. Townes, and M. J. Stevenson, "Ground State Doubling Transitions of OH Radical," *Phys. Rev. Letters* **3**, 40–41 (1959).

The transition probabilities for the OH radio line have been calculated—although sometimes incorrectly—by several authors; for discussion and bibliography, see the following paper. (The values of the Einstein coefficients quoted in the text are taken from this reference.)

67. A Carrington and T. A. Miller, "Einstein A Coefficient for the 18 cm Transition of OH," *Nature* **214**, 998–999 (1967).

Mechanisms of radio emission of interstellar OH are discussed in Refs. 40, 43, and 47, and in the next eleven papers.

68. J. L. Symmonds, "Formation of Hydroxyl Molecules in Interstellar Space," *Nature* **208**, 1195–1196 (1965).
69. I. S. Shklovsky, "Emission of Mysterium as a Maser Effect," *Astron. Tzirk.* No. 372, 1–6 (1966).
70. F. Perkins, T. Gold, and E. E. Salpeter, "Maser Action in Interstellar OH," *Astrophys. J.* **145**, 361–366 (1966).
71. I. D. Johnson, "A Mechanism for Maser Action of OH Molecules in Interstellar Space," *Cornell-Sydney Univ. Astron. Center Report* No. 46 (1966).
72. M. M. Litvak, A. L. McWhorter, M. L. Meeks, and M. J. Zeiger, "Maser Model for Interstellar OH Microwave Emission," *Phys. Rev. Letters* **17**, 821–826 (1966).
73. A. H. Cook, "Suggested Mechanism for the Anomalous Excitation of OH Microwave Emission from H II Regions," *Nature* **210**, 611–612 (1966).
74. C. V. Meer, "Theory for the Polarization of Cosmic OH^- 18 cm Radiation," *Phys. Rev. Letters* **17**, 774–775 (1966).
75. P. L. Bender, "Polarization of Cosmic OH^- 18-cm Radiation," *Phys. Rev. Letters* **18**, 562–564 (1967).
76. A. H. Cook, "Brightness and Temporal Variation of Radio Emission from Galactic OH," *Nature* **214**, 689–690 (1967).
77. V. A. Hughes, "Mechanism for Anamolous OH Emission from H II Regions," *Nature* **215**, 942–943 (1967).
78. J. A. Ball and D. H. Staelin, "Classification of OH Radio Emission Sources," *Astrophys. J.* **153**, 141–46 (1968).

The excitation of OH in a region of neutral hydrogen is discussed in the next two papers.

79. A. E. E. Rogers and A. H. Barrett, "Excitation Temperature of the 18 cm Line of OH in H I Regions," *Astrophys. J.* **151**, 163–175 (1968).
80. W. Miller Goss and G. B. Field, "Collisional Excitation of Low Energy

Permitted Transition by Charged Particles," *Astrophys. J.* **151**, 177–185 (1968).

Detection of Λ-doublet radiation from the excited $^2\Pi_{1/2}$, $J = 1/2$ state of interstellar hydroxyl was reported in Ref. 81, and from the $^2\Pi_{3/2}$, $J = 5/2$ state of OH, in Ref. 82.

81. B. Zuckerman, P. Palmer, H. Penfield, and A. E. Lilley, "Detection of Microwave Radiation from the $^2\Pi_{1/2}$, $J = 1/2$ State of OH," *Astrophys. J.* **153**, L69–L76 (1969).
82. J. L. Yen, B. Zuckerman, P. Palmer, and H. Penfield, "Detection of the $^2\Pi_{3/2}$, $J = 5/2$ State of OH at 5-Centimeter Wavelength," *Astrophys. J.* **156**, L27–L32 (1969).

Detection of interstellar ammonia was first reported in Ref. 83. Further observations of ammonia lines were reported in Ref. 84.

83. A. C. Cheung. D. M. Rank, C. H. Townes, D. D. Thornton, and W. J. Welch, "Detection of NH_3 Molecules in the Interstellar Medium by Their Microwave Emission," *Phys. Rev. Letters* **21**, 1701–1705 (1968).
84. A. C. Cheung, D. M. Rank, C. H. Townes, and W. J. Welch, "Further Microwave Emission Lines and Clouds of Ammonia in Our Galaxy," *Nature* **221**, 917–919 (1969).

Observations of interstellar water were reported in the next two papers and in Ref. 84, although the possibility of detecting water had been discussed earlier by Snyder and Buhl (Ref. 87).

85. A. C. Cheung, D. M. Rank, C. H. Townes, D. D. Thornton, and W. J. Welch, "Detection of Water in Interstellar Regions by its Microwave Radiation," *Nature* **221**, 626–628 (1969).
86. S. H. Knowles, C. H. Mayer, A. C. Cheung, D. M. Rank, and C. H. Townes, "Spectra, Variability, Size and Polarization of H_2O Microwave Emission Sources in the Galaxy," *Science* **163**, 1055–1057 (1969).
87. L. E. Snyder and D. Buhl, "Water-Vapor Clouds in the Interstellar Medium," *Astrophys. J.* **155**, L65–L69 (1969).

Formaldehyde was observed in the interstellar medium by Snyder, Buhl, Zuckerman, and Palmer, and the hyperfine structure of the relevant energy levels of formaldehyde was discussed by Oka, Takagi, and Morino.

88. L. E. Snyder, D. Buhl, B. Zuckerman, and P. Palmer, "Microwave Detection of Interstellar Formaldehyde," *Phys. Rev. Letters* **22**, 679–681 (1969).
89. T. Oka. K. Takagi, and Y. Morino, "Microwave Spectrum of Formaldehyde in Vibrationally Excited States," *J. Mol. Spectry.* **14**, 27–52 (1964).

The reader can become familiar with microwave spectroscopy of gases by reading the following volume:

90. C. H. Townes and A. L. Schawlow, *Microwave Spectroscopy*, McGraw-Hill, New York, 1955.

Fig. 8.1 is a modification of Fig. 1 of Ref. 87; Figs. 8.2, 8.3 and 8.4 follow figures in Refs. 64, 83, and 87; and Fig. 8.5 is a modification of a figure in Ref. 88.

8.4. Radio observations of recombination lines in galactic regions of ionized hydrogen were suggested by Kardashev in the following paper.

91. N. S. Kardashev, "On the Possibility of Detection of Allowed Lines of Atomic Hydrogen in the Radio Frequency Spectrum," *Astron. Zh.* **36**, 838–844 (1959).

The 104α and 90α lines of hydrogen were detected by Dravskikh and Dravskikh, and by Sorochenko and Borodzich. (Sorochenko and Borodzich's findings were reported by Vitkevich at the 12th General Assembly of the I. A. U. in 1964.)

92. Z. V. Dravskikh and A. F. Dravskikh, "An Attempt of Observation of an Excited Hydrogen Radioline," *Astron. Tzirk.* No. 282, 2–4 (1964).

Observations of other hydrogen recombination lines (109α, 126α, 156α, 158α, 166α, 253α) were reported in the following papers.

93. B. Höglund and P. G. Mezger, "Hydrogen Emission Line $n_{110} \rightarrow n_{109}$ Detection at 5009 Megahertz in Galactic H II Regions," *Science* **150**, 339–340 and 347–348 (1965).
94. A. E. Lilley, D. H. Menzel, H. Penfield, and B. Zuckerman, "Detection of Hydrogen Emission Lines $n_{159} \rightarrow n_{158}$ and $n_{157} \rightarrow n_{156}$ in Galactic H II Regions," *Nature* **209**, 468–470 (1966).
95. P. Palmer and B. Zuckerman, "Detection of Hydrogen Emission Line 166α in M 17," *Nature* **209**, 1118 (1966).
96. H. Penfield, P. Palmer, and B. Zuckerman, "Detection of the Hydrogen Emission Line 253α," *Astrophys. J.* **148**, L25–L28 (1967).
97. R. X. McGee and F. F. Gardner, "Hydrogen Recombination Lines 126α and 166α observed in Galactic H II Regions," *Nature* **213**, 579 (1967).
98. P. G. Mezger and B. Höglund, "Galactic H II Regions. II," *Astrophys. J.* **147**, 490–518 (1967).

The 94α and 148δ lines of hydrogen were observed by Gordon and Meeks; observations of the 137β and 148δ lines were made by Zuckerman, Palmer, Penfield, and Lilley; observations of the 158β and 159β lines were reported by Gardner and McGee.

99. M. A. Gordon and M. L. Meeks, "Observations of the 94α and 148δ Hydrogen and 94α Helium Emission Lines in the Orion Nebula," *Astrophys. J.* **149**, L21–25 (1967).
100. B. Zuckerman, P. Palmer, H. Penfield, and A. E. Lilley, "On the Electron Temperatures of H II Regions," *Astrophys. J.* **149**, L61–L64 (1967).
101. F. F. Gardner and R. X. McGee, "Detection of β Transitions in the Recombination Spectrum of Hydrogen near 9 cm Wavelength," *Nature* **213**, 480–481 (1967).

Detection of the 156α, 158α and 159α lines of helium was reported in the following paper; the 94α line of helium was reported in Ref. 99.

102. A. E. Lilley, P. Palmer, H. Penfield, and B. Zuckerman, "Radio Astronomical Detection of Helium," *Nature* **211**, 174–175 (1966).

The 109α line of carbon, detected by Palmer and co-workers (Ref. 103), was identified as such by Goldberg and Dupree (Ref. 104).

103. P. Palmer, B. Zuckerman, H. Penfield, A. E. Lilley, and P. G. Mezger, "Detection of a New Microwave Spectral Line," *Nature* **215**, 40–41 (1967).
104. L. Goldberg and A. K. Dupree, "Population of Atomic Levels by Dielectronic Recombination," *Nature* **215**, 41–43 (1967).

The frequencies for recombination lines were computed and tabulated by Lilley and Palmer.

105. A. E. Lilley and P. Palmer, "Tables of Radio Frequency Recombination Lines," *Astrophys. J. Supplement* **16**, 143–174 (1968).

The Stark broadening of recombination lines was discussed by Griem.

106. M. R. Griem, "Stark Broadening by Electron and Ion Impacts of $n\alpha$ Hydrogen Lines of Large Principal Quantum Number," *Astrophys. J.* **148**, 547–558 (1967).

The influence of departures from thermodynamic equilibrium on the populations of levels with large principal quantum numbers and the associated enhancement of recombination lines are discussed in the following paper and in Ref. 104.

107. L. Goldberg, "Stimulated Emission of Radio Frequency Lines of Hydrogen," *Astrophys. J.* **144**, 1225–1229 (1966).

For a review of problems related to observations of recombination lines and their interpretation, see

108. P. G. Mezger and P. Palmer, "Radio Recombination Lines: A New Observational Tool in Astrophysics," *Science* **160**, 29–42 (1968).

APPENDIX 1

The Radiation Field

The vibrations of the electric vector of a monochromatic electromagnetic wave can be represented in the plane perpendicular to the direction of propagation as

$$E_x = E_x^0 \sin(\omega t - \epsilon_x),$$
$$E_y = E_y^0 \sin(\omega t - \epsilon_y), \tag{A.1}$$

where E_x^0 and E_y^0 are the amplitudes of vibrations in two mutually perpendicular directions and ω is the circular frequency equal to $2\pi\nu$. If the ratio of the amplitudes $E_y^0/E_x^0 = \tan\alpha$, $(0 \leq \alpha \leq \pi/2)$ and the difference in phase $\delta = \epsilon_x - \epsilon_y$ are both absolute constants, we will call the beam of waves described by equation (A.1) a totally elliptically polarized beam. In this case E_x and E_y describe an ellipse in the (x, y) plane perpendicular to the direction of wave propagation and moving with the velocity of the wave. If we rotate the coordinate system by an angle φ such that $\tan 2\varphi = \tan\alpha \cos\delta$, we will have the coincidence of the coordinate axes with the principle axes of the ellipse. The vibrations in the new coordinate system will be represented by

$$E_\varphi = E^0 \cos\beta \sin\omega t,$$
$$E_{\varphi+\pi/2} = E^0 \sin\beta \cos\omega t, \tag{A.2}$$

where β is the ellipticity:

$$\cot \beta = \mp \frac{\text{Major axis}}{\text{Minor axis}}, \quad -\frac{\pi}{4} \le \beta \le +\frac{\pi}{4}. \tag{A.3}$$

In equation (A.3) the minus sign stands for left-handed polarization and the plus sign for right-handed polarization.† Between the parameters α and δ, characterizing the ellipse in the (x, y) system of coordinates, and the parameters β and φ, characterizing the ellipse in the system coinciding with the principal axes, there are the following relations:

$$\begin{aligned} \sin 2\beta &= \sin 2\alpha \sin \delta, \\ \tan 2\varphi &= \tan 2\alpha \cos \delta, \end{aligned} \tag{A.4}$$

and

$$\begin{aligned} \cos 2\alpha &= \cos 2\beta \cos 2\varphi, \\ \tan \delta &= \tan 2\beta \operatorname{cosec} 2\varphi. \end{aligned} \tag{A.5}$$

From equations (A.4) and (A.5) it follows that

$$\begin{aligned} \frac{c}{4\pi} 2E_x{}^0 E_y{}^0 \cos(\epsilon_x - \epsilon_y) &= I_\nu \cos 2\beta \sin 2\varphi, \\ \frac{c}{4\pi} 2E_x{}^0 E_y{}^0 \sin(\epsilon_x - \epsilon_y) &= I_\nu \sin 2\beta, \end{aligned} \tag{A.6}$$

where I_ν is the intensity of the beam of waves:‡

$$I_\nu = \frac{c}{4\pi}(E^0)^2 = \frac{c}{4\pi}[(E_x{}^0)^2 + (E_y{}^0)^2] = I_{\nu x} + I_{\nu y}. \tag{A.7}$$

Equation (A.7) follows from the Pointing theorem, which relates the flux of energy of the wave through a unit surface area to the amplitude of the electric vector of the wave, since the intensity is defined through the equation,

---

† In physics, if the rotation of the electric vector in a plane perpendicular to the direction of wave propagation is clockwise when the wave is approaching the observer, or counter-clockwise when the wave is receding from the observer, then the polarization of the wave is referred to as right-handed. In radio engineering such a wave will be called left-handed. In this book we use the classical physics definitions of right- and left-handed polarization.

‡ In reality we do not have absolutely monochromatic waves, and the amplitudes and phases vary with time. In elliptically polarized radiation the amplitude ratio and the phase difference are always constant regardless of changes of the amplitudes and phases. The relation of equation (A.7) between the intensity and the amplitudes of vibration has to be modified in the sense that the squares of the amplitudes appearing in this equation should be understood as time averages.

$$dE_\nu d\nu = I_\nu \cos\vartheta \, d\nu \, d\sigma \, d\Omega \, dt, \tag{A.8}$$

where $dE_\nu d\nu$ is the energy flowing across an area $d\sigma$ in a frequency interval from ν to $\nu + d\nu$ in a direction confined to a solid angle $d\Omega$ during a time dt, and ϑ is an angle between the direction in which the intensity is considered and the direction of an outward normal to the area $d\sigma$. The intensity I_ν is then the amount of radiant energy dE_ν in a unit frequency interval flowing in the directions confined to a unit solid angle centered on a given direction, across a unit area perpendicular to this direction in a unit of time (see Figure 1.3). The intensity is, in general, a function of the point in space, the direction, and the time. A completely elliptically polarized wave is therefore characterized by its intensity and by two more parameters describing the polarization: the parameters could be α and δ, for example, or β and φ. Instead of using these mentioned parameters to characterize fully elliptically polarized radiation, the so-called *Stokes parameters* can be used. They are related to the parameters I_ν, α, and δ or I_ν, β, and φ in the following way:

$$\begin{aligned}
Q_\nu &= \frac{c}{4\pi}\left[(E_x{}^0)^2 - (E_y{}^0)^2\right] = I_\nu \cos 2\alpha = I_\nu \cos 2\beta \cos 2\varphi \\
&= I_{\nu x} - I_{\nu y}, \\
U_\nu &= \frac{c}{4\pi} 2E_x{}^0 E_y{}^0 \cos(\epsilon_x - \epsilon_y) = I_\nu \sin 2\alpha \cos\delta = I_\nu \cos 2\beta \sin 2\varphi \\
&= (I_{\nu x} - I_{\nu y}) \tan 2\varphi, \\
V_\nu &= \frac{c}{4\pi} 2E_x{}^0 E_y{}^0 \sin(\epsilon_x - \epsilon_y) = I_\nu \sin 2\alpha \sin\delta = I_\nu \sin 2\beta \\
&= (I_{\nu x} - I_{\nu y}) \tan 2\beta \sec 2\varphi.
\end{aligned} \tag{A.9}$$

The Stokes parameters are in many cases more convenient to use than the parameters I_ν, α, and δ or I_ν, β, and φ for reasons given below (page 211). The equations:

$$\begin{aligned}
I_\nu{}^2 &= Q_\nu{}^2 + U_\nu{}^2 + V_\nu{}^2, \\
\tan 2\varphi &= U_\nu / Q_\nu, \\
\sin 2\beta &= \frac{V_\nu}{\sqrt{Q_\nu{}^2 + U_\nu{}^2 + V_\nu{}^2}},
\end{aligned} \tag{A.10}$$

give the relations between I_ν, α, and δ and I_ν, β, and φ, which are the inverse relations to equation (A.9).

The Stokes parameters Q_ν, U_ν, and V_ν can be considered as Cartesian coordinates of a point P on a sphere of radius I_ν such that 2β and 2φ are the spherical coordinates of this point; this is called the Poincaré representation, and the sphere is called the Poincaré sphere. The Poincaré representation of the state of a monochromatic wave on a sphere is unique —every possible state of polarization corresponds to one point on the Poincaré sphere and vice versa. The Poincaré sphere is illustrated in Figure A.1. The north pole represents the state of right-handed circular polarization: $\delta = \pi/2$, $Q_\nu = U_\nu = 0$, and $V_\nu = I_\nu$. In the northern hemisphere we have $\beta > 0$, and the points represent right-handed elliptical polarization. On the equator, V_ν is equal to zero, and the points on the equator correspond to linearly polarized states with $\delta = 0$ or $n\pi$. The southern hemisphere is the locus of points representing left-handed elliptical polarization ($\beta < 0$). At the south pole we have $Q_\nu = U_\nu = 0$, and $V_\nu = -I_\nu$. At this point $\delta = -(\pi/2)$, and the south pole therefore represents a left-handed circular polarization. The relations of spherical trigonometry on the Poincaré sphere are very useful in finding the relationships between parameters characterizing a totally elliptically polarized beam of radiation.

Arbitrarily polarized radiation can be represented by equation (A.1), where the amplitude and phases are subjected to irregular variations and the ratio of amplitudes $\tan\alpha$ and the difference in phase δ in two perpendicular directions are not necessarily constant. For arbitrarily polarized light we define the Stokes parameters as

$$
\begin{aligned}
I_\nu &= \frac{c}{4\pi}\left[\langle (E_x{}^0)^2\rangle + \langle (E_y{}^0)^2\rangle\right],\\
Q_\nu &= \frac{c}{4\pi}\left[\langle (E_x{}^0)^2\rangle - \langle (E_y{}^0)^2\rangle\right],\\
U_\nu &= \frac{c}{4\pi}\, 2\langle E_x{}^0 E_y{}^0 \cos\delta\rangle,\\
V_\nu &= \frac{c}{4\pi}\, 2\langle E_x{}^0 E_y{}^0 \sin\delta\rangle,
\end{aligned}
\tag{A.11}
$$

Since in the arbitrarily polarized beam of radiation the amplitude ratio and the phase difference are not constant, we need four parameters in order to specify the polarization state fully, while in the case of totally elliptically polarized radiation we need only three Stokes parameters. We recall that for a totally elliptically polarized beam there was a relation between the intensity I_ν and the Stokes parameters Q_ν, U_ν, and V_ν [the first relation

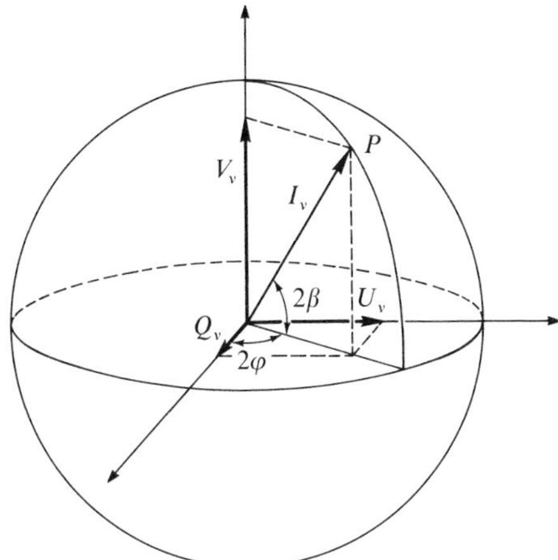

Fig. A.1 Poincaré sphere representation of elliptically polarized radiation.

of equation (A.10)]. This relation is not valid for an arbitrarily polarized beam. One can prove that for arbitrarily polarized radiation the inequality

$$I_\nu^2 \geq Q_\nu^2 + U_\nu^2 + V_\nu^2 \tag{A.12}$$

is always valid. The sign of equality in equation (A.12) refers to the particular case of totally elliptically polarized radiation. The parameter I_ν is therefore independent of the parameters Q_ν, U_ν, and V_ν in the case of arbitrary polarization.

The Stokes parameters I_ν, Q_ν, and V_ν, or any set of four independent parameters uniquely related to the Stokes parameters, specify an arbitrarily polarized beam of waves completely. This can be shown if one realizes that the process of the measurement of radiation consists of the determination of the intensity as a function of the position angle ψ and of an arbitrary constant phase shift η introduced by the measuring device between the two perpendicular components of the electric vector in the plane perpendicular to the direction of propagation of the beam. This measured intensity is equal to

$$I_\nu(\psi;\eta) = \frac{1}{2}\left[I_\nu + Q_\nu \cos 2\psi + (U_\nu \cos\eta - V_\nu \sin\eta)\sin 2\psi\right] \tag{A.13}$$

(see, for example, Ref. 1). We can conclude from equation (A.13) that the measurements do not permit one to distinguish between the two beams of waves characterized by the same Stokes parameters I_ν, Q_ν, U_ν, and V_ν. The Stokes parameters enter equation (A.13) linearly, and all of them have the dimensions of intensity. Therefore, if we have a mixture of several independent beams of waves (by independence we mean the inability to interfere mutually, i.e., the lack of a permanent phase relationship between the beams), the Stokes parameters characterizing the mixture of those beams of waves will be equal to the sum of the corresponding Stokes parameters characterizing the individual beams.

For unpolarized (natural) waves the measured intensity $I_\nu(\psi; \eta)$ is independent of ψ and of η; consequently for natural radiation the Stokes parameters Q_ν, U_ν, and V_ν must vanish according to equation (A.13). A beam of natural radiation can therefore be represented as a mixture of two oppositely polarized beams (i.e., beams for which the ellipses have their major axes mutually perpendicular, and the sense of rotation of the electric vector in one beam is opposite to that in the other). The Stokes parameters for two such beams will be characterized by the values (β, φ) and $(-\beta, \varphi + \pi/2)$, and their sum will be zero. The intensity of each of the component beams has to be equal to one half the intensity of the beam of natural radiation. Similarly, the most general mixture of arbitrary polarization can be represented as the sum of a beam of natural radiation and a beam of totally elliptically polarized radiation. The beams, of course, have to be independent. Among many other representations of an arbitrarily polarized beam of waves there is the useful representation as the sum of two independent oppositely polarized beams of unequal intensity.

Instead of intensity we can use other quantities like average intensity, flux, and so on, to describe the radiation field. The Stokes parameters can be expressed in terms of these new quantities instead of in terms of the intensity, as in equation (A.9). The average intensity J_ν is defined as

$$J_\nu = \frac{1}{4\pi} \int I_\nu \, d\Omega = \frac{1}{4\pi} \int_{\vartheta=0}^{\pi} \int_{\varphi=0}^{2\pi} I_\nu(\vartheta, \varphi) \sin\vartheta \, d\vartheta \, d\varphi, \qquad \text{(A.14)}$$

where 4π is the number of steradians in a sphere, and the element of solid angle $d\Omega$ defined by the ranges $(\vartheta, \vartheta + d\vartheta)$ and $(\varphi, \varphi + d\varphi)$ in cylindrical coordinates with the z-axis along the normal to $d\sigma$ is

$$d\Omega = \sin\vartheta \, d\vartheta \, d\varphi. \qquad \text{(A.15)}$$

The amount of radiant energy flowing through a unit area in a unit frequency interval and in a unit of time is called the flux:

$$F_\nu = \int I_\nu \cos\vartheta \, d\Omega = \int_{\vartheta=0}^{\pi} \int_{\varphi=0}^{2\pi} I_\nu(\vartheta, \varphi) \cos\vartheta \sin\vartheta \, d\vartheta \, d\varphi. \qquad \text{(A.16)}$$

Flux is a function of the direction of the outward normal to $d\sigma$, and this functional dependence has the character of a vector.

To better understand the physical difference between intensity and flux let us comment briefly. As long as the sun is visible as a disk and the limb darkening is neglected, the intensity in the directions confined within the solid angle defined by the solar disk does not depend on the distance from the sun. The flux, however, will depend on distance and will vary as the inverse square of the distance. We can remark further that optical systems change only the solid angle from which the radiation of a given intensity is received. Therefore they do change the flux (the amount of energy passing through the focus), but they do not increase the intensity of the radiation. On the contrary, the absorption in optical systems decreases the intensity of radiation passing through the system.

We have defined the quantities I_ν, J_ν, F_ν, and so forth, referring them to a frequency band from ν to $\nu + d\nu$. Of course, it is possible to introduce the quantities I_λ, J_λ, F_λ, and so forth, referring them to a wavelength band from λ to $\lambda + d\lambda$. They will be related to I_ν, J_ν, F_ν, and so on, as follows:

$$I_\nu = I_\lambda \left| \frac{d\lambda}{d\nu} \right| = \frac{\lambda^2}{c} I_\lambda. \tag{A.17}$$

If we are interested in the total intensity (at all frequencies), we can integrate I_ν over all frequencies (or integrate I_λ over all wavelengths):

$$I = \int_0^\infty I_\nu \, d\nu = \int_0^\infty I_\lambda \, d\lambda. \tag{A.18}$$

The energy density $u_{\text{rad},\nu}\, d\nu$ of the radiation at any given point in space is the amount of energy per unit volume in the frequency interval between ν and $\nu + d\nu$ which is flowing through the immediate neighborhood of that point. The energy density of the radiation field is therefore related to the intensity by the formula,

$$u_{\text{rad},\nu} = \frac{1}{c} \int I_\nu \, d\Omega = \frac{4\pi}{c} J_\nu. \tag{A.19}$$

Since a photon has a momentum $h\nu/c$ in its direction of propagation, the radiant energy E will carry a momentum E/c in the direction of propagation of radiation. Therefore a pressure will be associated with the radiation. This pressure at a given point is defined as the rate of transfer of the momentum normal to an arbitrary, infinitesimal element of surface containing this point, per unit area, and is given in terms of intensity by the formula,

$$p_{\text{rad}}(\nu) = \frac{1}{c} \int I_\nu \cos^2 \vartheta \, d\Omega = \frac{1}{c} \int_{\vartheta=0}^{\pi} \int_{\varphi=0}^{2\pi} I_\nu \cos^2 \vartheta \sin \vartheta \, d\vartheta \, d\varphi. \tag{A.20}$$

For an isotropic radiation field,

$$p_{\text{rad}}(\nu) = \frac{1}{3} u_{\text{rad},\nu}. \tag{A.21}$$

The intensity I_ν of the radiation field can be affected by the interaction of radiation with matter. The process of absorption of radiation by matter characterized by the *absorption coefficient* $\tilde{\kappa}_\nu$ will reduce the intensity of the radiation I_ν passing through a slab of matter of thickness ds by the amount

$$dI_\nu = -\tilde{\kappa}_\nu I_\nu \, ds. \tag{A.22}$$

On the other hand, an element of matter of unit volume may emit in a unit of time in a unit frequency interval within a unit solid angle the amount of energy equal to its *emission coefficient* ε_ν. The ratio S_ν of the emission to the absorption coefficient,

$$S_\nu = \frac{\varepsilon_\nu}{\tilde{\kappa}_\nu} \tag{A.23}$$

is called the source function. The emission and absorption processes can be described in terms of the *Einstein probability coefficients* A_{nm}, B_{nm}, and B_{mn}, instead of in terms of the emission and absorption coefficients, $\tilde{\kappa}_\nu$ and ε_ν. The *coefficient of spontaneous emission* A_{nm} is defined by the probability $A_{nm}(d\Omega/4\pi)dt$ that an atom passing from an excited state E_n to the state E_m emits a quantum of energy $h\nu_{nm}$ within an element of solid angle $d\Omega$ in an interval of time dt in the absence of an external field. The spontaneous emission, that is, the emission in the absence of an external field, is isotropic. The *coefficient of stimulated emission* (or of negative absorption) B_{nm} is defined by the probability $B_{nm}I_\nu(d\Omega/4\pi)dt$ that an external radiation field of intensity I_ν stimulates a transition from the state E_n to the state E_m accompanied by the emission of a quantum of energy $h\nu_{nm}$ in an interval of time dt within a solid angle $d\Omega$. The stimulated emission of radiation occurs in the same direction and with the same phase as the direction and phase of the incident radiation. The *coefficient of absorption* B_{mn} is defined by the probability $B_{mn}I_\nu(d\Omega/4\pi)dt$ that an atom absorbs a quantum of energy $h\nu$ in a time dt from directions within a solid angle $d\Omega$ from an external radiation field of intensity I_ν and passes from the state E_m to the state E_n. The Einstein coefficients A_{nm}, B_{nm}, and B_{mn}, and the emission and absorption coefficients $\tilde{\kappa}_\nu$ and $\mathcal{E}_\nu$ are related in the following way:

$$\mathcal{E}_\nu = \frac{N_n}{4\pi} [A_{nm} + B_{nm} I_\nu] h\nu, \tag{A.24}$$

$$\tilde{\kappa}_\nu = \frac{N_m}{4\pi} B_{mn} h\nu, \tag{A.25}$$

where N_n and N_m are the number of atoms in the states E_n and E_m, respectively.

The change in energy of the radiation passing through an element of matter of length ds must be equal to the difference in the rate of absorption and emission within this element,

$$\frac{dI_\nu}{ds} = -\tilde{\kappa}_\nu I_\nu + \mathcal{E}_\nu. \tag{A.26}$$

This equation is called the *equation of transfer of radiation*. Introducing the *optical thickness* τ_ν, defined as

$$\tau_\nu = \int_0^s \tilde{\kappa}_\nu \, ds, \tag{A.27}$$

and the source function, S_ν, we can write the equation of transfer in the form,

$$-\frac{dI_\nu}{d\tau_\nu} = I_\nu - S_\nu. \tag{A.28}$$

With the use of the Einstein coefficients A_{nm}, B_{nm}, and B_{mn}, the equation of transfer can be written in the form,

$$4\pi \frac{dI_\nu}{ds} = N_n A_{nm} h\nu - N_m B_{mn} h\nu \left[1 - \frac{N_n B_{nm}}{N_m B_{mn}}\right] I_\nu. \tag{A.29}$$

If the source function S_ν were not dependent on the intensity I_ν, the equation of transfer would be a first-order linear differential equation. Its solution would be

$$I_\nu(s) = I_\nu(0) e^{-\tau(s,0)} + \int_0^s e^{-\tau(s,s')} \tilde{\kappa}_\nu S_\nu \, ds'. \tag{A.30}$$

Since S_ν ordinarily depends on I_ν, equation (A.30) is not a solution of the equation of transfer, but is another form of the equation. The equation of transfer is, in general, an integro-differential equation.

For a system in *thermodynamic equilibrium* (an adiabatically enclosed system) the intensity of the radiation field does not depend on the properties of the medium but depends only on the temperature. For such a system the source function is equal to the *Planck function*

$$B_\nu(T) = \frac{2h\nu^3}{c^2}\frac{1}{e^{h\nu/kT} - 1}, \qquad \text{(A.31)}$$

where h is the Planck constant and k is the Boltzmann constant. The energy density of radiation in a system in thermodynamic equilibrium is proportional to the fourth power of the temperature (*Stefan's law*):

$$u = \int_0^\infty u_\nu \, d\nu = \frac{4\pi}{c}\int_0^\infty B_\nu \, d\nu = \frac{8\pi^5 k^4}{15c^3 h^3} T^4 = aT^4. \qquad \text{(A.32)}$$

For large $h\nu/kT$ (the ultraviolet region of the spectrum), *Wien's asymptotic form of the Planck formula* can be used:

$$B_\nu(T) \approx \frac{2h\nu^3}{c^2} e^{-(h\nu/kT)}. \qquad \text{(A.33)}$$

For small $h\nu/kT$ (the far infrared and radio regions) one can use the *Rayleigh-Jeans* asymptotic formula for the Planck function:

$$B_\nu(T) \approx \frac{2kT}{c^2}\nu^2. \qquad \text{(A.34)}$$

The Planck formula can be expressed in wavelength units, instead of in frequency units as in equation (A.30), and represented as a function of wavelength:

$$B_\lambda(T) = \frac{2hc^2}{\lambda^5}\frac{1}{e^{hc/\lambda kT} - 1}. \qquad \text{(A.35)}$$

By differentiating equation (A.34) we can specify the wavelength $\lambda_{\max}$(cm) at which B_λ attains maximum for a given temperature T(°K):

$$\lambda_{\max} T = 0.2898 \qquad \text{(A.36)}$$

Note that the maximum of the Planck function B_ν will occur for the same temperature at a different frequency than $\nu = c/\lambda_{\max}$. The Planck functions B_λ and B_ν are represented on Fig. A.2.

Introducing equations (A.24) and (A.25) into equation (A.23) and remembering that for a system in thermodynamic equilibrium S_ν and I_ν are equal to B_ν, we can obtain an expression for B_ν, which, when com-

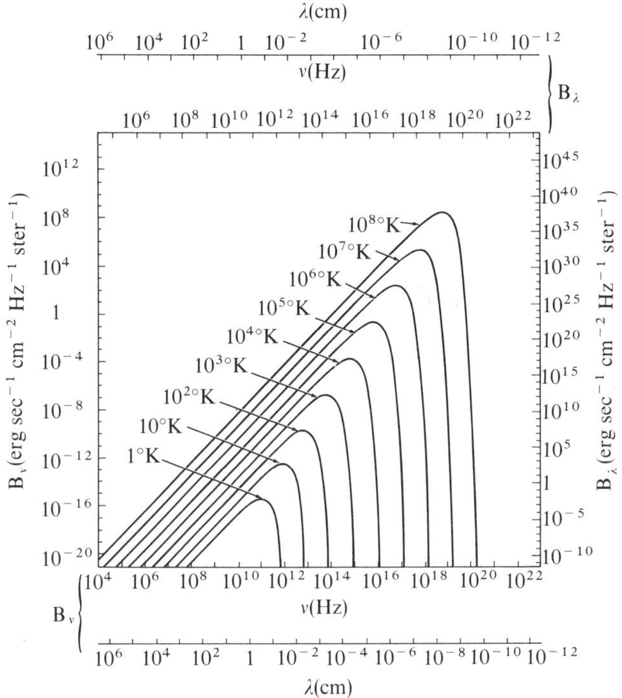

Fig. A.2 The Planck functions B_ν and B_λ as functions of frequency and wavelength for a range of temperatures. [Adapted from Kraus (Ref. 20, Chapter 1).]

pared with equation (A.35), will give the following relations between the Einstein coefficients:

$$\frac{A_{nm}}{B_{nm}} = \frac{2h\nu^3}{c^2}, \tag{A. 37}$$

$$\frac{B_{mn}}{B_{nm}} = \frac{N_n}{N_m} e^{h\nu/kT}. \tag{A.38}$$

For bound-bound transitions the populations N_m and N_n of the two levels E_n and E_m, respectively, are related by the Boltzmann formula,

$$\frac{N_n}{N_m} = \frac{g_n}{g_m} \exp\left(\frac{h\nu}{kT}\right) \tag{A.39}$$

where g_n, equal to $2J + 1$, is the statistical weight of the nth level, and J is the total angular momentum quantum number for the nth level (g_m has a corresponding definition). Introducing equation (A.39) into equation (A.38) we obtain

$$\frac{B_{mn}}{B_{nm}} = \frac{g_n}{g_m}. \tag{A.40}$$

The relations of equations (A.37) and (A.40) involve only atomic constants. Therefore if the validity of these relations has been proved for one particular state of the system as it was for the state of thermodynamical equilibrium, we can conclude that these relations have a general validity. If for a given transition one of the Einstein coefficients is calculated or determined experimentally, the remaining two can be determined from equations (A.37) and (A.40).

If the temperature gradients are small and the absorption coefficient is large, we can describe the local properties of a system by assuming that this system is locally in thermodynamic equilibrium. Therefore at every point in the system we can introduce a temperature T which will be a function of the position of the point in the system. In the neighborhood of every point we can apply the formulae developed for the case of thermodynamic equilibrium with the provision that the temperature is not constant throughout the system, but that it is a local temperature.

Using equations (A.37) and (A.38) and introducing the effective absorption coefficient κ_ν defined by

$$\kappa_\nu = \tilde{\kappa}_\nu \left[1 - \exp\left(\frac{h\nu}{kT}\right)\right], \tag{A.41}$$

we can write the equation of transfer (A.26) in the form,

$$\frac{dI_\nu}{ds} = \kappa_\nu B_\nu - \kappa_\nu I_\nu. \tag{A.42}$$

The effective coefficient of absorption κ_ν includes the effect of negative absorption (stimulated emission). We see from equation (A.41) that in the spectral region where $h\nu/kT \gg 1$, negative absorption is relatively unimportant, and we can replace the effective absorption coefficient κ by the coefficient $\tilde{\kappa}$. However, in the far infrared and radio region where $h\nu/kT \ll 1$, negative absorption is very important and can even be dominant.

Bibliographical Notes to Appendix 1

This appendix summarizes briefly some of the material on the radiation field contained in the following books.

1. S. Chandrasekhar, *Radiative Transfer*, Chap. I, Dover, New York, 1950.
2. S. Chandrasekhar, *Introduction to the Study of Stellar Structure*, Chap. V, Dover, New York, 1957.
3. W. A. Shurcliff, *Polarized Light Production and Use*, Harvard University Press, Cambridge, 1966.
4. H. C. van der Hulst, *Light Scattering by Small Particles*, Chap. 5, Wiley & Sons, New York, 1957.
5. M. Born and E. Wolf, *Principles of Optics*, Pp. 24–35 and 550–552, Pergamon Press, 1959.

APPENDIX 2

Tables of Special Functions

Table 1

The functions:

$$F(x) = x \int_x^{\infty} K_{5/3}(z)\, dz$$

$$K(x) = K_{5/3}(x)$$

$$S(x) = F(x)/K(x)$$

x	$F(x)$	$K(x)$	$S(x)$
1.00 E–04	9.96 E–02	6.65 E 06	1.50 E–08
2.00 E–04	1.25 E–01	2.10 E 06	5.98 E–08
5.00 E–04	1.70 E–01	4.55 E 05	3.73 E–07
1.00 E–03	2.13 E–01	1.43 E 05	1.49 E–06
2.00 E–03	2.70 E–01	4.51 E 04	5.92 E–06
5.00 E–03	3.58 E–01	9.80 E 03	3.66 E–05
1.00 E–02	4.45 E–01	3.09 E 03	1.44 E–04
2.00 E–02	5.47 E–01	9.72 E 02	5.63 E–04
3.00 E–02	6.13 E–01	4.95 E 02	1.24 E–03
4.00 E–02	6.63 E–01	3.06 E 02	2.17 E–03
5.00 E–02	7.02 E–01	2.12 E 02	3.31 E–03
6.00 E–02	7.33 E–01	1.56 E 02	4.70 E–03
7.00 E–02	7.60 E–01	1.20 E 02	6.33 E–03
8.00 E–02	7.82 E–01	9.63 E 01	8.12 E–03
9.00 E–02	8.01 E–01	7.91 E 01	1.01 E–02
1.00 E–01	8.18 E–01	6.63 E 01	1.23 E–02
1.10 E–01	8.33 E–01	5.65 E 01	1.47 E–02

Table 1. cont.

x	$F(x)$	$K(x)$	$S(x)$
1.20 *E*–01	8.45 *E*–01	4.88 *E* 01	1.73 *E*–02
1.30 *E*–01	8.56 *E*–01	4.27 *E* 01	2.00 *E*–02
1.40 *E*–01	8.66 *E*–01	3.77 *E* 01	2.30 *E*–02
1.50 *E*–01	8.74 *E*–01	3.36 *E* 01	2.60 *E*–02
1.60 *E*–01	8.82 *E*–01	3.01 *E* 01	2.93 *E*–02
1.70 *E*–01	8.89 *E*–01	2.72 *E* 01	3.27 *E*–02
1.80 *E*–01	8.95 *E*–01	2.47 *E* 01	3.63 *E*–02
1.90 *E*–01	9.00 *E*–01	2.25 *E* 01	3.99 *E*–02
2.00 *E*–01	9.04 *E*–01	2.07 *E* 01	4.38 *E*–02
2.10 *E*–01	9.08 *E*–01	1.90 *E* 01	4.77 *E*–02
2.20 *E*–01	9.11 *E*–01	1.76 *E* 01	5.18 *E*–02
2.30 *E*–01	9.13 *E*–01	1.63 *E* 01	5.60 *E*–02
2.40 *E*–01	9.15 *E*–01	1.52 *E* 01	6.04 *E*–02
2.50 *E*–01	9.17 *E*–01	1.41 *E* 01	6.50 *E*–02
2.60 *E*–01	9.17 *E*–01	1.32 *E* 01	6.94 *E*–02
2.70 *E*–01	9.17 *E*–01	1.24 *E* 01	7.40 *E*–02
2.80 *E*–01	9.18 *E*–01	1.16 *E* 01	7.89 *E*–02
2.90 *E*–01	9.18 *E*–01	1.10 *E* 01	8.39 *E*–02
3.00 *E*–01	9.18 *E*–01	1.03 *E* 01	8.88 *E*–02
3.10 *E*–01	9.17 *E*–01	9.77 *E* 00	9.39 *E*–02
3.20 *E*–01	9.16 *E*–01	9.25 *E* 00	9.90 *E*–02
3.30 *E*–01	9.15 *E*–01	8.77 *E* 00	1.04 *E*–01
3.40 *E*–01	9.14 *E*–01	8.32 *E* 00	1.10 *E*–01
3.50 *E*–01	9.12 *E*–01	7.92 *E* 00	1.15 *E*–01
3.60 *E*–01	9.10 *E*–01	7.54 *E* 00	1.21 *E*–01
3.70 *E*–01	9.08 *E*–01	7.18 *E* 00	1.26 *E*–01
3.80 *E*–01	9.06 *E*–01	6.85 *E* 00	1.32 *E*–01
3.90 *E*–01	9.03 *E*–01	6.55 *E* 00	1.38 *E*–01
4.00 *E*–01	9.01 *E*–01	6.26 *E* 00	1.44 *E*–01
4.10 *E*–01	8.98 *E*–01	6.00 *E* 00	1.50 *E*–01
4.20 *E*–01	8.96 *E*–01	5.75 *E* 00	1.56 *E*–01
4.30 *E*–01	8.93 *E*–01	5.51 *E* 00	1.62 *E*–01
4.40 *E*–01	8.91 *E*–01	5.29 *E* 00	1.69 *E*–01
4.50 *E*–01	8.88 *E*–01	5.08 *E* 00	1.75 *E*–01
4.60 *E*–01	8.85 *E*–01	4.89 *E* 00	1.82 *E*–01
4.70 *E*–01	8.82 *E*–01	4.70 *E* 00	1.88 *E*–01
4.80 *E*–01	8.78 *E*–01	4.53 *E* 00	1.94 *E*–01
4.90 *E*–01	8.75 *E*–01	4.36 *E* 00	2.01 *E*–01

Table 1. cont.

x	$F(x)$	$K(x)$	$S(x)$
5.00 *E*–01	8.72 *E*–01	4.21 *E* 00	2.07 *E*–01
5.20 *E*–01	8.64 *E*–01	3.92 *E* 00	2.21 *E*–01
5.40 *E*–01	8.55 *E*–01	3.66 *E* 00	2.34 *E*–01
5.60 *E*–01	8.48 *E*–01	3.42 *E* 00	2.48 *E*–01
5.80 *E*–01	8.40 *E*–01	3.21 *E* 00	2.62 *E*–01
6.00 *E*–01	8.32 *E*–01	3.01 *E* 00	2.77 *E*–01
6.20 *E*–01	8.23 *E*–01	2.83 *E* 00	2.91 *E*–01
6.40 *E*–01	8.14 *E*–01	2.67 *E* 00	3.05 *E*–01
6.60 *E*–01	8.05 *E*–01	2.52 *E* 00	3.19 *E*–01
6.80 *E*–01	7.97 *E*–01	2.38 *E* 00	3.36 *E*–01
7.00 *E*–01	7.88 *E*–01	2.25 *E* 00	3.51 *E*–01
7.20 *E*–01	7.79 *E*–01	2.13 *E* 00	3.66 *E*–01
7.40 *E*–01	7.70 *E*–01	2.02 *E* 00	3.82 *E*–01
7.60 *E*–01	7.60 *E*–01	1.92 *E* 00	3.96 *E*–01
7.80 *E*–01	7.51 *E*–01	1.82 *E* 00	4.13 *E*–01
8.00 *E*–01	7.42 *E*–01	1.73 *E* 00	4.29 *E*–01
8.20 *E*–01	7.32 *E*–01	1.65 *E* 00	4.44 *E*–01
8.40 *E*–01	7.22 *E*–01	1.57 *E* 00	4.60 *E*–01
8.60 *E*–01	7.13 *E*–01	1.50 *E* 00	4.75 *E*–01
8.80 *E*–01	7.04 *E*–01	1.43 *E* 00	4.92 *E*–01
9.00 *E*–01	6.94 *E*–01	1.37 *E* 00	5.07 *E*–01
9.20 *E*–01	6.85 *E*–01	1.31 *E* 00	5.23 *E*–01
9.40 *E*–01	6.77 *E*–01	1.25 *E* 00	5.42 *E*–01
9.60 *E*–01	6.69 *E*–01	1.20 *E* 00	5.58 *E*–01
9.80 *E*–01	6.63 *E*–01	1.15 *E* 00	5.77 *E*–01
1.00 *E* 00	6.55 *E*–01	1.10 *E* 00	5.95 *E*–01
1.05 *E* 00	6.31 *E*–01	9.89 *E*–01	6.38 *E*–01
1.10 *E* 00	6.10 *E*–01	8.94 *E*–01	6.82 *E*–01
1.15 *E* 00	5.87 *E*–01	8.11 *E*–01	7.24 *E*–01
1.20 *E* 00	5.66 *E*–01	7.37 *E*–01	7.68 *E*–01
1.25 *E* 00	5.46 *E*–01	6.71 *E*–01	8.14 *E*–01
1.30 *E* 00	5.24 *E*–01	6.13 *E*–01	8.55 *E*–01
1.35 *E* 00	5.07 *E*–01	5.61 *E*–01	9.04 *E*–01
1.40 *E* 00	4.86 *E*–01	5.14 *E*–01	9.46 *E*–01
1.45 *E* 00	4.67 *E*–01	4.72 *E*–01	9.89 *E*–01
1.50 *E* 00	4.46 *E*–01	4.34 *E*–01	1.03 *E* 00
1.55 *E* 00	4.30 *E*–01	4.00 *E*–01	1.08 *E* 00
1.60 *E* 00	4.14 *E*–01	3.68 *E*–01	1.13 *E* 00

Table 1. cont.

x	$F(x)$	$K(x)$	$S(x)$
1.65 *E* 00	3.99 *E*–01	3.40 *E*–01	1.17 *E* 00
1.70 *E* 00	3.85 *E*–01	3.14 *E*–01	1.22 *E* 00
1.75 *E* 00	3.68 *E*–01	2.91 *E*–01	1.26 *E* 00
1.80 *E* 00	3.54 *E*–01	2.69 *E*–01	1.32 *E* 00
1.85 *E* 00	3.40 *E*–01	2.50 *E*–01	1.36 *E* 00
1.90 *E* 00	3.29 *E*–01	2.32 *E*–01	1.42 *E* 00
1.95 *E* 00	3.15 *E*–01	2.15 *E*–01	1.47 *E* 00
2.00 *E* 00	3.01 *E*–01	2.00 *E*–01	1.51 *E* 00
2.10 *E* 00	2.73 *E*–01	1.73 *E*–01	1.58 *E* 00
2.20 *E* 00	2.54 *E*–01	1.50 *E*–01	1.69 *E* 00
2.30 *E* 00	2.35 *E*–01	1.31 *E*–01	1.80 *E* 00
2.40 *E* 00	2.17 *E*–01	1.14 *E*–01	1.90 *E* 00
2.50 *E* 00	2.00 *E*–01	9.94 *E*–02	2.01 *E* 00
2.60 *E* 00	1.84 *E*–01	8.70 *E*–02	2.11 *E* 00
2.70 *E* 00	1.68 *E*–01	7.63 *E*–02	2.20 *E* 00
2.80 *E* 00	1.53 *E*–01	6.69 *E*–02	2.29 *E* 00
2.90 *E* 00	1.41 *E*–01	5.88 *E*–02	2.39 *E* 00
3.00 *E* 00	1.30 *E*–01	5.18 *E*–02	2.51 *E* 00
3.10 *E* 00	1.19 *E*–01	4.56 *E*–02	2.61 *E* 00
3.20 *E* 00	1.08 *E*–01	4.02 *E*–02	2.69 *E* 00
3.30 *E* 00	9.98 *E*–02	3.55 *E*–02	2.81 *E* 00
3.40 *E* 00	9.23 *E*–02	3.14 *E*–02	2.94 *E* 00
3.50 *E* 00	8.45 *E*–02	2.78 *E*–02	3.04 *E* 00
3.60 *E* 00	7.76 *E*–02	2.46 *E*–02	3.15 *E* 00
3.70 *E* 00	7.12 *E*–02	2.18 *E*–02	3.27 *E* 00
3.80 *E* 00	6.52 *E*–02	1.93 *E*–02	3.38 *E* 00
3.90 *E* 00	5.96 *E*–02	1.71 *E*–02	3.49 *E* 00
4.00 *E* 00	5.41 *E*–02	1.52 *E*–02	3.56 *E* 00
4.10 *E* 00	5.00 *E*–02	1.35 *E*–02	3.70 *E* 00
4.20 *E* 00	4.59 *E*–02	1.20 *E*–02	3.83 *E* 00
4.30 *E* 00	4.19 *E*–02	1.07 *E*–02	3.92 *E* 00
4.40 *E* 00	3.79 *E*–02	9.50 *E*–03	3.99 *E* 00
4.50 *E* 00	3.39 *E*–02	8.46 *E*–03	4.01 *E* 00
4.60 *E* 00	3.15 *E*–02	7.53 *E*–03	4.18 *E* 00
4.70 *E* 00	2.81 *E*–02	6.71 *E*–03	4.19 *E* 00
4.80 *E* 00	2.62 *E*–02	5.98 *E*–03	4.38 *E* 00
4.90 *E* 00	2.34 *E*–02	5.33 *E*–03	4.40 *E* 00
5.00 *E* 00	2.14 *E*–02	4.75 *E*–03	4.50 *E* 00

Table 1. cont.

x	$F(x)$	$K(x)$	$S(x)$
5.25 *E* 00	1.70 *E*–02	3.58 *E*–03	4.75 *E* 00
5.50 *E* 00	1.35 *E*–02	2.70 *E*–03	5.00 *E* 00
5.75 *E* 00	1.07 *E*–02	2.04 *E*–03	5.25 *E* 00
6.00 *E* 00	8.45 *E*–03	1.54 *E*–03	5.49 *E* 00
6.25 *E* 00	6.64 *E*–03	1.17 *E*–03	5.68 *E* 00
6.50 *E* 00	5.26 *E*–03	8.86 *E*–04	5.94 *E* 00
6.75 *E* 00	4.16 *E*–03	6.73 *E*–04	6.18 *E* 00
7.00 *E* 00	3.29 *E*–03	5.11 *E*–04	6.44 *E* 00
7.25 *E* 00	2.60 *E*–03	3.89 *E*–04	6.68 *E* 00
7.50 *E* 00	2.06 *E*–03	2.97 *E*–04	6.94 *E* 00
7.75 *E* 00	1.63 *E*–03	2.26 *E*–04	7.21 *E* 00
8.00 *E* 00	1.28 *E*–03	1.73 *E*–04	7.40 *E* 00
8.25 *E* 00	1.03 *E*–03	1.32 *E*–04	7.80 *E* 00
8.50 *E* 00	8.00 *E*–04	1.01 *E*–04	7.92 *E* 00
8.75 *E* 00	6.31 *E*–04	7.70 *E*–05	8.19 *E* 00
9.00 *E* 00	4.98 *E*–04	5.89 *E*–05	8.46 *E* 00
9.25 *E* 00	3.92 *E*–04	4.51 *E*–05	8.69 *E* 00
9.50 *E* 00	3.09 *E*–04	3.45 *E*–05	8.96 *E* 00
9.75 *E* 00	2.44 *E*–04	2.65 *E*–05	9.22 *E* 00
1.00 *E* 01	1.92 *E*–04	2.03 *E*–05	9.46 *E* 00
1.20 *E* 01	2.82 *E*–05	2.46 *E*–06	1.15 *E* 01
1.40 *E* 01	4.09 *E*–06	3.04 *E*–07	1.85 *E* 01
1.60 *E* 01	5.89 *E*–07	3.81 *E*–08	1.55 *E* 01
1.80 *E* 01	8.42 *E*–08	4.82 *E*–09	1.75 *E* 01
2.00 *E* 01	1.20 *E*–08	6.14 *E*–10	1.95 *E* 01
2.50 *E* 01	8.96 *E*–11	3.66 *E*–12	2.45 *E* 01
3.00 *E* 01	6.58 *E*–13	2.23 *E*–14	2.95 *E* 01
4.00 *E* 01	3.43 *E*–17	8.69 *E*–19	3.95 *E* 01
5.00 *E* 01	1.74 *E*–21	3.51 *E*–23	4.95 *E* 01

Table 2

The function

$$J(\tau_m, x) = \frac{S(x)}{S(0.29)}\left[1 - e^{-\tau_m\,[K(x)/K(0.29)]}\right]$$

x	τ_m				
	0.01	0.1	1	10	100
1.00 *E*–04	1.79 *E*–05	1.79 *E*–06	1.79 *E*–07	1.79 *E*–08	1.79 *E*–09
2.00 *E*–04	7.14 *E*–05	7.14 *E*–06	7.14 *E*–07	7.14 *E*–08	7.14 *E*–09
5.00 *E*–04	4.45 *E*–04	4.45 *E*–05	4.45 *E*–06	4.45 *E*–07	4.45 *E*–08
1.00 *E*–03	1.78 *E*–03	1.78 *E*–04	1.78 *E*–05	1.78 *E*–06	1.78 *E*–07
2.00 *E*–03	7.06 *E*–03	7.06 *E*–04	7.06 *E*–05	7.06 *E*–06	7.06 *E*–07
5.00 *E*–03	4.36 *E*–02	4.36 *E*–03	4.36 *E*–04	4.36 *E*–05	4.36 *E*–06
1.00 *E*–02	1.62 *E*–01	1.72 *E*–02	1.72 *E*–03	1.72 *E*–04	1.72 *E*–05
2.00 *E*–02	3.95 *E*–01	6.72 *E*–02	6.72 *E*–03	6.72 *E*–04	6.72 *E*–05
5.00 *E*–02	6.97 *E*–01	3.40 *E*–01	3.99 *E*–02	3.99 *E*–03	3.99 *E*–04
1.00 *E*–01	8.66 *E*–01	6.69 *E*–01	1.47 *E*–01	1.48 *E*–02	1.48 *E*–03
1.50 *E*–01	9.39 *E*–01	8.21 *E*–01	2.97 *E*–01	3.11 *E*–02	3.11 *E*–03
2.00 *E*–01	9.75 *E*–01	8.97 *E*–01	4.43 *E*–01	5.22 *E*–02	5.22 *E*–03
2.50 *E*–01	9.91 *E*–01	9.36 *E*–01	5.61 *E*–01	7.74 *E*–02	7.74 *E*–03
3.00 *E*–01	1.00 *E* 00	9.54 *E*–01	6.47 *E*–01	1.06 *E*–01	1.06 *E*–02
3.50 *E*–01	9.94 *E*–01	9.59 *E*–01	7.08 *E*–01	1.38 *E*–01	1.38 *E*–02
4.00 *E*–01	9.83 *E*–01	9.55 *E*–01	7.49 *E*–01	1.71 *E*–01	1.72 *E*–02
4.50 *E*–01	9.67 *E*–01	9.45 *E*–01	7.74 *E*–01	2.07 *E*–01	2.09 *E*–02
5.00 *E*–01	9.49 *E*–01	9.31 *E*–01	7.88 *E*–01	2.42 *E*–01	2.47 *E*–02
6.00 *E*–01	9.06 *E*–01	8.94 *E*–01	7.92 *E*–01	3.09 *E*–01	3.30 *E*–02
7.00 *E*–01	8.55 *E*–01	8.50 *E*–01	7.76 *E*–01	3.65 *E*–01	4.19 *E*–02
8.00 *E*–01	8.09 *E*–01	8.03 *E*–01	7.48 *E*–01	4.06 *E*–01	5.12 *E*–02
9.00 *E*–01	7.59 *E*–01	7.55 *E*–01	7.14 *E*–01	4.34 *E*–01	6.09 *E*–02
1.00 *E* 00	7.10 *E*–01	7.07 *E*–01	6.76 *E*–01	4.49 *E*–01	7.09 *E*–02
1.25 *E* 00	5.94 *E*–01	5.94 *E*–01	5.76 *E*–01	4.44 *E*–01	9.68 *E*–02
1.50 *E* 00	4.91 *E*–01	4.91 *E*–01	4.82 *E*–01	4.06 *E*–01	1.22 *E*–01
1.75 *E* 00	4.03 *E*–01	4.03 *E*–01	3.98 *E*–01	3.54 *E*–01	1.41 *E*–01
2.00 *E* 00	3.29 *E*–01	3.29 *E*–01	3.26 *E*–01	3.01 *E*–01	1.51 *E*–01
2.50 *E* 00	2.16 *E*–01	2.16 *E*–01	2.16 *E*–01	2.07 *E*–01	1.42 *E*–01
3.00 *E* 00	1.40 *E*–01	1.40 *E*–01	1.40 *E*–01	1.37 *E*–01	1.12 *E*–01
3.50 *E* 00	9.02 *E*–02	9.02 *E*–02	9.02 *E*–02	8.90 *E*–02	7.97 *E*–02
4.00 *E* 00	5.77 *E*–02	5.77 *E*–02	5.77 *E*–02	5.73 *E*–02	5.39 *E*–02
4.50 *E* 00	3.67 *E*–02	3.67 *E*–02	3.67 *E*–02	3.67 *E*–02	3.53 *E*–02

Table 2. cont.

x	τ_m				
	0.01	0.1	1	10	100
5.00 *E* 00	2.33 *E*–02	2.33 *E*–02	2.33 *E*–02	2.33 *E*–02	2.28 *E*–02
6.25 *E* 00	7.31 *E*–03	7.31 *E*–03	7.31 *E*–03	7.31 *E*–03	7.27 *E*–03
7.50 *E* 00	2.26 *E*–03	2.26 *E*–03	2.26 *E*–03	2.26 *E*–03	2.26 *E*–03
8.75 *E* 00	6.92 *E*–04	6.92 *E*–04	6.92 *E*–04	6.92 *E*–04	6.92 *E*–04
1.00 *E* 01	2.09 *E*–04	2.09 *E*–04	2.09 *E*–04	2.09 *E*–04	2.09 *E*–04
1.20 *E* 01	3.07 *E*–05	3.07 *E*–05	3.07 *E*–05	3.07 *E*–05	3.07 *E*–05
1.40 *E* 01	4.46 *E*–06	4.46 *E*–06	4.46 *E*–06	4.46 *E*–06	4.56 *E*–06
1.60 *E* 01	6.41 *E*–07	6.41 *E*–07	6.41 *E*–07	6.41 *E*–07	6.41 *E*–07
1.80 *E* 01	9.17 *E*–08	9.17 *E*–08	9.17 *E*–08	9.17 *E*–08	9.17 *E*–08
2.00 *E* 01	1.30 *E*–08	1.30 *E*–08	1.30 *E*–08	1.30 *E*–08	1.30 *E*–08
2.50 *E* 01	9.75 *E*–11	9.75 *E*–11	9.75 *E*–11	9.75 *E*–11	9.75 *E*–11
3.00 *E* 01	7.17 *E*–13	7.17 *E*–13	7.17 *E*–13	7.17 *E*–13	7.17 *E*–13
4.00 *E* 01	3.73 *E*–17	3.73 *E*–17	3.73 *E*–17	3.73 *E*–17	3.73 *E*–17
5.00 *E* 01	1.89 *E*–21	1.89 *E*–21	1.89 *E*–21	1.89 *E*–21	1.89 *E*–21

Table 3

The function

$$J(z, \gamma) = z^{5/2}[1 - \exp(-z^{-(\gamma+4)/2})]$$

z	γ										
	1.0	1.5	2.0	2.5	3.0	3.5	4.0	4.5	5.0	5.5	6.0
1.0 *E*–02	1.00 *E*–05	1.00 *E*–05	1.00 *E*–05	1.00 *E*–05	1.00 *E*–05	1.00 *E*–05	1.00 *E*–05	1.00 *E*–05	1.00 *E*–05	1.00 *E*–05	1.00 *E*–05
1.0 *E*–01	3.16 *E*–03	3.16 *E*–03	3.16 *E*–03	3.16 *E*–02	3.16 *E*–03	3.16 *E*–03	3.16 *E*–03	3.16 *E*–03	3.16 *E*–03	3.16 *E*–03	3.16 *E*–03
2.0 *E*–01	1.79 *E*–02	1.79 *E*–02	1.79 *E*–02	1.79 *E*–02	1.79 *E*–02	1.79 *E*–02	1.79 *E*–02	1.79 *E*–02	1.79 *E*–02	1.79 *E*–02	1.79 *E*–02
5.0 *E*–01	1.76 *E*–01	1.77 *E*–01	1.77 *E*–01	1.77 *E*–01	1.77 *E*–01	1.77 *E*–01	1.77 *E*–01	1.77 *E*–01	1.77 *E*–01	1.77 *E*–01	1.77 *E*–01
7.0 *E*–01	3.74 *E*–01	3.81 *E*–01	3.88 *E*–01	3.93 *E*–01	3.97 *E*–01	4.01 *E*–01	4.04 *E*–01	4.06 *E*–01	4.07 *E*–01	4.08 *E*–01	4.09 *E*–01
8.0 *E*–01	4.73 *E*–01	4.82 *E*–01	4.91 *E*–01	5.00 *E*–01	5.08 *E*–01	5.16 *E*–01	5.23 *E*–01	5.79 *E*–01	5.35 *E*–01	5.40 *E*–01	5.45 *E*–01
9.0 *E*–01	5.59 *E*–01	5.66 *E*–01	5.74 *E*–01	5.81 *E*–01	5.87 *E*–01	5.94 *E*–01	6.01 *E*–01	6.08 *E*–01	6.14 *E*–01	6.21 *E*–01	6.27 *E*–01
1.0 *E* 00	6.32 *E*–01	6.32 *E*–01.	6.32 *E*–01	6.32 *E*–01	6.32 *E*–01	6.32 *E*–01	6.32 *E*–01	6.32 *E*–01	6.32 *E*–01	6.32 *E*–01	6.32 *E*–01
1.2 *E* 00	7.41 *E*–01	7.17 *E*–01	6.93 *E*–01	6.70 *E*–01	6.47 *E*–01	6.25 *E*–01	6.04 *E*–01	5.82 *E*–01	5.62 *E*–01	5.42 *E*–01	5.22 *E*–01
1.5 *E* 00	8.39 *E*–01	7.70 *E*–01	7.07 *E*–01	6.46 *E*–01	5.92 *E*–01	5.41 *E*–01	4.94 *E*–01	4.50 *E*–01	4.10 *E*–01	3.74 *E*–01	3.40 *E*–01
1.7 *E* 00	8.78 *E*–01	7.81 *E*–01	6.94 *E*–01	6.15 *E*–01	5.45 *E*–01	4.81 *E*–01	4.25 *E*–01	3.75 *E*–01	3.31 *E*–01	2.91 *E*–01	2.56 *E*–01
2.0 *E* 00	9.17 *E*–01	7.81 *E*–01	6.65 *E*–01	5.64 *E*–01	4.79 *E*–01	4.05 *E*–01	3.43 *E*–01	2.90 *E*–01	2.45 *E*–01	2.06 *E*–01	1.74 *E*–01
3.0 *E* 00	9.69 *E*–01	7.42 *E*–01	5.67 *E*–01	4.33 *E*–01	3.30 *E*–01	2.51 *E*–01	1.91 *E*–01	1.46 *E*–01	1.11 *E*–01	8.42 *E*–02	6.40 *E*–02
5.0 *E* 00	9.91 *E*–01	6.65 *E*–01	4.45 *E*–01	2.98 *E*–01	2.00 *E*–01	1.34 *E*–01	8.94 *E*–02	5.98 *E*–02	4.00 *E*–02	2.67 *E*–02	1.79 *E*–02
7.0 *E* 00	9.96 *E*–01	6.13 *E*–01	3.77 *E*–01	2.32 *E*–01	1.43 *E*–01	8.78 *E*–02	5.40 *E*–02	3.32 *E*–02	2.04 *E*–02	1.25 *E*–02	7.71 *E*–03
1.0 *E* 01	9.98 *E*–01	5.62 *E*–01	3.16 *E*–01	1.78 *E*–01	1.00 *E*–01	5.62 *E*–02	3.16 *E*–02	1.78 *E*–02	1.00 *E*–02	5.62 *E*–03	3.16 *E*–03
1.0 *E* 02	1.00 *E* 00	3.16 *E*–01	1.00 *E*–01	3.16 *E*–02	1.00 *E*–02	3.16 *E*–03	1.00 *E*–03	3.16 *E*–04	1.00 *E*–04	3.16 *E*–05	1.00 *E*–05
1.0 *E* 03	1.00 *E* 00	1.78 *E*–01	3.16 *E*–02	5.62 *E*–03	1.00 *E*–03	1.78 *E*–04	3.16 *E*–05	5.62 *E*–06	1.00 *E*–06	1.78 *E*–07	3.16 *E*–02

Table 4

The function:

$$I(x_m) = \frac{1}{x_m} \int_0^\infty z^2 \exp(-z)\ F(x_m/z^2)\,dz$$

x_m	$I(x_m)$	x_m	$I(x_m)$
1 *E*–06	2.56 *E* 04	1 *E*–01	1.04 *E* 01
2 *E*–06	1.61 *E* 04	2 *E*–01	6.10 *E* 00
5 *E*–06	8.75 *E* 03	5 *E*–01	2.86 *E* 00
1 *E*–05	5.51 *E* 03	1 *E* 00	1.52 *E* 00
2 *E*–05	3.47 *E* 03	2 *E* 00	7.48 *E*–01
5 *E*–05	1.88 *E* 03	5 *E* 00	2.50 *E*–01
1 *E*–04	1.19 *E* 03	1 *E* 01	9.24 *E*–02
4 *E*–04	7.47 *E* 02	2 *E* 01	2.81 *E*–02
5 *E*–04	4.05 *E* 02	5 *E* 01	3.90 *E*–03
1 *E*–03	2.54 *E* 02	1 *E* 02	5.85 *E*–04
2 *E*–03	1.60 *E* 02	2 *E* 02	5.59 *E*–05
5 *E*–03	8.58 *E* 01	5 *E* 02	9.98 *E*–07
1 *E*–02	5.34 *E* 01	1 *E* 03	1.92 *E*–08
2 *E*–02	3.31 *E* 01	2 *E* 03	1.35 *E*–10
5 *E*–02	1.73 *E* 01	5 *E* 03	2.64 *E*–14

Table 5

The function:

$$G(x) = xK_{2/3}(x)$$

$$\Pi(x) = G(x)/F(x)$$

x	$G(x)$	$\Pi(x)$
0.001	0.107	0.502
0.005	0.184	0.514
0.010	0.231	0.519
0.025	0.312	0.535
0.050	0.388	0.553
0.100	0.475	0.581
0.200	0.560	0.619
0.300	0.596	0.649
0.400	0.607	0.674
0.500	0.603	0.692
0.800	0.547	0.737
1.000	0.494	0.754
1.400	0.386	0.794
1.800	0.290	0.819
2.000	0.250	0.831
2.500	0.168	0.840
3.000	0.111	0.854
3.500	0.0726	0.859
4.000	0.0470	0.869
5.000	0.0192	0.897
6.000	0.00772	0.914
7.000	0.00306	0.930
8.000	0.00120	0.938
9.000	0.000469	0.942
10.000	0.000182	0.948

Table 6

The constants c_1, c_2, c_3, c_4 and c_7

Constant	cgs
$c_1 = \frac{3e}{4\pi m^3 c^5}$	$= 6.27 \ E \ 18$
$c_2 = \frac{2e^4}{3m^4 c^7}$	$= 2.37 \ E\text{–}03$
$c_3 = \frac{\sqrt{3}\, e^3}{4\pi mc^2}$	$= 1.87 \ E\text{–}23$
$c_4 = c_1^{3/2} c_3 c^2$	$= 2.63 \ E \ 26$
$c_7 = \frac{c_1}{c_2^2}$	$= 1.12 \ E \ 24$

Table 7

The functions:

$$c_5 = \frac{\sqrt{3}}{16\pi}\frac{e^3}{mc^2}\left(\frac{\gamma + 7/3}{\gamma + 1}\right)\Gamma\left(\frac{3\gamma - 1}{12}\right)\Gamma\left(\frac{3\gamma + 7}{12}\right)$$

$$c_6 = \frac{\sqrt{3}\pi}{72}\, em^5 c^{10}\left(\gamma + \frac{10}{3}\right)\Gamma\left(\frac{3\gamma + 2}{12}\right)\Gamma\left(\frac{3\gamma + 10}{12}\right)$$

$$c_8 = \int_0^\infty x^{(\gamma-3)/2} F(x)\, dx$$

$$c_9 = \int_0^{\pi/2} (\sin\theta)^{(\gamma+3)/2}\, d\theta = \frac{\sqrt{\pi}}{2}\frac{\Gamma\left(\frac{\gamma+5}{4}\right)}{\Gamma\left(\frac{\gamma+7}{4}\right)}$$

$$c_{10} = \int_0^\infty x^{(2/3)(\gamma-1)} F(x)\, dx$$

$$c_{11} = \int_0^1 (1 - x^{3/2})^{\gamma-2}\, x^{(\gamma+3)/2}\, dx$$

$$c_{14} = \frac{1}{4}\sqrt{\frac{6}{\pi}}\left(\frac{e}{m^3c}\right)^{1/2}\frac{(\gamma+1)(3\gamma+10)}{(3\gamma+7)}\frac{\Gamma\left(\frac{3\gamma+2}{12}\right)\Gamma\left(\frac{3\gamma+10}{12}\right)}{\Gamma\left(\frac{3\gamma-1}{12}\right)\Gamma\left(\frac{3\gamma+7}{12}\right)}$$

γ	c_5	c_6	c_8	c_9	c_{10}	c_{11}	c_{14}
0.5	2.66 E–22	1.62 E–40		0.826	19.0	12.8	3.38 E 29
1.0	4.88 E–23	1.18 E–40		0.785	20.2	2.80	1.33 E 30
1.5	2.26 E–23	9.69 E–41		0.750	22.7	0.775	2.38 E 30
2.0	1.37 E–23	8.61 E–41	2.08	0.719	26.7	0.286	3.48 E 30
2.5	9.68 E–24	8.10 E–41	1.75	0.691	33.1	0.131	4.65 E 30
3.0	7.52 E–24	7.97 E–41	1.61	0.667	42.8	0.0682	5.89 E 30
3.5	6.29 E–24	8.16 E–41	1.61	0.645	57.4	0.0381	7.22 E 30
4.0	5.56 E–24	8.55 E–41	1.69	0.624	80.6	0.0222	8.51 E 30
4.5	5.16 E–24	9.24 E–41	1.87	0.606	116	0.0134	9.94 E 30
5.0	4.98 E–24	1.03 E–40	2.14	0.589	172	0.00820	1.14 E 31
5.5	4.97 E–24	1.16 E–40	2.55	0.574	262	0.00511	1.30 E 31
6.0	5.11 E–24	1.34 E–40	3.12	0.559	408	0.00323	1.45 E 31

Table 8

The functions:†

$$c_{12} = c_2^{-1} c_1^{1/2} \frac{2\alpha - 2}{2\alpha - 1} \cdot \frac{\nu_1^{(1-2\alpha)/2} - \nu_2^{(1-2\alpha)/2}}{\nu_1^{1-\alpha} - \nu_2^{1-\alpha}}$$

$$c_{13} = 0.921 \cdot c_{12}^{4/7}$$

for $\nu_1 = 10^7$ Hz and $\nu_2 = 10^{10}$ and 10^{11} Hz.

α	$\nu_2 = 10^{10}$ Hz		$\nu_2 = 10^{11}$ Hz	
	c_{12}	c_{13}	c_{12}	c_{13}
0.2	2.5 *E* 07	1.6 *E* 04	8.3 *E* 06	8.3 *E* 03
0.3	2.8 *E* 07	1.7 *E* 04	9.8 *E* 06	9.1 *E* 03
0.4	3.2 *E* 07	1.8 *E* 04	1.2 *E* 07	1.0 *E* 04
0.5	3.7 *E* 07	2.0 *E* 04	1.6 *E* 07	1.2 *E* 04
0.6	4.5 *E* 07	2.2 *E* 04	2.0 *E* 07	1.4 *E* 04
0.7	5.4 *E* 07	2.5 *E* 04	2.8 *E* 07	1.7 *E* 04
0.8	6.5 *E* 07	2.7 *E* 04	3.9 *E* 07	2.0 *E* 04
0.9	7.8 *E* 07	3.0 *E* 04	5.4 *E* 07	2.4 *E* 04
1.0	9.3 *E* 07	3.3 *E* 04	7.1 *E* 07	2.8 *E* 04
1.1	1.1 *E* 08	3.6 *E* 04	9.3 *E* 07	3.3 *E* 04
1.2	1.3 *E* 08	4.0 *E* 04	1.1 *E* 08	3.7 *E* 04

† For $\alpha = 1/2$ and 1 the functions c_{12} and c_{13} have values following from the appropriate formulae resulting from the integration of equations (7.4) and (7.5).

APPENDIX 3

A Few Useful Nomograms

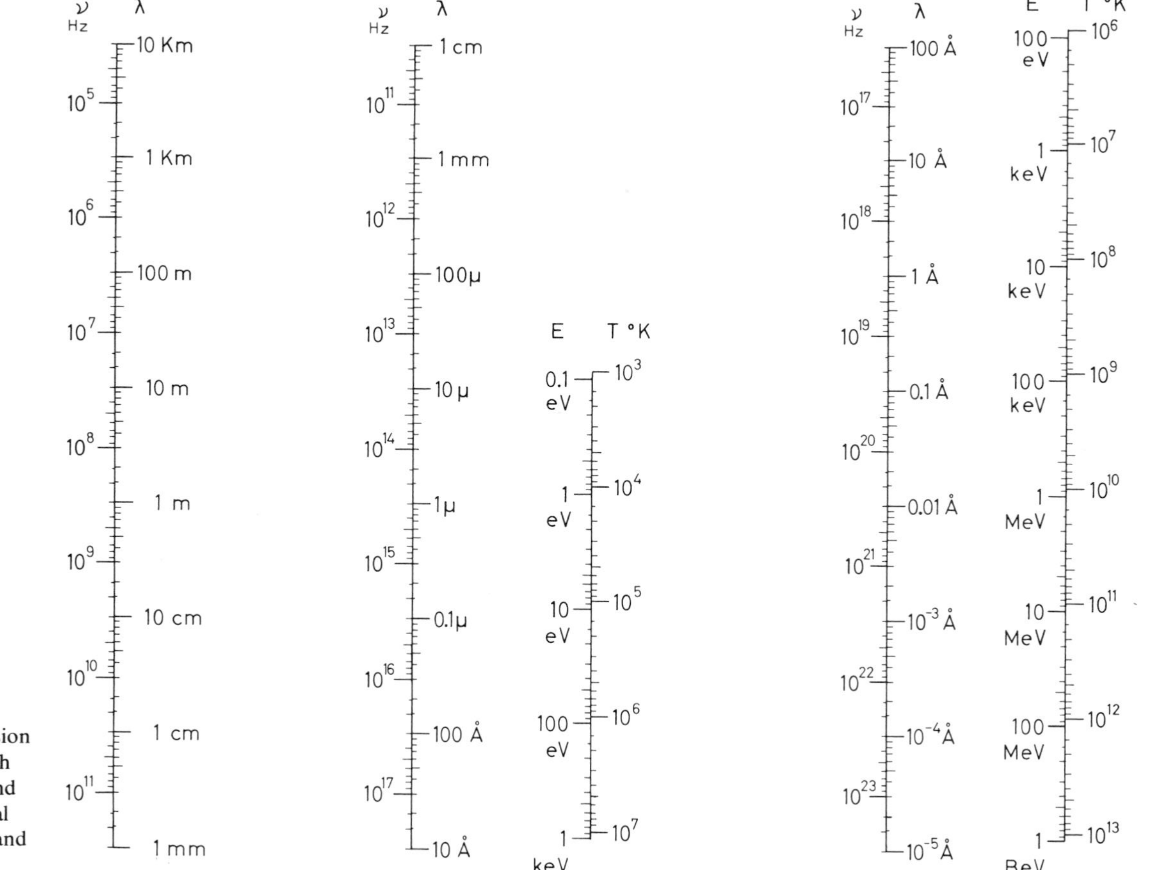

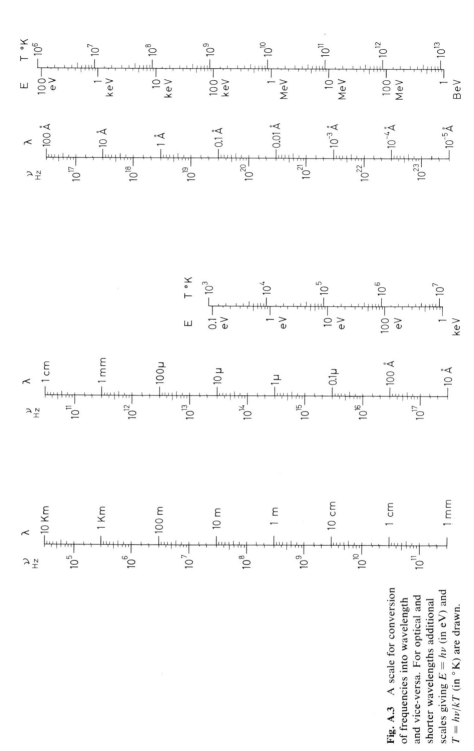

Fig. A.3 A scale for conversion of frequencies into wavelength and vice-versa. For optical and shorter wavelengths additional scales giving $E = h\nu$ (in eV) and $T = h\nu/kT$ (in °K) are drawn.

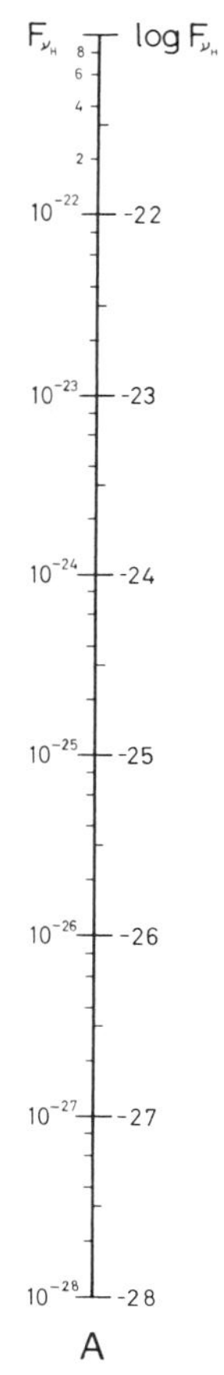

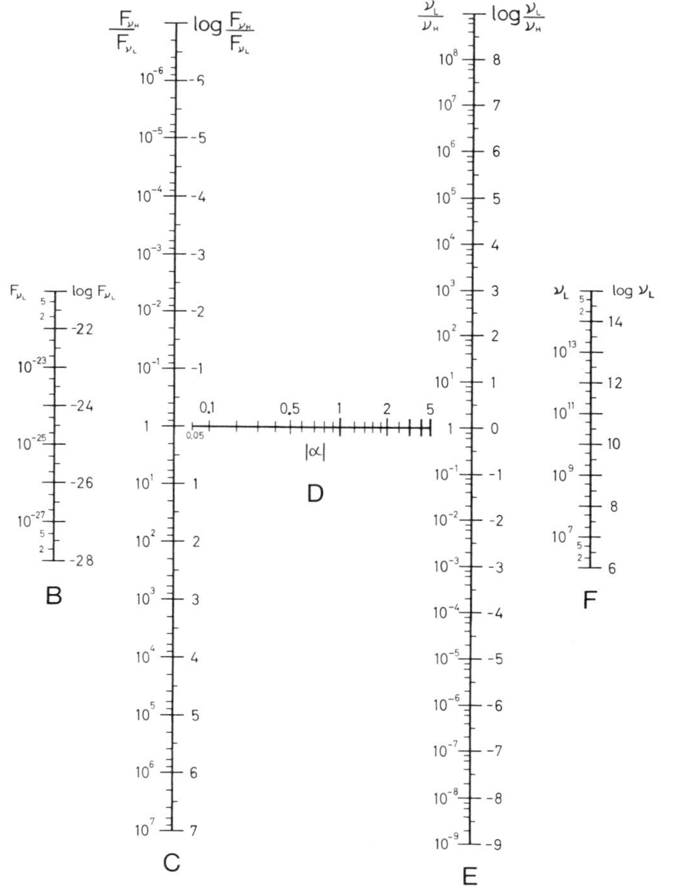

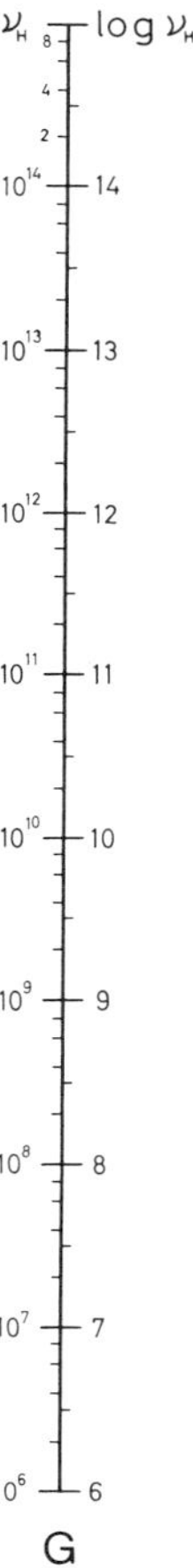

Fig. A.4 A nomogram illustrating the relation between fluxes at two frequencies and spectral index α for a source with a power law spectrum. Subscripts H and L refer to fluxes at the higher and lower of the two frequencies considered, respectively. Three straight lines should be drawn: one connecting points on the A, B, and C scales, another on the C, D, and E scales, and the other on the E, F, and G scales.

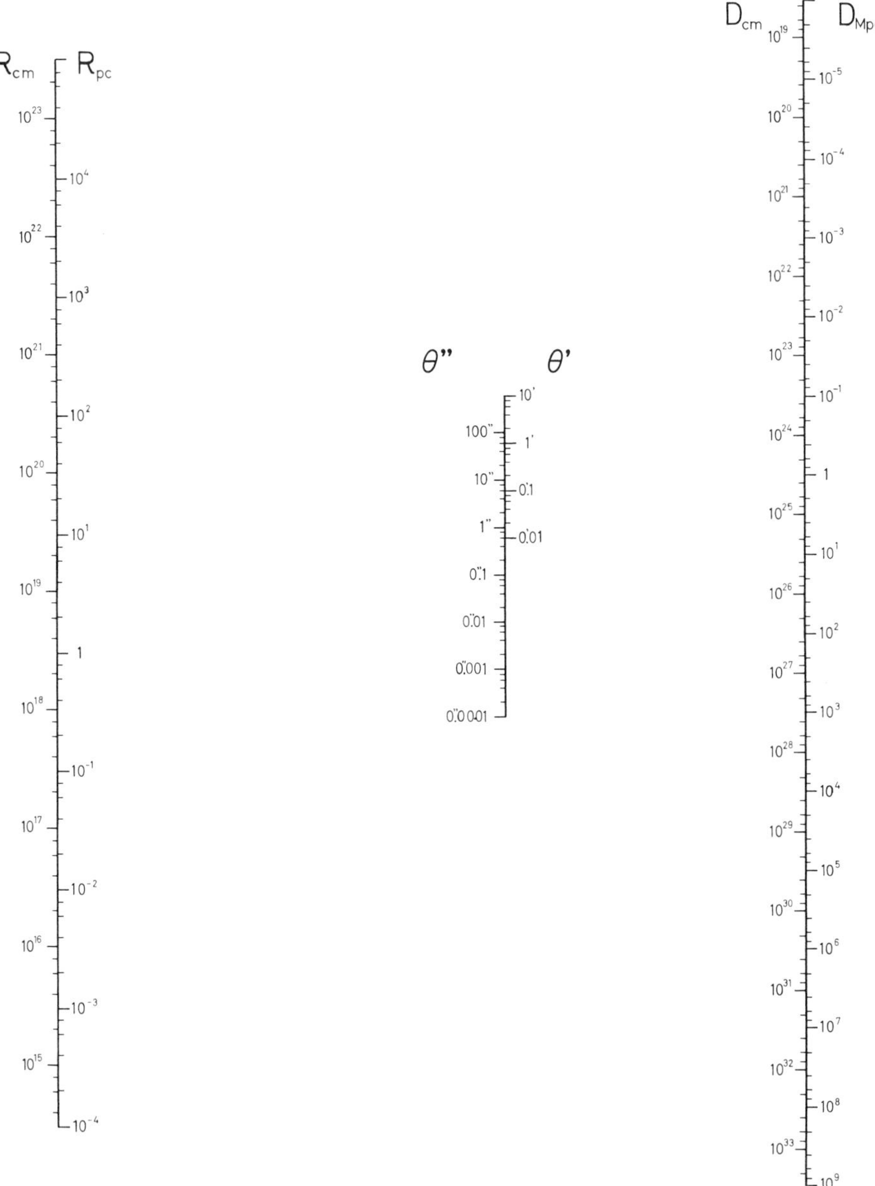

Fig. A.5 A nomogram for converting angular θ and linear R diameters of objects at a distance D in Euclidean space. One line connects all three scales.

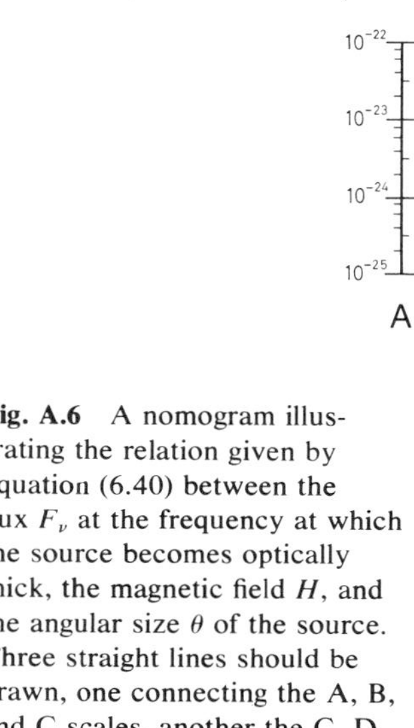

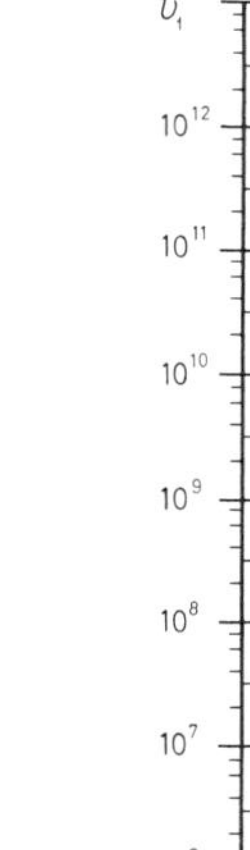

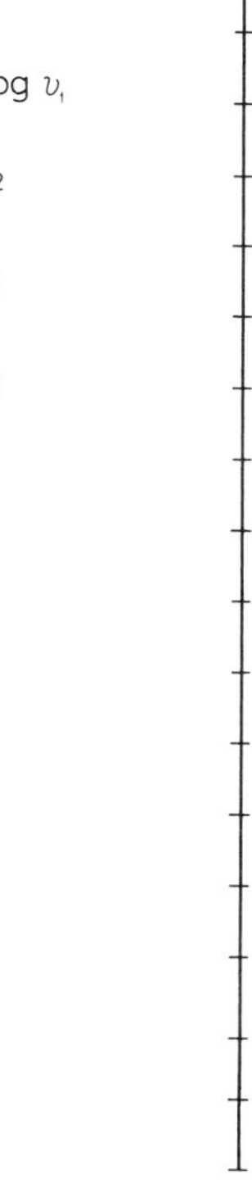

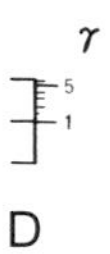

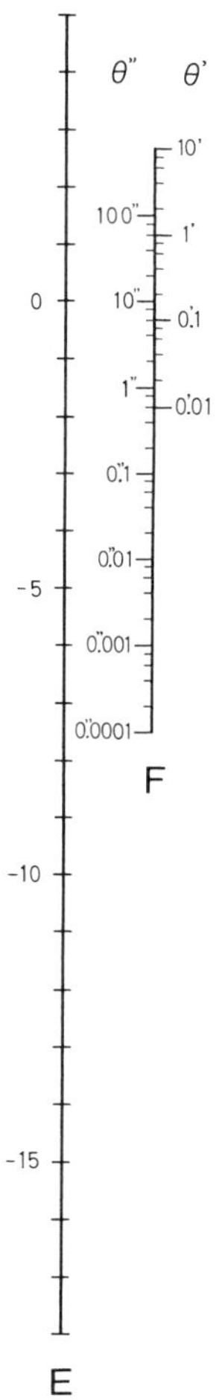

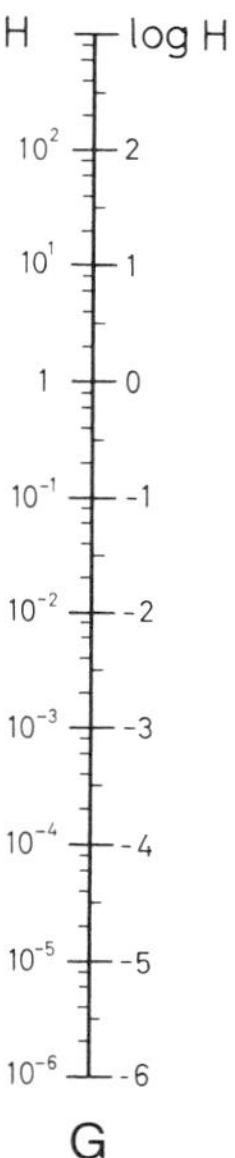

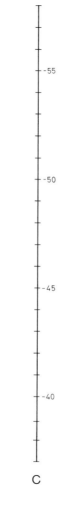

Fig. A.6 A nomogram illustrating the relation given by equation (6.40) between the flux F_ν at the frequency at which the source becomes optically thick, the magnetic field H, and the angular size θ of the source. Three straight lines should be drawn, one connecting the A, B, and C scales, another the C, D, and E scales, and the other the E, F, and G scales.

APPENDIX 4

Surveys of Discrete Radio Sources: A Bibliography

A4.1. Historical

While investigating the continuous cosmic radio emission Hey, Parsons, and Phillips discovered a variable discrete source in Cygnus. The relative variation of intensity was about 15%.

1. J. S. Hey, S. J. Parsons, and J. W. Phillips, "Fluctuations in Cosmic Radiation at Radio Frequencies," *Nature* **158**, 234 (1946).

This discovery was confirmed by Bolton and Stanley, who used a sea interferometer. They determined the coordinates of a source in Cygnus and set a limit of 8′ on its angular diameter. Their observations were made at 60, 85, 100, and 200 MHz; at 200 MHz the variable component could not be detected.

2. J. G. Bolton and G. J. Stanley, "Variable Source of Radio-Frequency Radiation in the Constellation of Cygnus," *Nature* **161**, 312–313 (1948).

Another confirmation of the discovery was made by Ryle and Smith who also discovered another source (in Cassiopeia) at 81.5 MHz with a two antenna interferometer with a 500 m spacing.

3. M. Ryle and F. G. Smith, "A New Intense Source of Radio-Frequency Radiation in the Constellation of Cassiopeia," *Nature* **162**, 462–463 (1948).

Bolton detected four new discrete sources with a sea interferometer: in Taurus, Coma Berenices (an accurate determination of coordinates located this source in Virgo), Hercules, and Centaurus. Positions of three of these sources were measured by Bolton and co-workers.

4. J. G. Bolton, "Discrete Sources of Galactic Radio-Frequency Noise," *Nature* **162**, 141–142 (1948).
5. J. G. Bolton, G. J. Stanley, and O. B. Slee, "Positions of Three Discrete Sources of Galactic Radio Frequency Radiation," *Nature* **164**, 101–102 (1949).

A catalogue of 18 sources (of which 13 were new) containing the first spectra of Cyg A, Tau A, Vir A and Cen A was published by Stanley and Slee.

6. G. J. Stanley and O. B. Slee, "Galactic Radiation at Radio Frequencies, II. The Discrete Sources," *Australian J. Sci. Res.* **3A**, 234–250 (1950).

In Ref. 6 and the two following papers the discussion of correlation in intensity variations in discrete sources observed with two antennas spaced at a certain distance led to the conclusion that the fluctuations of intensity were of ionospheric origin (they followed an annual cycle, depended on frequency decreasing at higher frequencies and disappearing at 200 MHz, were particularly noticeable when the source was smaller than 2°, and were correlated for small antenna spacings).

7. F. G. Smith, "Origin of the Fluctuations in the Intensity of Radio Waves from Galactic Sources—Cambridge Observations," *Nature* **165**, 422–423 (1950).
8. C. G. Little and A. C. B. Lovell, "Origin of the Fluctuations in the Intensity of Radio Waves from Galactic Sources—Jodrell Bank Observations," *Nature* **165**, 423–424 (1950).

A 1952 paper by Mills listed 77 discrete sources at a wavelength of 3 m. The instrument used was an interferometer consisting of three antenna arrays of 24 in half-wave dipoles, each East-West line having a maximum spacing of 250 m. The main lobe was 40′ wide and the spacing of lobes was 3°. The sky coverage was $+50° < \delta < -90°$. Three sources appeared to be extended: Vela, Sagittarius, and Centaurus. Centaurus was identified with NGC 5128.

9. B. Y. Mills, "The Distribution of Discrete Sources of Cosmic Radio Radiation," *Australian J. Sci. Res.* **5A**, 266–287 (1952).

Brown and Hazard observed 23 sources between declinations +38° and +68° with the 218-foot fixed reflector of the University of Manchester. The sources were observed in transit at a wavelength of 1.89 m with a pencil beam 2° wide. The weakest source had a flux of 5 f.u.

10. R. Hanbury Brown and C. Hazard, "A Survey of 23 Localized Radio Sources in the Northern Hemisphere," *Monthly Notices Roy. Astron. Soc.* **113**, 123–133 (1953).

A catalogue of 104 discrete sources was published in 1954 by Bolton and co-workers. Observations were made with a sea interferometer at a frequency of 100 MHz. The coverage of the sky was $+50° < \delta < -50°$ and the lobe width was 1°.

11. J. G. Bolton, G. J. Stanley, and O. B. Slee, "Galactic Radiation at Radio Frequencies, VIII. Discrete Sources at 100 Mc/s Between Declinations +50° and −50° " *Australian J. Phys.* **7**, 110–129 (1954).

A survey of 207 sources was made with a helical antenna at Ohio State University at a wavelength of 1.20 m (250 MHz): 48 helices were used. The main lobe had dimensions of 1°.2 in right ascention and 17° in declination. The weakest flux recorded was smaller than 100 f.u. and the errors in determining flux were from 20% for strong sources to 100% for weak sources. Out of 47 sources in Ref. 11 and 27 sources in Ref. 9 that were within the region covered by the Ohio survey, 39 and 11 sources, respectively, coincided with sources listed in the survey.

12. J. D. Kraus, H. C. Ko, and S. Matt, "Galactic And Localized Source Observation at 250 Mc/s," *Astrophys. J.* **59**, 439–443 (1954).

Thirty-seven sources located between $-12° < \delta < -52°$ (23 of which coincide with sources given in Ref. 11) were observed at 18.3 MHz (16.4 m) with 30 fixed half-wave dipoles oriented approximately in the N–S direction.

13. C. A. Shain and C. S. Higgins, "Observations of the General Background and Discrete Sources of 18.3 Mc/s Cosmic Noise," *Australian J. Phys.* **7**, 130–149 (1954).

At the recommendation of the International Astronomical Union a list of reliably known radio sources was compiled. This catalogue introduced a new nomenclature of sources, but this has been largely superseded by that used in the Third Cambridge Catalogue of radio sources. The following schematic describes the IAU designation of radio sources:

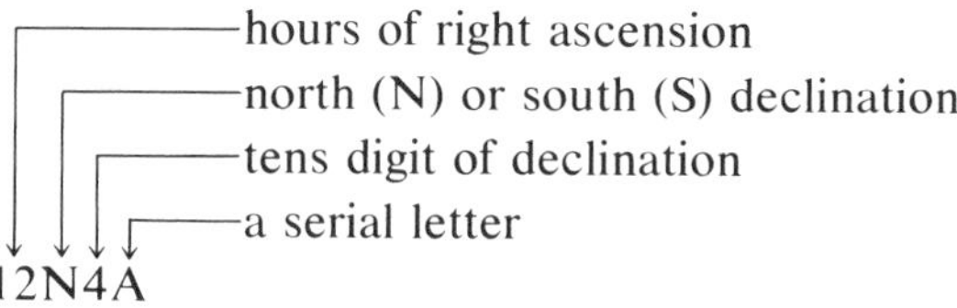

14. J. L. Pawsey, "A Catalogue of Reliably Known Discrete Sources of Cosmic Radio Waves," *Astrophys. J.* **121**, 1–5 (1955).

Heeschen observed 14 sources at frequencies of 440, 1200, 1400, and 8000 MHz and discussed their spectra.

15. D. S. Heeschen, "Observations of Radio Sources at Four Frequencies," *Astrophys. J.* **133**, 322–334 (1961).

The flux measurements made before 1964 were compiled in a catalogue that lists 1292 sources and contains an extensive bibliography of previous observations of radio sources.

16. W. E. Howard III and S. P. Maran, "The General Catalogue of Radio Sources," *Astrophys. J. Supplement* **10**, 1–330 (1965).

For a list of surveys of galactic sources see the bibliographical notes to Chapter 6 of this book. Some of the early identifications of radio sources with optical objects are described in the following articles.

17. W. Baade and R. Minkowski, "Identification of the Radio Sources in Cassiopeia, Cygnus A, and Puppis A," *Astrophys. J.* **119**, 206–214 (1954).
18. W. Baade and R. Minkowski, "On the Identification of Radio Sources," *Astrophys. J.* **119**, 215–231 (1954).
19. J. Basinski, B. J. Bok, and K. Gottlieb, "Optical Identification of Southern Radio Sources," *in* R. M. Bracewell, ed., *Paris Symposium on Radio Astronomy*, pp. 514–522, Stanford University Press, 1959.
20. J. A. Roberts, J. G. Bolton, and D. E. Harris, "Positions and Suggested Identifications for the Radio Sources Hydra A and Hercules A," *Publ. Astron. Soc. Pacific* **72**, 5–9 (1960).
21. B. Y. Mills, "On the Optical Identifications of Extragalactic Radio Sources," *Australian J. Phys.* **13**, 550–577 (1960).

A4.2. The Cambridge Surveys

1C Fifty sources compiled at 3.7 m with the aid of a fixed meridian interferometer were listed in the First Cambridge Catalogue (1C). The sources are numbered consecutively.

22. M. Ryle, F. G. Smith, and B. Elsmore, "A Preliminary Survey of the Radio Stars in the Northern Hemisphere," *Monthly Notices Roy. Astron. Soc.* **110**, 508–523 (1950).

2C The Second Cambridge Catalogue (2C) of radio sources was published in 1955. It contains 1936 sources observed at 3.7 m with an interferometer consisting of four similar aerials in the corners of a rectangle, the reception pattern of each aerial being 2°.0 in right ascension and 15° in declination. The sources are numbered consecutively and prefixed with 2C.

23. J. R. Shakeshaft, M. Ryle, J. E. Baldwin, B. Elsmore, and J. H. Thomson, "A Survey of Radio Sources Between Declinations −38° and +83°," *Mem. Roy. Astron. Soc.* **67**, 106–154 (1955).

Most of the 2C sources were found later to be confusion effects rather than real sources; see for example:

24. C. Hazard and D. Walsh, "A Survey of the Localized Radio Sources at a Frequency of 92 Mc/s," *Jodrell Bank Annals* **1**, 338–350 (1960).

3C The Second Cambridge Catalogue was superseded by the Third Cambridge Catalogue (3C) made at a frequency of 159 MHz with the same instrumentation as the 2C catalogue. Three methods of observations were used leading to three subsurveys: first, 3C(a) was made with the system responding to sources with diameters $< 7'$ (the coverage is $-10° < \delta \leq +55°$ and the beamwidth of each element is 1°.2 EW and 7°.7 NS with a separation of 308λ EW and 27λ NS); second, 3C(b) was made with the system responding to sources with diameters up to 1° and making possible measurements of diameters for sources with a diameter range of $2'$ to $10'$ (the coverage is $-25° \leq \delta \leq +60°$); third, 3C(c) registered sources of small angular diameters at $+52° \leq \delta \leq +70°$. In total 471 sources were observed. The 3C catalogue is confusion limited rather than noise limited, and the limiting flux is 8 f.u. Within an area of three steradians only 75 2C sources were confirmed. The 3C catalogue is in general agreement with the MSH catalogue (Refs. 69 to 71) for sources with fluxes larger than 10 f.u. at 159 MHz. The sources are numbered consecutively and prefixed with 3C.

25. D. O. Edge, J. R. Shakeshaft, W. B. McAdam, J. E. Baldwin, and S. Archer, "A Survey of Radio Sources at a Frequency of 159 Mc/s," *Mem. Roy. Astron. Soc.* **68**, 37–60 (1959).

3CR The revised Third Cambridge Catalogue (3CR) was published in 1961. It lists all point sources north of $\delta = -0^\circ\!.5$ (except in the areas near the ridge of galactic emission) with fluxes larger than the limiting flux of about 9 to 40 f.u. for sources of angular diameters from 1′ to 1°, respectively. The numbering system of the 3C catalogue is retained in the 3CR catalogue; the sources not in the 3C have the number of the preceding 3C source followed by a point and an additional digit (for example, 3C 175.1). In some of the later literature, a 3C source contained in the 3CR catalogue is referred to by its 3C number followed by a point and a zero (for example, 3C 192.0), while a 3C source not contained in the 3CR catalogue is referred to by its 3C number only (for example, 3C 193).

26. A. S. Bennett, "The Revised 3C Catalogue of Radio Sources," *Mem. Roy. Astron. Soc.* **68**, 163–172 (1961).

The catalogue was based on the 178 MHz survey, made with an interferometer consisting of a 1450 × 65 foot cylindrical paraboloid elongated in the EW direction plus a movable 190 × 65 foot cylindrical paraboloid on rails in the NS direction. The antenna separation was 465λ (P. R. R. Leslie, Thesis, Cambridge University). Measurements of the flux densities and positions of selected sources from the 3C and 3CR catalogues (and occasionally from other catalogues) were reported in the following papers (see also the bibliography to Chapter 6).

27. B. Elsmore, M. Ryle, and P. R. R. Leslie, "The Positions, Flux Densities and Angular Diameters of 64 Radio Sources Observed at a Frequency of 178 Mc/s," *Mem. Roy. Astron. Soc.* **68**, 61–67 (1959).
28. D. S. Heeschen and B. L. Meredith, "Observations of Discrete Sources at 10 cm and 40 cm Wavelengths," *Publ. Nat. Rad. Astron. Obs.* **1**, 121–128 (1961).
29. S. J. Goldstein, Jr., "Observation of Sixty Discrete Sources at 1423 Mc," *Astron. J.* **67**, 171–175 (1962).
30. M. E. Clark, "The Determination of the Positions of 88 Radio Sources," *Monthly Notices Roy. Astron. Soc.* **127**, 405–411 (1964).
31. K. L. Kellermann, "Measurements of the Flux Density of Discrete Radio Sources at Decimeter Wavelengths," *Astron. J.* **69**, 205–215 (1964).
32. G. B. Sholomitsky, V. N. Kurilchik, L. M. Matveenko, and G. S. Khromov, "Observations of Some Weak Sources of Radio Radiation at the Wavelength of 32 cm," *Astron. Zh.* **41**, 823–828 (1964).
33. R. G. Conway and M. Moran, "Observations of Discrete Radio Sources at Frequencies of 240 and 412 Mc/s," *Monthly Notices Roy. Astron. Soc.* **127**, 377–385 (1964).

34. R. G. Conway, E. J. Daintree, and R. J. Long, "Observations of Radio Sources at 612 and 1400 Mc/s," *Monthly Notices Roy. Astron. Soc.* **131**, 159–171 (1965).
35. N. W. Broten, B. F. C. Cooper, F. F. Gardner, H. C. Minnett, R. M. Price, F. G. Tonking, and D. E. Yabsley, "Some Observations at 6 cm Wavelength with the Australian 210-foot Radio Telescope," *Australian J. Phys.* **18**, 85–90 (1965).
36. K. I. Kellermann, "Measurements of the Flux Density of Discrete Radio Sources at 6 cm Wavelength," *Australian J. Phys.* **19**, 577–581 (1966).
37. D. Wills and E. A. Parker, "The Positions and Flux Densities of 74 Radio Sources from the 3C Catalogue," *Monthly Notices Roy. Astron. Soc.* **131**, 503–519 (1966). (Measurements made at 178 MHz.)
38. A. Maxwell and R. Rinehart, "Flux Densities of Radio Sources at 5 Gc/sec." *Astron. J.* **71**, 927–930 (1966).
39. V. C. Artiukh, V. V. Vitkevich, P. D. Dagkesamansky, and V. N. Kozhukhov, "Fluxes and Spectral Indices of Sources from the 3C and 3CR Catalogues Measured at the Frequency of 86 MHz," *Astron. Zh.* **45**, 712–725 (1968).
40. K. I. Kellerman, I. I. K. Pauliny-Toth, and P. S. J. Williams, "The Spectra of Radio Sources in the Revised 3C Catalogue," *Astrophys. J.* **157**, 1–34 (1969).

New measurements of right ascensions and declinations of sources in the 3C and 3CR catalogues were reported in the following papers.

41. E. B. Fomalont, T. A. Matthews, D. Morris, and J. D. Wyndham, "Accurate Right Ascensions for 226 Radio Sources," *Astron. J.* **69**, 772–784 (1964).
42. R. B. Read, "Accurate Measurements of the Declinations of Radio Sources," *Astrophys. J.* **138**, 1–29 (1963).
43. J. D. Wyndham and R. B. Read, "Further Accurate Declinations of Radio Sources," *Astron. J.* **70**, 120–123 (1965).
44. E. B. Fomalont, J. D. Wyndham, and J. F. Bartlett, "Positions for 3C Revised Radio Sources," *Astron. J.* **72**, 445–452 (1967).
45. C. M. Wade, B. G. Clark, and D. E. Hogg, "Accurate Radio Source Position Measurements With the NRAO Interferometer," *Astrophys. J.* **142**, 406–409 (1965).
46. R. L. Adgie and H. Gent, "Positions of Radio Sources Determined by the Interferometer at the Royal Radar Establishment," *Nature* **209**, 549–551 (1966).
47. E. A. Parker, B. Elsmore, and J. R. Shakeshaft, "Positions of Radio Sources Measured with the One-Mile Radio Telescope," *Nature* **210**, 22–23 (1966).

Identifications of sources from the 3C and 3CR catalogues with optical objects are described in the following papers. For identifications of quasistellar sources, see the bibliography contained in Ref. 20 of Chapter 7.

48. R. F. Griffin, "Positions of Optical Objects in the Fields of 42 Radio Sources," *Astron. J.* **68**, 421–428 (1963).
49. J. D. Wyndham, "A Search for Optical Objects Associated with 50 Radio Sources," *Astron. J.* **70**, 384–392 (1965).
50. P. Véron, "Optical Positions for Radio Sources in the 3C Revised Catalogue," *Astrophys. J.* **144**, 861–865 (1966).

SRH The first survey employing the method of aperture synthesis was made with the Cambridge telescope at 178 MHz. 175 sources were found within the area between right ascensions $20^h\,40^m$ to $19^h\,15^m$ and declinations 40° to 44°. 67 sources are listed within the declinations of 49°.5 to 52°. The limiting flux is 2 f.u.

51. P. F. Scott, M. Ryle, and A. Hewish, "First Results of Radio Star Observations Using the Method of Aperture Synthesis," *Monthly Notices Roy. Astron. Soc.* **122**, 95–111 (1961).

LHE This survey of 559 sources was made at 408 MHz with the Cambridge four-element interferometer. The survey is complete down to 2.5 f.u. over the region of declination −10° to +13° and +27° to +61°, but only the 3C sources are listed in the paper.

52. R. J. Long, J. B. Haseler, and B. Elsmore, "A Survey of Radio Sources at 408 Mc/s," *Monthly Notices. Roy. Astron. Soc.* **125**, 313–324 (1963).

4C The Fourth Cambridge Catalogue (4C) of radio sources made with the Cambridge interferometer at 178 MHz covers the sky between declinations −07° and 80° and lists 4843 sources brighter than 2 f.u. at 178 MHz. The designation of sources is according to the following scheme:

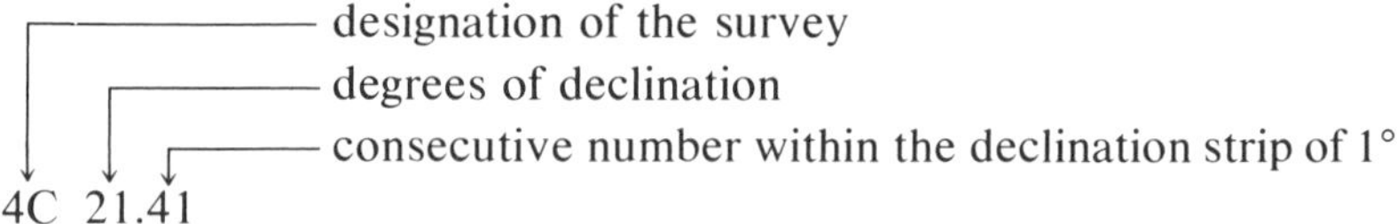

The catalogue consists of the following two papers, the first of which lists 1219 sources, and the second, 3624.

53. J. D. H. Pilkington and P. F. Scott, "A Survey of Radio Sources Between Declinations 20° and 40°." *Mem. Roy Astron. Soc.* **69**, 183–224 (1965).

54. J. F. R. Cower, P. F. Scott, and D. Wills, "A Survey of Radio Sources in the Declination Ranges −07° to 20° and 40° to 80°," *Mem. Roy. Astron. Soc.* **71**, 49–144 (1967).

More accurate determinations of positions and identifications of 4C sources with optical objects were reported in the following papers.

55. J. D. H. Pilkington, "Radio Sources and Rich Clusters of Galaxies," *Monthly Notices Roy. Astron. Soc.* **128**, 103–111 (1964).
56. P. A. G. Scheuer and D. Wills, "Identifications of Radio Sources with Haro Luyten Objects," *Astrophys. J.* **143**, 274–276 (1966).
57. D. Wills, "Radio Sources in Clusters of Galaxies," *Observatory* **86**, 140–145 (1966).
58. D. Wills, "4C Radio Sources and Blue Stellar Objects," *Observatory* **86**, 245–246 (1966).
59. J. L. Caswell and D. Wills, "Identifications of Radio Sources with Bright Galaxies," *Monthly Notices Roy. Astron. Soc.* **135**, 231–242 (1967).
60. D. Wills, "Optical Identifications of Selected 4C Radio Sources," *Monthly Notices Roy. Astron. Soc.* **135**, 339–343 (1967).
61. E. T. Olsen, "Accurate Positions of Selected 4C Sources," *Astron. J.* **72**, 738–746 (1967).

For measurements of 4C sources at different frequencies and discussion of their spectra, and the identification of sources, see the bibliography to Chapter 6 and the two papers below.

62. J. A. Bailey and G. G. Pooley, "Fan-Beam Observations of Radio Sources at 408 and 1407 MHz," *Monthly Notices Roy. Astron. Soc.* **138**, 51–66 (1968).
63. K. Aizu, "A Search for Identification of Some Radio Sources in the First Section of the 4C Catalogue with Galaxies," *Publ. Astron. Soc. Japan* **18**, 219–228 (1966).

5C The Fifth Cambridge survey at the present time covers a few small regions of the sky up to a limiting flux of 0.025 f.u. at 408 MHz and gives the positions with an accuracy of about 5″ of arc. At present, the survey consists of two lists. The first covers an area 4° in diameter centered at $\alpha = 09^h\,40^m$ and $\delta = 50°$ and contains 106 sources. The second covers the region 4° in diameter centered on $\alpha = 11^h\,00^m$ and $\delta = 49°\,40'$ and includes 207 sources brighter than 0.0115 f.u. at 408 MHz. A few sources were also observed at 1407 MHz. The designation of sources is as follows:

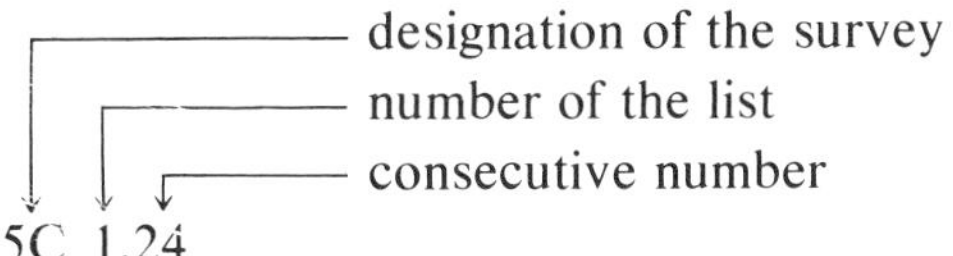

64. S. Kenderdine, M. Ryle, and G. G. Pooley, "Some Observations of Weak Radio Sources with the Cambridge One-Mile Telescope," *Monthly Notices Roy Astron. Soc.* **134**, 189–210 (1966).
65. G. G. Pooley and S. Kenderdine, "The 5C 2 Survey of Radio Sources," *Monthly Notices Roy. Astron. Soc.* **139**, 529–550 (1968).

WKB A 38 MHz survey of the sky north of declination $-10°$ down to 14 f.u. was made with the pencil beam Cambridge telescope. This survey lists 1,069 sources. The sources are labeled by the following method if their 4C number is not available:

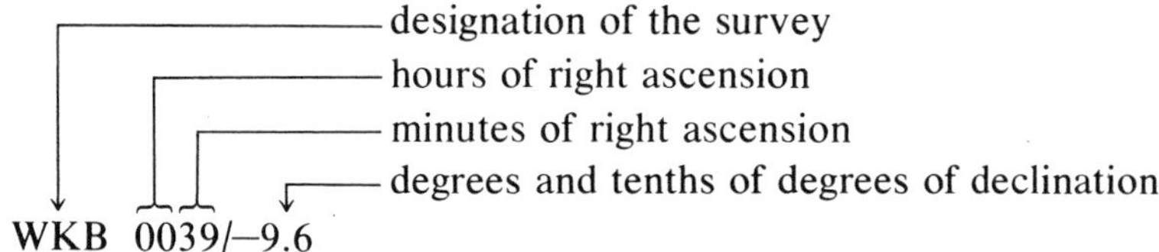

66. P. S. J. Williams, S. Kenderdine, and J. E. Baldwin, "A Survey of Radio Sources and Background Radiation at 38 Mc/s," *Mem. Roy. Astron. Soc.* **70**, 53–110 (1966).

RN A radio survey of the region of declinations higher than 86° was made with the use of the aperture synthesis method. This survey lists 87 sources with a flux density larger than 0.25, 0.55, 0.75, and 1.00 f.u. if the north polar distance of the sources is smaller than 2°.5, between 2°.5 and 3°, between 3° and 3°.5, and between 3°.5 and 4°, respectively. The frequency of observation is 178 MHz. The sources are numbered consecutively, so that the designation of sources in this survey is RN followed by the consecutive number (for example, RN 75).

67. M. Ryle and A. C. Neville, "A Radio Survey of the North Polar Region with a 4.5 Minute of Arc Pencil-Beam System," *Monthly Notices Roy. Astron. Soc.* **125**, 39–56 (1962).

NB The second survey of the region around the north pole was made using the technique of two-dimensional aerial synthesis with an effective pencil-beam response of 10 minutes of arc. The limiting flux density is 1.0 f.u. for declinations from 80° to 90°, 1.5 f.u. for declinations from 75° to 80° and 3.0 f.u. for declinations from 70° to 75°. The total number of sources recorded is 558. The designation of sources is according to the scheme which follows:

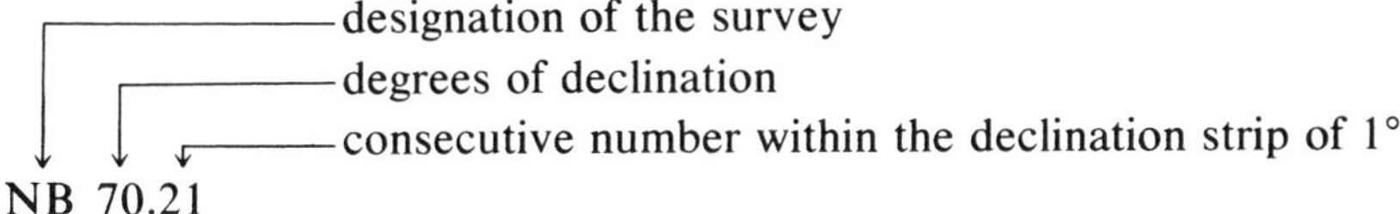

68. N. J. B. A. Branson, "A Radio Survey of the Sky North of Declination 70° at a Frequency of 81.5 Mc/s," *Monthly Notices. Roy. Astron. Soc.* **135**, 149–174 (1967).

A4.3. The Australian Surveys

MSH This survey was done with the Mills cross at 3.5 m. A total of 2270 sources down to the lower flux limit of 7 f.u. were recorded (1159 sources between +10° and −20°, 892 sources between −20° and −50°, and 219 sources between −50° and −80°). The designation of sources is illustrated by the following:

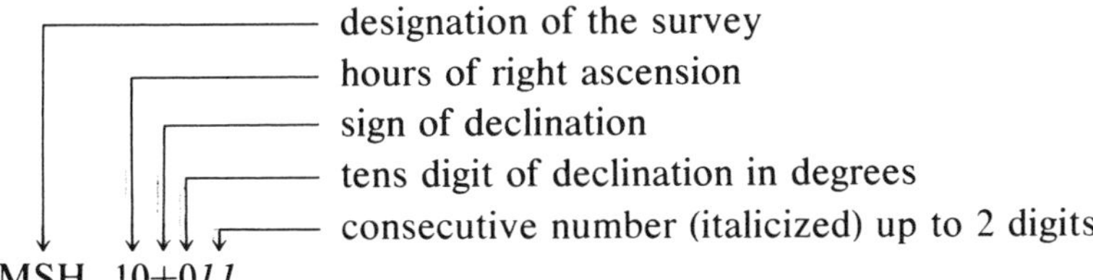

The MSH survey consists of three lists:

69. B. Y. Mills, O. B. Slee, and E. R. Hill, "A Catalogue of Radio Sources Between Declinations +10° and −20°," *Australian J. Phys.* **11**, 360–387 (1958).
70. B. Y. Mills, O. B. Slee, and E. R. Hill, "A Catalogue of Radio Sources Between Declinations −20° and −50°," *Australian J. Phys.* **13**, 676–699 (1960).
71. B. Y. Mills, O. B. Slee, and E. R. Hill, "A Catalogue of Radio Sources Between Declinations −50° and −80°," *Australian J. Phys.* **14**, 497–507 (1961).

PKS The Parkes Catalogue of radio sources consists of 5 lists and covers the area south of declination +27° except for a narrow strip along the galactic plane. The observations were made at 408 MHz, 1410 MHz and 2650 MHz with the 210 foot paraboloid at Parkes, Australia. The first list contains 297 sources brighter than 4 f.u. at 408 MHz. The basic finding survey for this list was made at 408 MHz, and then the sources were reobserved at 1410 MHz and 2650 MHz. The 247 sources in the second list were selected from an initial finding survey at 408 MHz in the zone −60° to −75° and from a 1410 MHz survey in the zone −75° to −90°. The list is essentially complete for sources brighter than 0.5 f.u. at 1410 MHz south of declinations of −75° and greater than 1 f.u. in the zone −75° to −60°. The third list, which contains 564 sources, is based on a finding survey made at 408 MHz. All the sources from the finding survey were reobserved at 1410 MHz. Sources brighter than 0.3 f.u. at 1410 MHz are included in the catalogue. The fourth list contains 628 sources brighter than 0.4 f.u. at 1410 MHz. The finding survey was made at 408 MHz. The fifth list contains 397 sources compiled from a finding survey at 635 MHz. The sources were also observed at 1410 MHz and 2650 MHz, and the catalogue is basically complete down to 1.5 f.u. at 635 MHz. The designation of sources in the Parkes catalogue is represented by the following

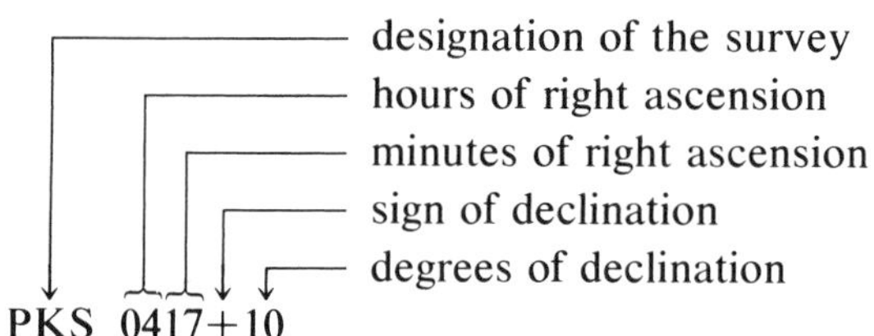

72. J. G. Bolton, F. F. Gardner, and M. B. Mackey, "The Parkes Catalogue of Radio Sources Declination Zone −20° to −60°," *Australian J. Phys.* **17**, 340–372 (1964).
73. R. M. Price and D. K. Milne, "The Parkes Catalogue of Radio Sources Declination Zone −60° to −90°," *Australian J. Phys.* **18**, 329–347 (1965).
74. G. A. Day, A. J. Shimmins, R. D. Ekers, and D. J. Cole, "The Parkes Catalogue of Radio Sources Declination Zone 0° to +20°," *Australian J. Phys.* **19**, 35–74 (1966).
75. A. J. Shimmins, G. A. Day, R. D. Ekers, and D. J. Cole, "The Parkes Catalogue of Radio Sources Declination Zone 0° to −20°," *Australian J. Phys.* **19**, 837–874 (1966).
76. A. J. Shimmins and G. A. Day, "The Parkes Catalogue of Radio Sources. Declination Zone +20° to +27°," *Australian J. Phys.* **21**, 377–403 (1968).

The first four lists were incorporated into one including more precise positions, more accurate flux densities, and additional information on polarization, structure, and optical identification of sources.

77. J. A. Ekers, ed., "The Parkes Catalogue of Radio Sources. Declination Zone +20° to −90°," *Australian J. Phys. Astrophys. Supplement* No. 7, 1–75 (1969).

The Parkes catalogue contains many identifications of sources with optical objects. Further identifications of optical objects with Parkes radio sources can be found in the following papers.

78. J. G. Bolton, M. E. Clarke, and R. D. Ekers, "Identification of Extra-galactic Radio Sources Between Declinations −20° and −44°," *Australian J. Phys.* **18**, 627–633, (1965).
79. J. G. Bolton and J. Ekers, "Identification of Radio Sources Between Declinations −20° and −30°," *Australian J. Phys.* **19**, 275–277 (1966).
80. M. E. Clarke, J. G. Bolton, and A. J. Shimmins, "Identification of Extra-galactic Radio Sources Between Declinations 0° and +20°," *Australian J. Phys.* **19**, 375–387 (1966).
81. J. G. Bolton and J. Ekers, "Further Identifications of Radio Sources Between Declinations 0° and 20°," *Australian J. Phys.* **19**, 471–473 (1966).
82. J. G. Bolton and J. Ekers, "Identification of Strong Extragalactic Radio Sources in the Declination Zone 0° to −20°," *Australian J. Phys.* **19**, 559–564 (1966).
83. J. G. Bolton and J. Ekers, "Further Identifications for Strong Extra-galactic Radio Sources in the Declination Zone 0° to −20°," *Australian J. Phys.* **19**, 713–715 (1966).
84. J. G. Bolton and J. Ekers, "Suggested Identifications for Weak Extra-galactic Radio Sources between Declinations 0° and −20°," *Australian J. Phys.* **20**, 109–116 (1967).
85. J. G. Bolton, A. J. Shimmins, and J. Merkelijn, "Identification of Radio Sources Between Declinations +27° and −30°," *Australian J. Phys.* **21**, 81–86 (1968).
86. B. E. Westerlund and L. F. Smith, "Optical Objects in the Fields of Southern Radio Sources," *Australian J. Phys.* **19**, 181–194 (1966).
87. B. Y. Mills, R. R. Shobbrook, and D. Stewart-Richardson, "Radio Sources in Clusters of Galaxies," *Australian J. Phys.* **21**, 511–521 (1968).
88. J. K. Merkelijn, "Accurate Positions and Identifications of 75 Radio Sources Between Declinations +20° and +27°," *Australian J. Phys.* **21**, 903–916 (1968).
89. J. K. Merkelijn, "Accurate Positions and Some Optical Identifications for 255 Radio Sources Between Declinations +20° and −33°," *Australian J. Phys.* **22**, 237–262 (1969).

Measurements of positions and fluxes of selected sources from the Parkes catalogue were reported in some of the above references and in the following papers.

90. A. J. Shimmins, M. E. Clarke, and R. D. Ekers, "Accurate Positions of 644 Radio Sources," *Australian J. Phys.* **19**, 649–685 (1966).
91. P. A. Hamilton and R. F. Haynes, "Source Flux Densities at 153 MHz," *Australian J. Phys.* **20**, 697–713 (1967).
92. A. J. Shimmins, "Accurate Positions of 210 Radio Sources," *Australian J. Phys.* **21**, 65–79 (1968).

93. R. F. Haynes and P. A. Hamilton, "Observations of 31 Radio Sources Between 40 and 130 MHz," *Australian J. Phys.* **21**, 87–94 (1968).
94. J. K. Merkelijn, A. J. Shimmins, and J. G. Bolton, "Accurate Positions and Some Optical Identifications for 67 Radio Sources Between Declinations +20° and +27°," *Australian J. Phys.* **21**, 523–537 (1968).
95. R. F. Haynes, P. A. Hamilton, and P. M. McCullough, "Observations of 11 Radio Sources Near 55 MHz," *Australian J. Phys.* **21**, 539–542 (1968).
96. A. J. Shimmins, R. N. Manchester, and B. J. Harris, "Accurate Flux Densities at 5009 MHz of 753 Radio Sources," *Australian J. Phys. Astrophys. Supplement* No. 8, 1–53 (1969).

A4.4. The California Institute of Technology Surveys

CTA The California Institute of Technology list A gives data on 106 sources, mainly from the 3C catalogue, at 906 MHz. The observations were made with the 90 foot paraboloid of the Owens Valley Radio Observatory. Six new sources, with a beam width of 0°.8 were discovered (CTA 1, CTA 21, CTA 26, CTA 80, CTA 97, CTA 102). The sources are numbered consecutively and prefixed with CTA.

97. D. E. Harris and J. A. Roberts, "Radio Source Measurements at 960 Mc/s," *Publ. Astron. Soc. Pacific* **72**, 237–255 (1960).

CTB List B gives the fluxes of 110 mainly galactic sources at 960 MHz; the instrumentation used was the same as in CTA. The sources are numbered consecutively and prefixed with CTB.

98. R. W. Wilson and J. G. Bolton, "A Survey of Galactic Radiation at 960 Mc/s," *Publ. Astron. Soc. Pacific* **72**, 331–347 (1960).

CTBR Wilson revised the CTB list. The revisions consisted of checking some positions and diameters by referring back to the original records, of adding interferometric diameters (NS) for most of the smaller sources, of computation of spectral indices for some sources observed at other frequencies, and of expansion of comments on optical fields. The CTBR list uses the same designation of sources as the CTB list.

99. R. W. Wilson, "Catalogue of Radio Sources in the Galactic Plane," *Astron. J.* **68**, 181–185 (1963).

CTC The CTC catalogue is a privately circulated list which is now obsolete.

CTD The CTD survey is a continuum survey at 1421 MHz carried out with the two-element interferometer of the Owens Valley Radio Observatory. The survey is essentially complete down to a flux of 1.15 f.u. Ref. 100 is the first list covering the region between the declinations of 23° 50′ and 30° 10′. The sources are numbered consecutively and prefixed with CTD.

100. K. I. Kellerman and R. B. Read, "A Continuum Survey for Discrete Radio Sources at 1421 Mc/s," *Publ. Owens Valley R. O.* **1**, No. 2 (1965).

A.4.5. The National Radio Astronomy Observatory Catalogues

NRAO The National Radio Astronomy Observatory catalogue of Radio sources gives positions and flux densities of 726 radio sources, mainly from the 3C and 3CR catalogues, measured at 750 and 1400 MHz with the 300 foot radio telescope at Green Bank. This catalogue is not a result of a sky survey but rather of observations of regions surrounding 3C and 3CR sources. In the course of observations a number of new sources were found. The sources are labeled by NRAO followed by a consecutive number (of up to three digits) in order of the right ascension. More recently, in (unpublished) lists used in the National Radio Astronomy Observatory the numbering system was expanded to include many additional sources; a fourth digit was added to the NRAO numbers; it is zero for sources contained in the above mentioned catalogue, but takes values from 1 to 9 for sources having right ascensions between those for the neighboring entries in the catalogue. The source NRAO 676 is thus referred to as NRAO 6760.

101. I. I. K. Pauliny-Toth, C. M. Wade, and D. S. Heeschen, "Positions and Flux Densities of Radio Sources," *Astrophys. J. Supplement* **13**, 65–124 (1966).

A region of the sky between +18° and +20° of declination was recently surveyed with the same equipment at the same frequencies. 458 sources with fluxes larger than 0.5 f.u. were detected. The numbering system is the same as in the Parkes catalogue.

102. B. Höglund, "Pencil-Beam Survey of Radio Sources Between Declinations +18° and +20° at 750 and 1410 MHz," *Astrophys. J. Supplement* **15**, 61–96 (1967).

A4.6. The Bologna Surveys

B1 This survey of radio sources was made with the EW arm of the Bologna cross radio telescope with an aperture of 30.0 × 564.3 meters and a beam of 1°.8 × 4′. The B1 list covers the right ascension region from 0 to 13 hours, and contains 629 sources brighter than 1 f.u. The Parkes system of designating sources is employed; but, instead of the prefix PKS, the prefix B1 is used.

103. A. Braccesi, M. Ceccarelli, R. Fanti, G. Gelatss, C. Giovannini, D. Harris, C. Rosatelli, G. Sinigaglia, and L. Volders, "A Catalogue of Radiosources from $\delta = -30°$ to $\delta = -20°$ at 408 MHz," *Nuovo Cimento* Ser. X, **40**, 267–294 (1965).

B1S The B1S list (also included in reference 103) gives 38 sources brighter than 0.6 f.u. located within a region between declinations −25°36′ and 20°00′ and right ascensions from $11^h\,00^m$ to $12^h\,50^m$. The Parkes system of designating sources is employed; but, instead of the prefix PKS, the prefix B1S is used.

GV This preliminary survey, made with the completed Bologna cross-type radio telescope, covers an area of sky between $07^h\,40^m$ and $18^h\,20^m$ in right ascension and 34° and 35° in declination. 328 sources down to 0.25 f.u. at 408 MHz were listed. The sources are numbered consecutively.

104. G. Grueff and M. Vigotti, "A Pencil-Beam Deep Sky Survey at 408 MHz," *Astrophys. Letters* **2**, 113–120 (1968).

B2 A list of 3235 radio sources stronger than 0.2 f.u., observed with the Bologna cross radio telescope at 408 MHz, covers the area of the sky extending from 34° 02′ to 29° 18′ (1968). The resolution is 3′ in right ascension and 10′ in declination. The Parkes system of designating sources is employed; but, instead of the prefix PKS, the prefix B2 is used.

105. Grouppo ROUB, "A Catalogue of 3235 Radiosources at 408 MHz," *Laboratorio Nazionale di Radioastronomia Università di Bologna Contribution* No. 55 (1969).

A4.7 The Ohio Survey

OA–OZ This survey was made at 1415 MHz with the 260 × 70 foot radio telescope of the Ohio State University. The first list contains

128 sources detected at 600 MHz and 1415 MHz with the fluxes larger than 2.0 and 0.5 f.u., respectively, within an area of $2^{h}.5$ in right ascension and 4° in declination around M31. The second list gives 236 sources within the region between right ascensions $08^{h}\,00^{m}$ and $16^{h}\,00^{m}$ and declinations $+25°\,00'$ and $+37°\,40'$. The sources listed are brighter than 0.37 f.u. The third list gives 1199 sources down to 0.3 f.u. located between right ascensions 00^{h} and 16^{h}. The fourth list gives 2101 sources with fluxes above 0.2 f.u. between declinations 0° and +20°. The designation of sources is represented by the following example:

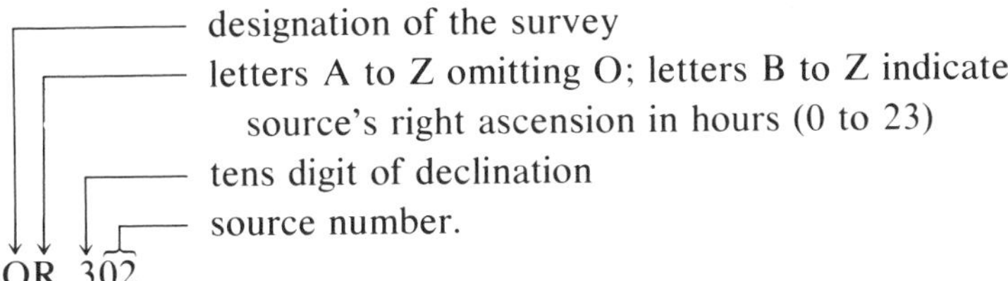

106. J. D. Kraus, "The Ohio (OA) List of Radio Sources," Appendix 3f in his *Radio Astronomy,* pp. 439–442, McGraw-Hill, New York, 1966.
107. D. J. Scheer and J. D. Kraus, "A High-Sensitivity Survey of the North Galactic Polar Region at 1415 MHz," *Astron. J.* **72**, 536–543 (1967).
108. R. S. Dixon and J. D. Kraus, "A High Sensitivity 1415 MHz Survey at North Declinations Between 19° and 37°," *Astron. J.* **73**, 381–407 (1968).
109. L. T. Fitch, R. S. Dixon, and J. D. Kraus, "A High-Sensitivity 1415-MHz Survey Between Declinations of 0° and 20° North," *Astron. J.* **74**, 612–688 (1969).

A4.8. The Vermillon River Observatory Survey

VRO A survey of the sky between declinations +9° to +69° at 610.5 MHz is being made with the 400 foot telescope of the Vermillon River Observatory of the University of Illinois. The first list of the survey contains a list of 239 sources brighter than 0.8 f.u. at 610.5 MHz. The second paper contains a list of 625 sources brighter than 0.8 f.u. The sources are designated according to the following procedure:

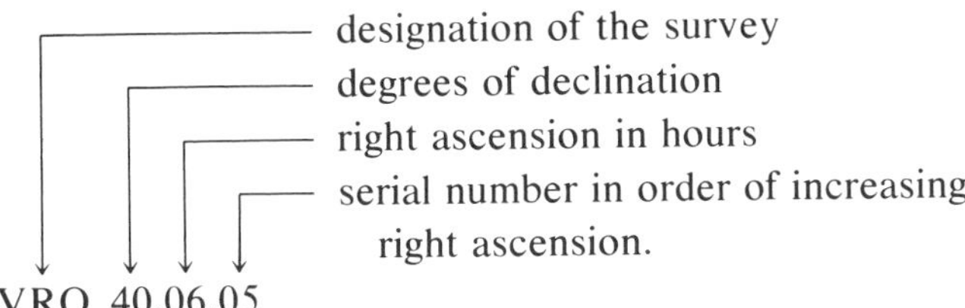

110. J. M. MacLeod, G. W. Swenson Jr., K. S. Yang, and J. R. Dickel, "A 610.5 Mc/sec Survey of the Sky between Declinations +40 and +44°," *Astron. J.* **70**, 756–764 (1965).
111. J. R. Dickel, K. S. Yang, G. C. McVittie, and G. W. Swenson, Jr., "A Survey of the Sky at 610.5 MHz. II. The Region Between Declinations +15° and +22°," *Astron. J.* **72**, 757–768 (1967).

A4.9 The Dominion Radio Observatory Survey

DA The Dominion list A contains 615 sources down to 2 f.u. at 1420 MHz observed with the 85 foot parabolic telescope of the Dominion Radio Observatory. The sources are numbered consecutively in order of increasing right ascension and are prefixed with DA.

112. J. A. Galt and J. E. D. Kennedy, "Survey of Radio Sources Observed in the Continuum near 1420 MHz, Declinations −5° to +70°," *Astron. J.* **73**, 135–151 (1968).

A4.10. The Dwingeloo Survey

DW The Dwingeloo list contains 188 sources down to 2.3 f.u. observed in the large regions of the northern sky with the 25m Dwingeloo telescope. The positions and the fluxes quoted were measured with the NRAO 300 foot radio telescope. The sources are numbered in the same way as the Parkes sources and are prefixed with DW.

113. M. M. Davis, "A 1417 MHz Search for Radio Sources Having a Flux Excess at Short Wavelengths," *Bull. Astron. Inst. Netherlands* **19**, 201–226 (1967).

A4.11. The Arecibo Occultation Survey

AO Occultation studies of weak radio sources are being carried out at the Arecibo Ionospheric Observatory with the 1000 foot radio telescope. Three lists of sources investigated at a frequency of 430 MHz (a few sources were investigated at 195 MHz) are published. The papers list 25 sources (13 of which are not listed in other catalogues). The sources are numbered according to the Parkes system and are prefixed by AO.

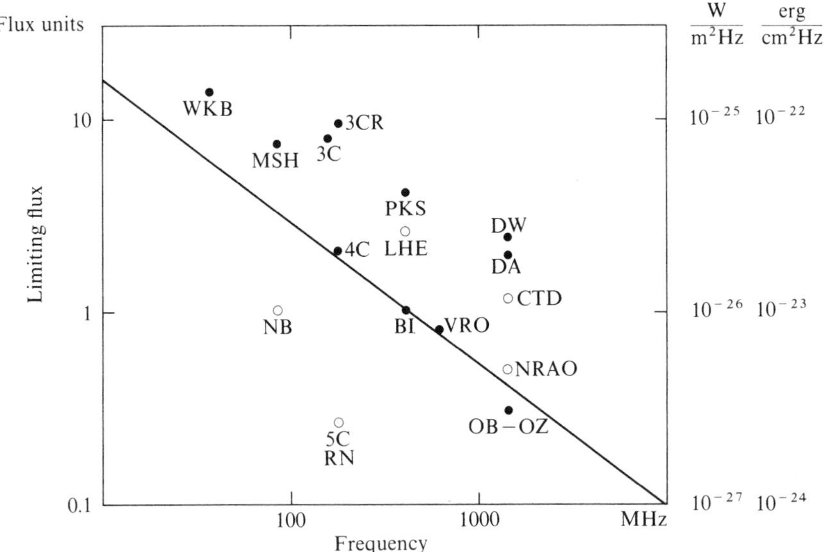

Fig. A.7 Frequencies and limiting fluxes of surveys of radio sources. Open circles refer to surveys covering only a very limited portion of the sky. If the limiting flux is a function of the angular size of the source or of its position on the sky, the lowest flux is plotted. The line represents a synchrotron spectrum with an index of 0.75 [After Davis, Ref. 113].

114. C. Hazard, S. Gulkis, and A. D. Bray, "Lunar Occultation Studies of Five Weak Radio Sources of Small Angular Size," *Astrophys. J.* **148**, 669–687 (1967).
115. C. Hazard, S. Gulkis, and J. Sutton, "Occultation Studies of Weak Radio Sources: List 2," *Astrophys. J.* **154**, 413–422 (1968).
116. S. Gulkis, J. Sutton, and C. Hazard, "Arecibo Occultation Studies: List 3," *Astrophys. J.* **157**, 1047–1053 (1969).

Author Index

Subject Index